WILEY FARM SERIES

The Wiley Farm Series is designed for agricultural students, farmers, and persons engaged in farm service employments. The books are based on accurate technical knowledge and tested experience in every field of agriculture.

Managing
the Farm Business

Managing
the Farm Business

RAYMOND R. BENEKE

Associate Professor, Department of Economics and Sociology
Iowa State College of Agriculture and Mechanical Arts

JOHN WILEY & SONS, INC., NEW YORK
CHAPMAN & HALL, LIMITED, LONDON

Preface

This text has been prepared primarily for students in vocational agriculture in secondary schools and for students in junior colleges and agricultural institutes. Farm operators interested in improving their business should also find the book helpful. It has been written with the conviction that success in the complex farm business of today requires a high degree of managerial skill as well as technical knowledge. To assist students in acquiring these skills each chapter centers about major "management problems" which in turn are considered from the standpoint of the economic principles and data that apply in making the decisions. When the principle involved has a broader application than to the problem discussed, other situations to which it applies are pointed out.

Emphasis has been given throughout the text to the basic principles underlying decision making, rather than to "cut and dried" answers. Admittedly, students prefer the simple, straightforward answer. But farm decisions are too complex and the environment in which they are made too changing for simple management formulas to work.

Considerable attention has been given to decisions involved in crop and livestock management. Every decision that farmers make has dollar and cents implications. It has not been possible in our brief space to take up all the problems of crop and livestock production. Rather, we discuss only those problems with the most important economic implications. It is assumed that students are familiar with the elementary technical aspects of crop and livestock production.

Marketing is treated only from the standpoint of the farm producer. The timing of production and marketing of livestock products to fit seasonal price patterns is discussed in the chapters on livestock management.

The principles discussed are basic to the organization and management of all types of farms, but, to be made meaningful, they must be supplemented with physical and economic data. Problems and illustrative materials used in the text have been drawn from a wide range of farm situations and research studies. However, the instructor will want to add to the illustrations presented in the text by using research and extension publications that apply to his locality.

The ability of students in farm management to analyze and make decisions will develop most effectively when they have an opportunity to apply principles to their home farm or other farms in the community. This is especially true of the material on organizing the cropping system, planning the livestock program, and analyzing the power and machinery organization. Experience in planning the organization of a farm can be provided by having the class use farms in the community as laboratory problems. The success of this method of study will depend in large measure on the availability of cropping histories, financial accounts, and other background data to supplement the students' own observations. If the work of the class is concentrated on one or two farms, the instructor can provide the student with more guidance with his problem than if each student worked with a separate farm. Later the student can gain additional experience by analyzing and making plans for his home farm situation.

Some instructors may prefer to follow a sequence of problem areas in their teaching that differs from the presentation in the text. Chapter 2 through 5, dealing with establishment in farming and controlling resources, can be postponed until later in the course with no difficulty. In organizing the text, I felt that the study of the use of records to improve the farm business should come only after the student is familiar with the principles underlying the organization and management of a farm. I also felt that there was some advantage in studying Chapters 20 and 21 in sequence. For this reason they were both presented at the end of the text. However, some instructors may want to consider the farm accounting problems presented in Chapter 20 earlier in the course.

I wish to express my appreciation for the helpful suggestions of Professors Lowell Hardin of Purdue University, Glen Johnson of Michigan State College, Howard Ottoson of the University of Nebraska, G. A. Peterson of the University of Illinois and J. B. McClelland of Iowa State College who read parts or all of the manuscript. I also would like to acknowledge my indebtedness to my colleagues, particularly Professors A. G. Ball, E. O. Heady, H. B. Howell, H. R. Jensen, W. G. Murray, and Wallace Ogg who have contributed greatly to a stimulating environment at Iowa State College.

RAYMOND R. BENEKE

April 1955

Contents

CHAPTER   PAGE

1. The Role of Management in the Farm Business . 1
2. Getting Established in Farming 16
3. Planning Farm Leasing Arrangements . . . 39
4. Buying a Farm 57
5. Using Credit in the Farm Business 79
6. Planning the Cropping Program 102
7. Fitting Conservation Measures to the Farm . . 138
8. Planning the Livestock Program 161
9. Managing the Hog Enterprise 194
10. Managing the Beef and Sheep Enterprises . . 217
11. Managing the Dairy Enterprise 234
12. Managing the Laying Flock 257
13. Using Farm Power and Machinery Efficiently . 269
14. Using Budgets in Farm Planning 292
15. Using Farm Labor Efficiently 313
16. Planning the Farmstead and Farm Building Arrangement 334
17. Adjusting Production to Prices and Markets . . 347
18. Adjusting to the Risks in Farming 369
19. Planning the Size of the Farm Business . . . 386
20. Keeping Farm Accounts 405
21. Using Records to Analyze the Farm Business . . 436
Index 453

vii

CHAPTER

1

The Role of Management
in the Farm Business

Understanding the Farm Manager's Function

The central task of the farm manager is to make and carry out farming decisions. Farm management is a process involving the following steps:

1. Observing and analyzing alternative courses of action.
2. Deciding which course of action to follow.
3. Taking the steps necessary to carry out the decision once it has been made.
4. Bearing the responsibility for the outcome of the decision.

Suppose you are wondering about changing from up-and-down-the-hill to contour farming. Your first step as a manager would be to observe the results other farmers are getting from contouring. You might read magazine articles and bulletins on the subject. In addition, you would consider the lay of the land, the severity of soil losses on your own farm, and the amount of fence that would have to be changed. Your observation and analysis of the pros and cons of contouring would give you the basis for choosing between contouring and continuing to farm up and down the hill. This choice represents the second step in the management process. Your third step, if you decided to contour, would be to take action. You would have to see that contour lines were laid out, fences changed, and crops actually planted and cultivated on the contour. As the final step in carrying out your function as a manager, you would have to bear the responsibility for the outcome of your decision. If you decided to contour and the results were good, you would be rewarded by higher returns. On the other hand, if your decision to contour worked out badly, you would suffer the consequences.

All management decisions involve substantially the process described above. However, the emphasis placed on each of the various steps often differs among managers and also according to the problem involved. Some managers may give more emphasis than others to observing and analyzing the problem before coming to a decision than others. Managers who ordinarily make a careful analysis before reaching a decision are sometimes forced by circumstances to make a hurried decision. Other managers may lack the initiative and self-discipline to carry out the decisions and plans they make.

Management is a continuing process

Managing a farm is a continuous process of decision making. Why is this true? Why is a farmer confronted day after day with decisions to make even after he has carefully planned and organized his farming program? The need for decisions arises out of changes both on his farm and elsewhere and the necessity of adjusting farming operations to them. The principal changes with which the farm manager must deal are as follows:

1. Fluctuations in Prices. Prices are constantly changing. The price of hogs may change in relationship to the price of corn. Or the price of hogs may change relative to the price of beef. Changes may also occur in the relative prices of the inputs used in farm production, such as protein feeds and corn or labor and machinery. Should the hog program be expanded when high hog prices are in prospect? How should the combination of corn and protein feeds be adjusted when the price ratio of corn and protein changes? How should production be adjusted to seasonal price changes? These are some of the management decisions that arise out of price changes.

2. Weather Variations and Disease. Suppose you are following a carefully planned crop-rotation system, but your stand of legume seeding is winter-killed. Should you plow up the seeding and put the land to corn? If so, what adjustments should you make in your feeding program? Or suppose pastures are unusually short owing to a drouth. What provisions should you make to provide feed for your livestock? These examples illustrate the types of problems that arise from changes in the weather. There are many more. Similarly, disease can give rise to management problems. Brucellosis or mastitis in cattle may force a farmer to sell some of his dairy herd. Or hog diseases may cause death loss and unthriftiness in the animals. Both these developments call for decisions and action on the part of the manager.

3. New Farming Methods. Present-day agriculture is characterized by rapid changes in farming methods. When a new oats variety is released, should you continue planting your present variety or change to the new variety? Should you buy a new sprayer to take advantage of new weed sprays? Should you install a hay drier to

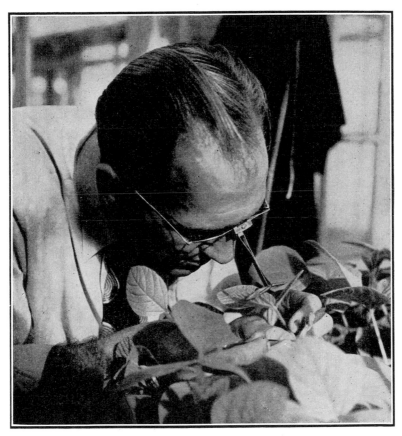

Figure 1. Agricultural scientists are constantly at work developing new crop varieties, improved feeding methods, and improved weed and insect sprays. The farm manager must decide which of these new developments he should adopt on his farm.

reduce weather damage to hay? These are some of the decisions the farmer has had to make in recent years concerning new farming methods. Although he cannot know what future problems will arise, the farm manager can be certain that he will have to make many similar decisions in the years ahead.

4. Changes in the People and Institutions with Which Farmers Deal. Sometimes individuals on whom the farmer is dependent cause difficulties. Hired workers may become ill or disgruntled. People with whom the farmer deals may not live up to their commitments. Changes in government regulations may force decisions on the farmer. For example, should a cornbelt farmer participate in the corn acreage allotment programs? If so, what adjustments should he make in his cropping system?

Gathering information

Before you have managed a farm business very long, you will find that you frequently must make decisions with incomplete knowledge of all the factors involved.

For example, in deciding whether to buy feeder cattle, what type

Figure 2. One of the tasks of a farm manager is to gather information to use in making decisions. Attending extension meetings is one way of obtaining information. (Courtesy Iowa Agr. Ext. Serv.)

and quantity of fertilizer to use on corn, or when to market hogs, the manager will never have all the information he would like to have to make a "perfect" decision. Knowledge of future prices and of physical production relationships is required for making a perfect decision in each of these cases. What will cattle sell for when they are ready for market? What will corn be worth? How rapidly will the cattle gain? How much will fertilizer increase yields? How much feed will be required per pound of added pork produced in carrying hogs to heavier weights? These are examples of the kinds of information needed to make the decisions referred to above.

One of the chief concerns of the manager is to increase his store of knowledge on which he must base his decisions. But a busy farmer has only a limited amount of time to devote to gathering information. He can draw on many sources, including neighbors, college bulletins, farm magazines, county agents, and farm radio programs. One way of improving the efficiency of the information-gathering process is to concentrate on the most important facts needed to make a decision. Many of the principles we will study in later chapters will help you to sort out and choose the facts that are most important in making a decision. The skillful manager learns where he can get dependable information with a minimum amount of effort. He learns to recognize which decisions are the most important among the many he must make and what types of information will be the most valuable to him. He avoids spending his time on making unimportant decisions or in trying to gather unimportant information.

The farmer is both manager and worker

The major proportion of the labor and management used on farms in the United States is supplied by the farm family. Typically, the farm operator does most of the managing. However, his wife also may play an important role in helping to make decisions. In some families, major decisions are talked over with the other members of the family as well. On rented farms the management is also shared with the farm owner.

Unlike most industrial firms where management and labor are performed by different people, the operator of a farm typically makes most of the decisions and does a large part of the work as well. Drawing a sharp line between doing the work and managing the farm is difficult. The alert farm operator often analyzes and makes important management decisions as he works. Even the hired farm laborer finds it difficult to escape making some decisions. Indeed one of the most frequent complaints farmers make of hired workers is that they are hesitant and inept when forced to make minor decisions in their work.

Specialized managers

A few farms are managed by men who devote their full time to making the decisions on one or more farms. In addition, some farm owners hire trained managers to look after their interests on tenant-operated farms. Although these specialized farm managers are becoming increasingly common, decision making on most farms is still done by the farm operator and his family. This book deals primarily with the problems of this second and most common group of managers. When we use the term *farm manager,* we refer to the farmer managing his own business.

Management is important

Every community has examples of hard-working farmers who are unable to make their farm businesses pay. Often they perform some of their operations, such as planting and cultivating their crops and feeding their livestock, in a satisfactory way. At the same time, they may make costly mistakes in their management. For example, they

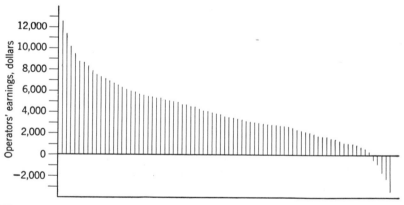

Figure 3.   Operators' earnings of 78 farmers in southeastern Minnesota, 1952. (Div. Agr. Econ., Univ. Minn.)

may raise the wrong kind of crops or livestock or make mistakes in timing their production and marketing. Frequently they invest too much money in machinery and equipment. Consistent errors in making important farm management decisions such as these may make the farm business unprofitable in spite of hard work.

A number of studies indicate that large differences exist among farm businesses in the amount of profit they return to their operators. Even when farms of the same size and type are compared, the amount of income earned from them varies a great deal. The return to the farm operator's labor and management on 78 southeastern Minnesota farms varied from a low of minus $3,400 to a high of $12,600 in 1952 (Figure 3). Although weather conditions and elements of luck accounted for some of the differences in returns among these farms, differences in the management ability of the farmers themselves were responsible for much of the variation.

Qualities of a superior manager

What personal qualities should you possess if you expect to succeed as a farm manager? You, of course, must have the traits required for success in any occupation, such as health, ambition, and intelligence. But, in addition, you need several qualifications that are of particular importance for making and carrying out decisions:

1. Ability to Analyze and Think through a Problem. The central task of the farm manager is to make decisions. Major decisions should be reached only after a careful analysis and weighing of the alternatives presented. The person who grows impatient with this type of mental activity and resorts to "playing hunches" in making decisions is not fitted for management responsibility.

2. The Initiative Necessary to Gather New Knowledge. Farm managers cannot acquire a storehouse of economic and technical knowledge and then stop learning. Facts soon become out of date in this age of rapid change. Knowing all of the current best ways of doing things is much less important than keeping up to date through a continuous process of learning.

3. Ability to Take Action and Get Things Done. Part of the manager's function is to see that action is taken, once a decision is made. Many farm managers stumble at this point. They may make wise decisions, but they lack the drive to carry them out. Perhaps the most common failing is to approach a new project with great enthusiasm and then gradually lose interest before the success of the project is assured. Starting a conservation program will lead to financial difficulty if the farm operator loses interest before he has worked out a livestock program to use his forage. Or time and money spent on a swine sanitation system will be wasted if the manager does not see that it is carefully followed. Carrying through, once a decision has been made, requires determination as well as initiative. This is especially true when things go badly and the success of the venture is in doubt.

4. Willingness and Ability to Accept Responsibility and a Reasonable Amount of Risk. One of the functions of a manager is to accept financial responsibility for the decisions he makes. Because of the many uncertainties and hazards that surround farming, the plans and decisions of even the best managers often turn out badly. Some people find living with these uncertainties difficult; others learn to accept them without discomfort; a few actually enjoy them. Managers who are overly sensitive to risk often take too many precautions and conduct their businesses too conservatively. As a result, their earnings suffer. The individual who worries unduly about the uncertainties that farming involves often would be happier and better off financially to consider some other occupation where he is called on to make fewer decisions and to bear less risk.

The resources used in farming

Farming is a production process. Resources are invested in the process, and products are taken from it. Resources are all of the things that are used to produce crops and livestock on the farm. They consist of such items as land, labor, fertilizer, feed, and the services of machines. These inputs are generally classified into four broad categories:

1. Land.
2. Capital.
3. Labor.
4. Management.

Land is usually thought of as including the air and sunshine above the surface, as well as the plant nutrients in the soil. The meaning of the term capital is not nearly so well understood as is the meaning of land. Some people think of capital as including only money. But it can be defined more accurately as consisting of all the materials and devices produced by man that aid in production. Thus farm capital consists of machinery, equipment, livestock, feed, and many other items. The money that is kept on hand or in the bank in order to do business should also be regarded as farm capital. Such money is important because it can always be used to obtain production resources. Labor includes all of the operator's labor, that of his family, and that which he hires.

Management is the special type of effort that the operator exerts in deciding how the land, labor, and capital are to be combined and used in the farming operation. Many successful farmers think that management is the most important of all the resources that enter into farming.

Getting the most out of resources

Farmers differ in the amounts and kinds of resources they have to use in their farming operations. Typically they have limited resources with which to work. The test of a good manager is his ability to make the best possible use of what he has. Some people make the mistake of confusing good land, buildings, and equipment with superior management. Although a high level of management may have contributed to a farmer's owning a well-equipped farm, the best managers often do not have the most or the best resources to start with.

Limited capital

Farmers with limited finances cannot make all the investments that would be profitable on their farm. Instead they must look for the most profitable of all the alternative uses to which their limited capital can be put. A feeding floor, for example, may be a highly profitable investment for a farmer who has an ample supply of capital. But the good manager with limited capital would put his capital into fertilizer and livestock instead, if these uses promise greater returns.

Limited labor

Some farmers occasionally find that they do not have enough labor to do all the jobs that should be done. When this situation arises, if more labor cannot be hired, the wise manager will use his available labor to do the most important jobs first. This may mean postponing cutting weeds in the fence row or cleaning up around the farmstead until higher-priority jobs are out of the way.

Appraising management performance

In appraising the management performance of a farmer, you should consider not only what he has been able to accomplish. You must also take into account the resources he has had to work with. Often some of the best management performances are achieved by farmers with limited resources even though their farms do not look impressive.

Fitting enterprises together

You may assume your first management responsibility with a single enterprise, such as a sow and litter or a dairy project. Although this management experience is valuable, managing the entire farming unit involves additional problems that are not encountered in managing a single enterprise. Farm businesses in the United States, for the most part, consist of a number of enterprises that must be fitted together. Some farmers have unusual technical skill in one enterprise but lack the ability to fit all the enterprises on the farm together into a well-organized unit. As a result, their farms are not so profitable as they could be.

Timing

Timing is a difficult problem when a number of enterprises are involved. For example, if you have only the hog enterprise to worry about, you can have the pigs farrowed at the time of year that will result in the greatest profit from hogs alone. But, if your responsibility includes a flock of breeding ewes or a cattle-feeding enterprise as well as a cropping system, the farrowing must be fitted in with the other projects to avoid excessive peaks in the labor load.

Allocating feed supplies

On farms with several types of livestock, available feed supplies must be divided among the livestock in such a way as to yield the greatest return to the whole farm rather than to any one enterprise. On a dairy-hog farm, for example, it may be profitable to feed more grain to dairy cows. But, from the standpoint of the entire farm business, income may be increased by using some of the grain to raise a greater number of hogs. Learning how much emphasis to give each enterprise is one of the most difficult farm management lessons. Learning how to adjust this emphasis as price relationships change is an even more difficult task.

Looking at the whole farm

Often young farmers learn how to manage effectively an enterprise in which they are particularly interested, but they do not learn how to fit a number of enterprises together and to allocate their time, labor, and capital among them so that they have a profitable farm business. This can happen easily because students spend much of their time studying livestock enterprises one at a time. Projects are also often built around a single enterprise.

In your study of farm management, you will spend much time discussing problems that arise out of fitting enterprises together. In the process you will draw upon the training you have had in animal husbandry, in farm crops and soils, and in farm mechanics. Your goal should be to learn how to fit all this knowledge together to make the entire farming unit a profitable business.

Choosing Goals for the Farm Business

In the previous section, we pointed out that the test of a good manager is his ability to get the most out of his limited resources. But what is it that the farm manager wishes to accomplish? The

Figure 4. One of the goals of most farm families is a modern home. A satisfactory money income from the farm business is usually necessary in achieving this goal. (Courtesy DeLaval Separator Co.)

answer to this question depends on the goals of the farm operator and his family. These goals differ among families. Furthermore, most families probably hope to achieve several different objectives through their farming operations. The principal goals of most farm families include the following:

1. Making money.
2. Providing security for their old age.
3. Avoiding excessive risk.

4. Having some time for leisure and recreation.

5. Achieving personal and family satisfactions, such as having a fine home, rearing and educating a family, and improving their own knowledge and abilities.

6. Having friends and being accepted in the community.

Figure 5. Farm families often have goals other than making money. Having a fine home and time for leisure and recreation frequently rank high on the list. However, making money is often necessary in order to achieve many of their goals such as an education for their children, travel, and modern conveniences in the home. (Courtesy J. I. Case Co.)

In a democratic society, the choice of goals is left to the individual as long as he lives within the law. For example, if a family prefers to have a great deal of leisure even though it must live poorly because of the low income that results, it is free to do so. It is not the purpose of a course in farm management to teach people what their goals should be, but rather to help them make progress toward achieving their goals.

Making money

One goal that is important on almost every farm is making money. Money of itself is not important to most people. However, a sizable income is necessary before the farm family can achieve other goals, such as a comfortable living and security during old age. In our society, your making more money means that your family can have better food, housing, and clothing. It means better education and medical care for them and an opportunity to enjoy many luxuries such as television, vacations, and modern household appliances. Earning as high an income as possible is particularly important to young farmers just getting started.

Avoiding risk

Keeping their business financially solvent is another primary goal of most farmers. Many farming ventures involve risk. Farmers can exercise some control over the risk they take through the way they organize their farm. For example, feeding lambs or heavy cattle, although generally profitable over a period of several years, may result in heavy losses during any one year. On the other hand, dairying generally provides a relatively stable and dependable income from year to year.

Some farmers pass up what appear to be promising opportunities to make money because of the possibility of losses. Operators of this type are called conservative. A few people enjoy risky enterprises. They are often referred to as "gamblers." Still others are willing to take large risks even though they do not enjoy the practice, because they have their eye on the large gains that are possible.

The amount of risk the farm operator is justified in taking depends on his financial condition and his family situation. If he is operating on a narrow margin and has heavy family responsibilities, he probably will want to avoid risky enterprises. On the other hand, the operator who is well established and has accumulated a financial backlog is in a better position to take risks.

Leisure

In addition to making money and achieving security, most farm families also want to have some time for leisure and recreation. Often farmers could make more money if they were willing to work harder and for longer hours. For example, they could milk more cows, raise more hogs, or farm more land. However, they may prefer the free time to the added income. Sometimes farmers keep no livestock because they want to be free in the winter. The enjoyment they get from having their winters free is worth more to them than the money income they forfeit as a consequence.

Farmers have more freedom than most workers in deciding on the amount of their time to spend working. No one tells the farm operator what time he should begin work and when he should stop. But, when he neglects his work, he also suffers the consequences. Therefore, this freedom to choose between work and leisure places an added responsibility on him to use his time wisely. Some farmers fail financially because they do not have enough self-discipline to do the work required for financial success.

Personal satisfactions

Earning money, for most people, is a means of satisfying more fundamental wants. But some satisfactions that go with farming cannot be purchased with money. For example, some farm families like to have an attractive, well-kept farmstead. In keeping the farmstead neat they may consume considerable time and energy that could have been spent in making more money instead. Other farmers enjoy keeping a certain class of livestock, even though it may not fit the resources of the farm so well as some other enterprise. Many farmers like to work with good machinery and, as a result, invest more in this way than can be justified on a dollar-and-cents basis.

Having friends and being accepted in the community

Farmers like most other people want to have friends and to be well thought of by people in the community. Often they take the attitude of their neighbors into consideration in making decisions on the farm. For example, they may participate in a government acreage-allotment program because they feel their neighbors think they should. Or they may be reluctant to try out new farming methods that the neighbors do not approve.

Goals sometimes conflict

One of the most important tasks of the farmer is to decide what he wants to get out of his farm business. In examining his goals, he will often find that one goal conflicts with another. Making more money will sometimes mean working harder and having less time for leisure. Avoiding risk often will mean giving up potential income. Investing in good machinery may result in a lower net farm income. It is important that the farm operator recognize where his goals conflict and decide which are the most important to him and his family.

Family goals that require money must be geared to the income-producing capacity of the farm business. The family must learn to live within its income. In addition, the family must decide how much income to use for family living and how much to put back into the business with a view to increasing future income. This is a particularly difficult problem for farm families because of the large amounts of capital that can be used profitably on most farms.

The farmer must use judgment in balancing his goals. He has to decide whether the personal satisfaction he may get out of a fine but expensive machine is worth the money it costs. In deciding whether to buy a new television set or to take a fishing trip, he must determine which, if either, he can afford. Similarly, when he keeps a crop or livestock enterprise which is unprofitable but which he enjoys, he must decide whether he can afford the decrease in income that will result.

Problems

1. List the decisions that had to be made on your home farm during the last week.

2. What goals other than making money are important on your home farm? How, if at all, do they interfere with making the highest possible farm income?

3. Select the farm operator from among the farmers you know who you think is the best manager. Then pick the one you regard as the poorest manager. Make a list of the characteristics of each and compare them.

4. Explain some of the factors that you think account for the wide differences in income shown in Figure 3.

References

Case, H. C. M., and Paul E. Johnston, *Principles of Farm Management*, Chapter 1, J. B. Lippincott Co., Chicago, Philadelphia, New York, 1953.

Efferson, J. Norman, *Principles of Farm Management*, Chapter 1, McGraw-Hill Book Co., New York, 1953.

"Farming Opportunities in the Midwest," *Purdue Ext. Bull.* 325, 1946.

Forster, G. W., *Farm Organization and Management*, 3d Ed., Chapter 1, Prentice-Hall, New York, 1953.

Hopkins, John A., and William G. Murray, *Elements of Farm Management*, 4th Ed., Chapter 1, Prentice-Hall, New York, 1953.

Howell, H. B., Earl O. Heady, and L. J. Bodensteiner, "Farming Today," *Iowa Agr. Expt. Sta. and Ext. Serv. Coop. Bull.* P. 82, 1946.

Malone, Carl C., *How to Make Your Farm Pay*, Chapter 1, Iowa State College Press, 1950.

Robertson, Lynn S., and Ralph H. Woods, *Farm Business Management*, Chapter 1, J. B. Lippincott Co., Chicago, Philadelphia, New York, 1950.

2

Getting Established in Farming

The large amount of capital needed in present-day farming makes it difficult for most young men to get established on their own. As a result, more and more farm youths begin by working out a partnership on the home farm. Sometimes this arrangement leads directly to the son taking over the home farm. In other instances it may help him to accumulate livestock and save money to start later on another farm.

What are the advantages of having a definite arrangement? What type of agreement should you work out? What should be included in the agreement? How should income and expenses be shared? These are the problems that we will discuss in the first section of this chapter. In the second part, the problems you will encounter in getting started on your own are considered.

Management Problems

1. Understanding the advantages of a definite income-sharing arrangement.
2. Making preliminary agreements.
3. Making income-sharing arrangements.
4. Adopting standard leases to family farming arrangements.
5. Getting established on your own.

Understanding the Advantages of a Definite Income-Sharing Arrangement

Many young men work on the home farm after they have finished school without making a definite agreement on the role they are to play in the business. This comes about naturally, because most farm boys have worked on the farm while they were in school without any clear-cut agreement. Typically, there is plenty of work to be done on the farm, and young men are apt to become absorbed in day-to-day farm operations. As a result, they postpone making a definite agreement, sometimes for years. Often they are well rewarded for the work they do, even though there is no clear-cut agreement on how they are to be paid.

However, even where the father and son work together smoothly, having a definite agreement offers several important advantages. Among them are:

1. The son has a greater incentive to do a good job.
2. The management is improved when the son takes an active role in both long-run planning and in making day-to-day decisions.
3. The family can make long-term plans for improving the business and eventually transferring it to the son.
4. Settling the estate is simplified in the event of the death of the father.

These advantages are often difficult to evaluate. But poor performance of the business is sometimes related directly to a lack of incentive on the part of the son. This lack of incentive may be caused by failure to define the son's responsibilities and his share in the returns from the farm. Maintaining the son's interest in the business and its management is particularly important when the father grows older and is unable to provide aggressive management himself.

Making Preliminary Agreements

Project agreements

Many persons who have started on their home farms received their first experience in working with their family, through a business-like project agreement. Agreements for sharing costs and returns from the project should be realistic and definite. Projects or supervised farming programs are an excellent place for you to learn to work with your family.

Wage agreements

In some instances the wage agreement may be a wise step for the son in taking over operation of the family farm. If you are waiting to go into the armed services or are not sure whether you want to become a farmer, beginning on a wage basis is generally desirable. If the son has already developed a project program, he may continue this, in addition to receiving wages for other work on the farm. Agreeing on a fair wage generally is not difficult, since the going wage rate is fairly well established in most communities. However, if you enter into a wage agreement, do not continue this phase of your farming experience any longer than is necessary. A prolonged hired-man and employer relationship between you and your father may cause both of you to develop attitudes that will be difficult to overcome later when a partnership farming arrangement is worked out. Under the typical hired-man arrangement, the farm operator has almost the entire responsibility for decision making. As long as you are working for wages, your father may fail to share management decisions with you. As a result, you may take less interest than you should in the success of the farming operation.

Enterprise agreement

In an enterprise agreement, the son usually draws a wage and receives as a bonus income from one of the major enterprises on the farm. Generally, this enterprise is one for which he has a major responsibility. This arrangement can be worked out very simply. Often the son receives a wage plus some fixed percentage of total sales from the enterprise.

The advantages of the enterprise agreement over a simple wage arrangement are (1) the son has more opportunity to develop his management talents and (2) he has a greater incentive to do a good job.

Some arrangements are designed especially to provide additional incentive for the son to improve the management of the enterprise in which he shares. For example, on farms where hogs are a major enterprise, the son sometimes receives wages and one third or one fourth of the income from any hogs marketed in excess of a seven-pigs-per-litter average. In dairying, he may receive a share of any increase in the average milk production per cow.

The chief disadvantage of the enterprise agreement is that it gives the son too narrow an interest in the business. Unless he is careful, he may give too much attention to the enterprise from which he receives his income. This is not good training for the time when he will have responsibility for managing the entire farm business.

Making Income-Sharing Arrangements

Once the father and son are convinced that they wish to farm together, they should enter into an income-sharing agreement. In this type of arrangement, the son gets a share of the income from the entire farm business. Often he furnishes part of the capital. He also shares the management with his father.

What are the advantages of an income-sharing agreement over a wage or enterprise agreement? An income-sharing plan provides a greater incentive for the son to do a good job. It also gives him broader management experience because he has some responsibility for the management of the whole farm.

Successful income-sharing agreements

The following conditions are necessary for a successful income-sharing agreement:

1. The farm business must be large enough. If a father–son arrangement is to be successful, the farm business must be large enough to make productive use of the labor and management of both father and son. If it is not already sufficiently large, land and capital should be available for expanding the business. The labor of both father and son must be used productively if both are to have an adequate income. A mistake made by many families is to give too little attention to the amount of income each partner will have after the income from the whole farm business is divided. After the son is married, two families instead of one must be supported from the farm. It is not unusual to see families trying to work out a successful income-sharing arrangement on a farm that has insufficient land and capital to support even one family adequately. If the business is too small, neither the father nor the son will have a good living. Under these circumstances, instead of attempting to work out a family farming agreement, it would be better for the son to work elsewhere.

How can you determine whether your home farm is large enough for a successful partnership? Generally farms that are below the community average in volume of business are poor prospects for income-sharing agreements. The best way to estimate the amount of income that the father and son each will make is to set up a budget. This can be done after the division of income has been determined. The fact that there is enough work to keep two men busy full time on the farm does not mean that the farm is large enough to support two operators. The need for two workers might be due to inefficient work methods rather than to a large, productive business.

The fact that the farm business is too small at the present does not always mean that a father–son arrangement would be unsuccessful. The possibilities for expanding the size of the business should be considered. Sometimes the partners can buy or rent more land, or the size of the livestock program can be expanded. These and other possibilities for increasing the size of the business are discussed more fully in Chapter 19.

2. *The father and son must be willing to cooperate in making decisions.* To form a successful partnership, both father and son should have a voice in the management. Often a smoothly functioning father-and-son team provides much better management than would either the father or the son working independently. Often the son furnishes imagination and initiative and is anxious to try new methods and to get things done. On the other hand, the father with his greater experience and caution may serve as a check on the son and sometimes steers the partnership away from unsuccessful ventures.

Though a difference in viewpoint between father and son can be an asset, it can also lead to trouble when the two partners are unwilling to cooperate. The son must recognize that his father is supplying most of the capital, and for this reason stands to lose the most if the farm business goes badly. This will often cause the father to be more conservative than the son thinks is necessary. There are no simple rules for cooperating as a management team. Young men who have worked together well with their families on 4-H club or FFA projects have a good basis on which to build a successful income-sharing agreement.

3. *There must be long-run opportunities for progress.* The purpose of the partnership arrangement should be considered in weighing long-run opportunities.

Is it to serve primarily as a way for you to accumulate capital to get started on your own on another farm? This is often the purpose of the agreement on farms where there are other sons who also want to get established in farming. If you are in this position, you will be less concerned about long-run opportunities on the home farm, and, consequently, you should look ahead and appraise realistically your chances of finding a farm of your own to rent when the time comes.

Or is the family arrangement designed to help you eventually take over complete operation of the home farm? If this is so, several other factors must be considered. Are there other sons who may also want to enter into the farming partnership? Although many family farming agreements with more than one son in the partnership have been successful, such agreements involve some additional problems. The size of the farm business must be large enough to furnish an adequate income to all of the partners. Where more people are involved in the management of the farm, making and carrying out decisions becomes more cumbersome.

Where the agreement is looked upon as a long-term arrangement, the availability of additional housing should be taken into account, even though the son is single. If the father is several years from

Figure 6. FFA and 4-H club projects are an excellent place to begin accumulating livestock with which to start farming. The experience gained in working with the family on farm projects can also be valuable later on when a family farming arrangement is established. (Courtesy Holstein Friesian Assoc.)

retirement age, the son will probably marry before the father is ready to leave the farm. It almost always is desirable for the two families to live in separate houses.

Whether or not the father owns the farm is important. There is no fundamental reason why father–son arrangements cannot be made to work successfully on rented farms. However, the unit must be larger in order to provide sufficient income for two families, plus a return to the landlord. In addition, rented farms typically offer less security and opportunity to make long-run plans. If the farm is rented, the prospects for continuing to rent it should be considered carefully.

Provisions to include in an income-sharing agreement

An income-sharing agreement should include the following provisions:

1. Whether the agreement is to run for a specified period or from year to year until either party wishes to end it.

2. A list of all items furnished by each partner at the start of the farming agreement, along with an estimate of their value.

3. How the income will be divided and how withdrawals for living expense will be made.

4. The way in which increases in the inventory of livestock, feed, and other items that are accumulated during the partnership will be divided.

5. The kinds of farm accounts that will be kept, and the way in which depreciation schedules and expenses on farm improvements will be handled.

6. The amount of food, fuel, electricity, and housing that the partnership will supply to both families.

7. How the agreement will be terminated. This should include provisions for dividing livestock, feed, and other items of farm capital owned by the partnership.

Basis for dividing income

How should we go about working out an agreement? This is a question farm families often ask. Although they want to be fair in dividing up the income from the business, they may have little information to guide them in working out the details of an arrangement. Custom and bargaining between landlords and tenants have fairly well established the terms of standard crop share and livestock share leases. But the terms of income-sharing agreements have not been established in this way.

The income from the farm business should be divided between the partners on the basis of what each contributes to it. Typically the father contributes most of the working capital in the form of livestock, feed, and machinery, and his own labor. If he owns the farm, he also supplies the land and buildings. The son contributes his own labor to the business and may also supply part of the working capital. The accompanying tabulation is an example showing how the division of income could be made.

Amount	Rate	Total
Son's Contributions:		
Labor 12 months	$150	$1,800
Livestock $1,000	5%	50
Machinery $1,000	5%	50
Total value of contributions		$1,900
Father's Contributions:		
Labor 9 months	$150	$1,350
Livestock $8,000	5%	400
Machinery and equipment $6,000	5%	300
Land $72,000	4½%	3,240
Total value of contribution		$5,290

Value of all contributions: $1,900 + $5,290 = $7,190

Per cent of contributions furnished by son: $\dfrac{\$1,900}{\$7,190} \times 100 = 26\%$

In figuring the net income for the farm, each party should be allowed any expenses that he has incurred during the year. Hence, taxes on the farm and depreciation on machinery supplied by the father would be paid to the father before the net income is divided. Or, if the son paid for some repairs on machinery during the year, he should be repaid before the income is divided.

In this example the son would receive 26 per cent of the income and the father the remaining 74 per cent. Supposing, for example, that the net income on the farming operations for the year were $10,000, the son's share would be $2,600 and the father's share $7,400. This division of income, based on the relative contributions furnished by each partner and the valuation we placed on them, assumes that each party contributed to the management in the same proportions in which he contributed other resources. According as the contributions of the two partners differ, the division of income would also differ.

Contribution of labor

Usually it is not difficult to estimate the number of months of labor each partner puts into the business. Both partners do not always work the full 12 months each year. Sometimes the father has reached the age where he wants to become less active and will work less than the full 12 months.

Determining the proper wage rate is more difficult. The prevailing wage in the community is often used as a base. Since the major contribution made by the son is his labor, putting a higher wage on labor will give him a proportionately larger share of the income. Similarly, putting a high price on land and equipment is usually advantageous to the father because he is supplying most of these inputs. Sometimes the younger partner believes that his labor should be figured at a higher rate than that of his father because he is able to work harder, or the father in turn may think that he should have a higher wage than the son because he takes more management responsibility. However, unless either of these differences is great, it is generally best to use the same wage rate for both partners. These problems can cause conflicts in working out an income-sharing agreement, and they illustrate how important it is for the father and son to be willing to cooperate with each other.

Evaluating contributions of land and capital

How should you evaluate the contributions of land and capital made by each party? Two steps are involved: (1) estimating the market value of the land, machinery, and livestock, and (2) determining what rate of interest to credit to the money tied up in these items. Here again the present market value of these items is probably the best basis to use. Farms of comparable value that have sold recently in the community can serve as a guide to estimating the value of land and buildings. Methods of putting a value on machinery and livestock are discussed in Chapter 20.

Once a value has been placed on these items, it is necessary to determine the rate of interest that will be used in estimating returns to them. This step often causes confusion. Why is an interest rate used in estimating the contributions of each party instead of the full value of the land, livestock, and machinery they furnish? The answer is that the annual service of each of these items is contributed rather than the items themselves. Land, for example, is not used up during the year but still remains intact at the end of the year. Depreciation on items such as machinery and equipment is an expense. The partner who furnishes machinery is allowed depreciation on it before the net income is divided.

What interest rate should you use in evaluating the services of the capital invested in land? One method is to use the rate prevailing on farm mortgages in the community. Capital invested in machinery and livestock is often figured at a somewhat higher rate than land because usually more risk is involved in the use of these items. The prevailing rate of interest charged on loans for investments of this type is a good guide to use.

Accounting procedures

In setting up the partnership arrangement, it is well to agree at the start who will keep the account books and how they will be kept. Questions can arise on several points. For example, how rapidly should the machinery be depreciated? For tax purposes it is often advantageous to depreciate machinery as rapidly as tax regulations permit. However, this works to the son's disadvantage when the father furnishes most of the machinery because it increases the amount of expense to be deducted for the father before the division of income is made.

The way in which inventories of livestock and feed will be handled should also be agreed upon. Will beef cows, for example, be valued according to the prevailing market prices each year, or will their values remain constant? Usually there will be no difficulty in arriving at satisfactory procedures for handling these matters. But it is always better if you agree on them at the start instead of waiting until the problem arises at the end of the first year. Methods of evaluating inventories are discussed in Chapter 20.

Increasing the son's share in the business

As he accumulates capital, the son will want to put it to work in the business. Similarly, as the father grows older he may want to turn over more of the work and management to the son. How will these changes affect the division of income? Fortunately the procedure we have shown here for arriving at a division of income is flexible. Once you have established the procedure and agreed on the accounting methods, re-evaluating the contributions being made by each partner to the business is a simple matter. If the proportion in which the contributions are supplied changes, the division of income can be changed accordingly. This should be done every year if significant changes take place in the contributions made by the two partners. If the contributions change but little, every two or three years may be often enough.

Low income

Young men are sometimes disappointed at the amount of income they can expect under an income-sharing arrangement. Frequently they blame the low income on the small share of the total farm income they receive. But more often the difficulty really arises out of the lack of adequate income from the whole farm business. Working out, in a systematic way, the share to which each partner is entitled focuses attention on this weakness. If the basic reason for the son's low income is recognized at the start, steps can be taken to remedy it. This usually will require increasing the size and the efficiency of the farm business. If this cannot be done, the young man who is dissatisfied with his income should seek an opportunity on some other farm or in some other occupation.

Unexpected losses

It is not unusual for farmers to have an occasional bad year. This may happen in a father–son partnership even though the farm business is well managed and will be profitable over the long run. What will the son live on during those years in which there is no income to share under an income-sharing agreement? If the son is well established and has accumulated a reserve of money on which he can draw during an emergency, he should be willing to share the "bad" along with the "good." But, if the low income comes during the first year or two of the arrangement, the son has not had a chance to get on his feet and as a result may have only small savings to tide him over. How should the partnership deal with this problem? The most widely used method is for the father to guarantee a minimum income or wage to the son until he is in a position to tide himself over a poor year. This income may be just enough to allow the son to subsist. The amount required will depend on the son's own family obligations and the proportion of his living that comes directly from the farm in the form of food, housing, and fuel.

Partners not related

So far in this discussion we have mentioned only partnerships between relatives. Income-sharing agreements are more common among family members than among non-related persons, as they require a degree of cooperation that is not easily achieved between two people who are not closely related. In spite of this difficulty, many farm operators work out successful farm operating agreements with young men not related to them. For the most part, these are operators who want to become less active or retire but who have no sons or sons-in-law interested in farming. Such an arrangement permits the operator to keep his investment in machinery and livestock and also work part of the time and keep a close hand on the management. But he does not bear the entire management responsibility and can usually count on better help from a partner than from a man he hires for wages. On the other hand, entering into an operating agreement with a nonrelated partner gives the young man with limited capital a good chance to get started. Unfortunately these opportunities are not easy to find.

The procedure suggested for working out a father–son agreement can also be followed in making arrangements between nonrelatives. It is even more important, however, to work out the agreement in detail and put it into writing. Obtaining legal advice is also a good idea, because agreements of this type can result in each partner being legally liable for the actions of the other.

Adapting Standard Leases to Family Farming Arrangements

Some families prefer to pattern their father–son agreements after the standard leases used in the community. The main advantage of this type of arrangement is that both parties are familiar with the rental terms that have been established by custom and bargaining in the community. This makes it easier for them to agree on what they consider a fair division of income.

The agreement can be based on a cash, crop-share, or livestock-share lease. If the father owns the farm, he becomes the landlord, receives the customary rent for his farm, and takes care of such expenses as taxes on the land, insurance, and building upkeep, which are ordinarily paid by the landlord. In addition to being the landlord, the father may also be the tenant along with his son. Often the father lends the son sufficient money so that the latter can furnish half of the tenant capital used on the farm. If the farm is to be set up on a livestock-share basis, the son must then have money enough to buy one fourth of the livestock and half of the machinery and tenant equipment. If a cash or crop-share leasing arrangement is agreed on, the son would need enough capital to finance half of the livestock, machinery, and other items typically supplied by the tenant.

After the father receives the landlord's share of the income from the farm business, the tenant's share should be divided equally between the father and son. If the son borrows money from the father or from some other source, he will have to pay interest out of his share of the income.

The amount of capital that must be supplied by the son under these arrangements depends on the terms of the lease. This is often a disadvantage. Under the income-sharing arrangement described above, the son puts in the capital that he has and shares in the income according to the labor and capital he furnishes. Some fathers hesitate to burden their son with a heavy debt, particularly at a time when farm prices are high and are likely to decline. If the son has enough capital of his own so that he does not have to borrow heavily, this type of arrangement works well.

Other problems involved in working out standard leasing arrangements are discussed in Chapter 3.

Getting Established on Your Own

Now let us turn to the problems of the young farmer who is starting on his own. Perhaps he has had some experience farming in partnership on the home farm. Or he may be starting out without this background. Where should he start? How should he go about finding a farm? How should he invest his limited capital?

Where to start

Beginning farmers often do not have much choice in the area in which they start to farm. The number of farms available for rent is limited. However, studies show that a high percentage of young men are successful in establishing themselves in the community in which they were reared.

There are two advantages in starting to farm in your home community. (1) You will be more familiar with the agriculture of the area, its problems, and the marketing facilities and farm services available in the community. (2) You also likely will be located near other members of your family who may be farming. Most beginning farmers receive aid from their parents and other relatives in getting started. If you are counting on help from this source, being located near them will make it easier for you to borrow machinery and equipment, exchange work, and obtain advice.

Finding a farm

Because, in most areas, buying a farm is out of the question for beginning farmers on account of the high price of land and the large down payment required, the greatest problem for beginners who cannot start on the home farm is finding a farm to rent. There is severe competition in the better farming areas for the land available to rent, for, in most communities, there are more young men who would like to farm than there are farms for rent. Also, many established farmers would like to expand their present unit by renting additional land. Many young men are fortunate enough to have a relative who owns a farm that they can rent. But others must watch their chance and start wherever and whenever they find a farm.

There is no organized "clearing house" to help you find landowners who have farms for rent. Usually the fact that a farm is for rent travels by word of mouth about the community. In most areas, competition for farms is so keen that landowners with good farms available for rent have numerous applicants without making much of an effort to contact prospective tenants. Therefore, if you want to rent a farm, you must take the initiative in contacting landowners with farms for rent.

In most communities, leases already in effect are either terminated or renewed in the summer or early fall, and so this is the time of the year you should actively look for a farm. You should make inquiries of professional farm managers, bankers, real estate brokers, and county agents. Such persons sometimes can suggest farms for rent or can pass the information along to landowners that you are looking for a farm.

The basic preparation for finding a farm, however, begins long before you actually are ready to farm for yourself. You take the first step when you start to accumulate livestock and equipment for farming and when you first set about learning how to do farm work and to manage a farm business. Once you have established a reputation for competence in doing farm work and in managing your own finances and for ambition and honesty, you have taken a big step toward finding a farm to rent.

Qualifications landowners desire in tenants

Because renting a farm is such a critical factor in getting established in farming, let us examine some of the qualifications that a landlord takes into consideration in selecting a tenant.

1. Background and Experience in Farming. Beginning farmers usually have not had a chance to demonstrate their ability as farm managers. Therefore, most landlords, in considering your qualifications as a prospective young farmer, will inquire about your home farm background. They will want to know what kind of farmer your father was and how much responsibility you had in the management of the home farm. A good 4-H club or FFA record is also considered important by many landlords.

2. *Available Equipment, Livestock, and Financial Position.* Most landowners want tenants to have sufficient equipment to get their work done well and on time. If you do not have enough machinery, the landlord will want to know what arrangements if any you have made to exchange work or hire machines. Often the assurance that your father or another relative living near by is well equipped and will help out in an emergency will help to strengthen your position as an applicant.

Other things being equal, landowners prefer renters who will develop a livestock program, even though the farm is rented on a crop-share basis. They are interested in maintaining fertility by having grain fed on the farm and the manure returned to the land. For this reason, they will frequently ask about your livestock plans.

Most landlords will be concerned about your financial position. They will inquire about the amount of money you owe and the cash you have on hand, and whether you are in a position to borrow more money if the need should arise.

Most landlords will not expect you to be so well equipped with machinery and livestock and in so favorable a financial position as someone who has been farming for several years. Some landowners consider the method by which you acquired your equipment, livestock, and money nearly as important as the amount you have. If you have saved a large proportion of your capital out of your own earnings, they consider this a good indication that you will do a creditable job of managing your financial affairs in the future.

3. *Ambition, Initiative, and Ability to Get Work Done.* In most rental arrangements, the primary resources that the tenant furnishes to balance the land and buildings supplied by the landlord are his labor and management. Tenants are often in a position where they can take short cuts that may be costly to landlords, such as failing to prepare the seedbed adequately to control weeds or to maintain buildings properly. Therefore, the landowner wants to assure himself of your intention and ability to do your work well. In addition to having the desire to make good, you also must have the physical capacity to work long hours and under unfavorable weather conditions when the occasion demands.

Youth and ambition are two advantages prospective young farmers have over their older, established competitors in renting a farm. Providing they have the training, equipment, and financial resources, most landlords would rather rent to younger than to older men.

4. Honesty. Most landlords are not in a position to supervise their farms closely. As a result, tenants have many opportunities to take unfair advantage of them. They can divide the grain unfairly, sell jointly owned fertilizer instead of applying it, or overcharge for minor purchases they make for the landlord. Landlords cannot determine whether you will prove to be honest by asking you. Instead they must look to your past performance and the reputation you have created for honesty among those who know you. They may also watch the frankness and accuracy with which you present your qualifications as an indication of your honesty.

Making the best use of limited capital

Young men starting to farm usually have had little chance to earn and to save money. As a result they lack sufficient capital to stock and equip their farm fully. How can they make their limited capital contribute most to their net income?

Let us examine a typical problem encountered by most beginning farmers because of limited capital. Suppose you have just completed your first year of farming. You have $2,500 from some corn that you sold recently to invest in your farm business. Since you started with a minimum investment in livestock and equipment, you have many possible uses for the money. However, four possibilities appear to be the most promising: (1) selling some of your poorer dairy cows and buying better ones, (2) buying more brood sows, (3) buying more equipment and (4) buying fertilizer.

Table 1. Example Showing Expected Returns from Each Additional $500 Invested in Four Different Ways

Money Invested	Better Dairy Cows	More Brood Sows	More Equipment	Fertilizer
1st $500	$300	$600	$200	$500
2d 500	150	275	175	250
3d 500	100	150	150	150
4th 500	50	100	125	75
5th 500	25	50	100	0

You estimate that each $500 invested in the four alternatives would add the amounts shown in Table 1 to net farm income. Thus,

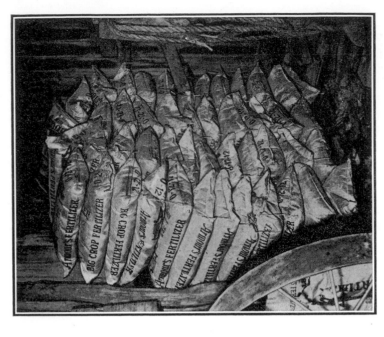

Figure 7. Beginning farmers who are short of capital usually have many uses for their limited funds. Would money spent on more brood sows, dairy cows, or fertilizer add the most to farm income? This is a decision many young farmers must make.

(Courtesy Union Pacific Railroad)

some additional investment in each of the four alternative uses would yield a high return. Returns do vary considerably among the different investments, however. Notice, too, that the returns from each additional $500 invested decreases as more money is used for each purpose. We will examine the reasons for this in later chapters. How should you invest your $2,500 so that it will make the greatest contribution to income?

The principle that should be followed in allocating capital among the four different uses is the principle of alternative returns. It may be stated as follows: If a resource is limited, all possible alternative uses for it should be examined, and each additional portion should be used where it will yield the greatest return. This principle applies wherever a resource is limited and can be put to more than one use on the farm. We shall refer to it often in our study of farm management problems.

The principle of alternative returns is sometimes also referred to as the principle of opportunity cost. The use of this term arises from the fact that the cost of using a limited resource in one enterprise is the opportunity to put it to some other use in the business that you give up.

According to the principle, the first $500 should be invested in brood sows, since this use promises a greater return for the first $500 than the other three alternatives. The second $500 should be invested in fertilizer and the third in better dairy cows. Even though returns decrease as more money is invested in brood sows, they are still the most profitable use for the fourth $500. The last $500 out of the $2,500 should be used for fertilizer. Thus the $2,500 should be invested as follows: $1,000 in brood sows, $1,000 in fertilizer and $500 in better dairy cows. Notice that none of the money should be used for equipment, even though money utilized in this way would add to income. There are too many alternative uses that promise a greater return to justify spending any of the $2,500 for additional equipment.

We have used the schedule of returns shown in Table 1 as an example only. You should not conclude from it that brood sows and fertilizer are always the most profitable use for additional capital. The pattern of returns might be quite different on another farm. However, the principle of alternative returns should always be used as a guide in making investments in the farm business when capital is limited.

The principle explained above should make clear to you why it may be unwise for the beginner to pattern his use of capital after that of well-established farmers with plenty of capital. Buying a pickup truck, a mechanical barn cleaner, or an electric welder or putting in a feeding floor may be profitable for the farmer with ample capital, but all may be poor investments for the beginner who is short on money. The well-financed operator does not have to give up the possibility of buying more brood sows, feed, fertilizer, or dairy cows if he buys a pickup truck or an electric welder. On the other hand, the young farmer just starting out must always weigh

Figure 8. Mechanical barn cleaners save labor but require a sizable outlay of capital. They fit best on farms that have adequate capital but are short on labor. Beginning farmers, short of capital, should consider returns from capital in other uses on their farm before making improvements of this type. (Courtesy Union Pacific Railroad)

the return from every investment against the income he would gain from an alternative use.

Competition from the household

In addition to the many competing uses that the beginning farmer has for his limited capital in the farm business, he usually also has household furniture and equipment to buy. How much should the family spend to furnish the house, and how much should they allocate to the farm business? When a young couple spends some of their limited funds on a new electric range or a refrigerator, they obviously cannot spend it for machinery, livestock, and feed. The more they spend for the one purpose, the less they will have for the other.

We cannot set forth any uniform rules that should be followed in making this decision. If the young couple puts off buying good household equipment and furnishings until they have no further need for capital in the farm business, they may have to wait a long time. The amount of capital that can be used to advantage in the farm business is very great in almost all types of farming. Perhaps the best procedure for young couples severely limited in capital is to take the middle way. They should not buy all new equipment and household furnishings because this would involve too great a sacrifice of farm income. Instead they should get along with some used equipment until they have had a chance to accumulate savings out of farm earnings. Putting a maximum amount of capital to work in the farm business during the first few years will help increase their income so that they will be in a better position to purchase modern conveniences and furniture later on.

Ways of reducing capital needs

The beginner is handicapped the first year because he has very little livestock and no inventory of home-raised grains to use for livestock feed. However, it is to his advantage, if possible, to get his livestock program under way during the first year without waiting to raise a crop for feed.

If the beginner's father or some other relative is well established in farming, exchange arrangements frequently can be worked out. For example, he can "borrow" a brood sow early in the spring and have it farrow one or perhaps two litters of pigs. Then he can either return the brood sow or sell it and give the proceeds to its owner. Usually, if the established farmer makes preparation in advance by breeding a sufficient number of sows, he can give the beginner this help without any financial sacrifice himself. A similar arrangement can be worked out whereby they can exchange feed. The established operator can provide corn and oats during the spring and early summer months. Then, when the new operator gets his first crop, he can repay the established farmer bushel for bushel. Again this exchange can be of great help to the beginner at small sacrifice to the established farm operator.

Studies show that beginning farmers are often long on labor and short on capital. For this reason it is often good business for them to exchange labor for machine services. The beginning operator may help a neighbor or a relative put up hay in exchange for the use of haying machinery, or he may help combine grain in return for the use of the combine on his own farm. This holds to a minimum the amount of capital the beginner must invest in machinery and permits him to use the capital elsewhere in his business.

Making management decisions

In making decisions, established farmers can be guided by what they have done in previous years. Usually they will be following more or less definite long-range programs, which will determine their decisions. But, because beginning farmers have no previous experience to guide them, they must make a great many new decisions during their first year or two of farming. They must work out a cropping system and plan a livestock program, in addition to solving the many day-to-day problems that farming involves. They will make many decisions completely on their own for the first time.

How well you can adjust to this responsibility will depend on your background. If you have had projects on the home farm and have been given responsibility for making decisions, you will find these new responsibilities less troublesome. Before making major decisions, you should not hesitate to seek the advice of others. You usually will find that successful farmers, relatives, and others are glad to give advice.

Problems

1. Make a list of all the young men who have started to farm in your community during the last five years. How many started on the home farm?

2. If you have no definite project agreement, work out the provisions that you think should be included in such an agreement. Ask your father if he agrees with the terms you have suggested.

3. Assume that your father raises 100 hogs which are sold at an average weight of 230 pounds and keeps 20 cows which produce an average of 10,000 pounds of grade A milk per cow each year. He has agreed to give you 10 per cent of the gross receipts from these two enterprises, plus a wage. How many dollars could you expect to realize from your share of hog and milk receipts?

4. Determine the approximate share of income you would be entitled to if you entered into an income-sharing agreement on your home farm. Assume that you contribute only your labor, on a full-time basis. Do you think the business is sufficiently large at the present to support a successful father–son agreement?

5. Graph the index of prices received by farmers from 1909 to the present. This information can be obtained from *Agricultural Outlook Charts* published yearly by the U.S. Department of Agriculture. Then extend the trend line for ten more years as follows: (1) prices rising fairly sharply during the ten-year period, (2) prices rising gradually, (3) prices remaining stable, (4) prices dropping slightly, and (5) prices dropping sharply. Label each line from the top to the bottom *A* through *E*, respectively. Which of these most nearly represents the direction in which you think prices will move in the next ten years? How would your appraisal of future prices influence the way you would start farming?

Ask the rest of the class to indicate which of the five price trends you have plotted on the graph they think is most likely to prevail in the next ten years.

6. Assume that you were starting to farm next spring on your home farm on a crop-share lease. Make a list of (1) equipment, livestock, and supplies you would need, (2) equipment, livestock, and supplies that you could do without but that you think would increase your income, and (3) items that you would like to have but that would not increase your income. Under what circumstances do you think you would be justified in buying any of the items you have listed in the third group?

7. Again assume you are starting to farm as in six above. What is the minimum amount of money you would need to get started? Be sure to allow for living and operating expenses until you begin to have income from the business. You will find that farm auction sales are an excellent source of information on prices of used machinery and equipment.

References

Beneke, Raymond R., and George A. Pond, "Starting Farming in Southeastern Minnesota," *Minn. Agr. Expt. Sta. Bull.* 405, June 1950.

Case, H. C. M., and Paul E. Johnston, *Principles of Farm Management,* Chapter 18, J. B. Lippincott Co., Chicago, Philadelphia, New York, 1953.

Cunningham, J. B., and H. C. M. Case, "Father–Son Farm Business Agreements," *Illinois Ext. Circ.* 587, 1944.

Efferson, J. Norman, *Principles of Farm Management,* Chapter 17, McGraw-Hill Book Co., New York, 1953.

"Farming Opportunities in the Midwest," *Purdue Ext. Bull.* 325, 1946.

Forster, G. W., *Farm Organization and Management,* 3d Ed., Chapter 13, Prentice-Hall, New York, 1953.

Harris, Marshall, and Elton B. Hill, "Family Farm-Transfer Agreements," *Illinois Ext. Circ.* 680, 1951.

Hill, Elton B., and Marshall Harris, "Family Farm-Operating Agreements," *Mich. Sta. Spec. Bull.* 368, 1951.

Hoglund, C. R., and A. W. Anderson, "Father–Son Farming Plans," *S. Dakota Agr. Expt. Sta. Bull.* 390, 1948.

Hopkins, John A., and William G. Murray, *Elements of Farm Management,* Chapter 2, 4th Ed., Prentice-Hall, New York, 1953.

Howell, H. B., Earl O. Heady, and L. J. Bodensteiner, "Farming Today," *Iowa Agr. Expt. Sta. and Ext. Serv. Coop. Bull.*, p. 82, 1946.

Johnson, O. R., "Transferring the Farm to the Next Generation," *Missouri Agr. Expt. Sta. Bull.* 515, 1948.

McNall, P. E., "Steps toward Farm Ownership," *Wisconsin Agr. Ext. Serv. Circ.* 368, Mar. 1946.

Moore, H. R., and R. C. Headington, "Father–Son Farming Plans and Arrangements," *Ohio Expt. Sta. Bull.* 686, 1949.

Parsons, Kenneth H., and Eliot D. Waples, "Keeping the Farm in the Family," *Wisconsin Agr. Expt. Sta. Res. Bull.* 157, 1945.

Parsons, Kenneth H., and Clara J. Legrid, "Planning for the Descent of Property in the Family," *Wisconsin Agr. Ext. Serv. Circ.* 364, 1945.

Robertson, Lynn S., and Ralph H. Woods, "Farm Business Management," Chapter 16, J. B. Lippincott Co., Chicago, Philadelphia, New York, 1950.

Smith, R. S., and S. W. Warren, "Father and Son Arrangements on the Farm," *Cornell Ext. Bull.* 892, 1953.

Tharp, Max M., and Harold H. Ellis, "Father–Son Farm Operating Agreements," *USDA Farmers Bull.* 2026, 1951.

3

Planning Farm Leasing Arrangements

In the previous chapter we have studied family farming agreements. They are actually a specialized type of leasing arrangement. In this chapter we will center our attention on standard leasing arrangements. Most farmers rent under one of these arrangements at some time during their farming career. In some cases renting may be a step to ownership. In others it may be a permanent status. Leasing enables many young men to farm who lack sufficient capital to own the land, equipment, and livestock needed. In some areas of the United States well over 50% of the land is farmed under some type of leasing arrangement (Figure 9).

Management Problems

1. Selecting the type of lease to use.
2. Drawing up the lease.
3. Improving farming on rented farms.

Selecting the Type of Lease to Use

We will study the characteristics of the following lease types:

1. Straight cash.
2. Sliding-scale cash.
3. Crop share.
4. Livestock share.

The crop-share lease is the most widely used of all the leasing types (Figure 10). The lease labeled "share cash" is essentially the same as the crop-share lease. For this reason we will discuss the two types together.

Straight cash leases

Under this arrangement the landlord furnishes the land and buildings and in return is paid a flat sum by the tenant. Cash leasing requires little supervision and management on the part of the land-

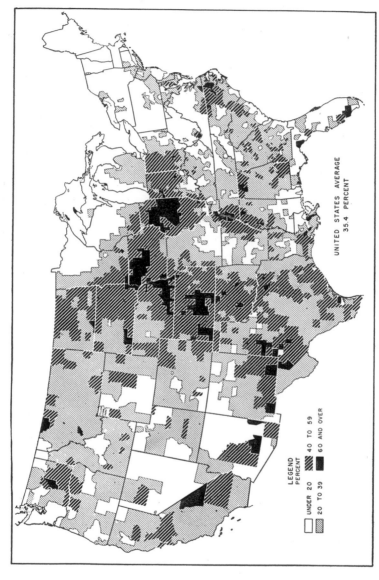

Figure 9. Percentage of all land in farms operated under lease, April 1, 1950—county unit basis. (From *Farm Tenure, a Graphic Summary*, 1950 Census of Agriculture)

LEGEND
PERCENT

UNDER 20

20 TO 39

40 TO 59

60 AND OVER

UNITED STATES AVERAGE
35.4 PERCENT

lord. He has few decisions to make aside from picking a tenant and determining the amount of rent to be charged. He can be fairly certain of the amount of rent he will get from the farm since this is not affected by changes in prices or yields taking place during the year.

How does the cash lease work out for the tenant? Some tenants like to rent on a cash basis because of the greater freedom it permits them in making decisions. They get the full amount of any in-

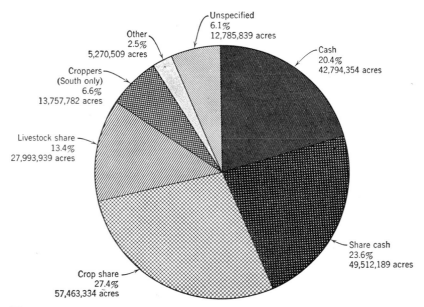

Figure 10. Land in farms operated by tenants, by class of tenant, for the United States, 1950. (From *Farm Tenure, a Graphic Summary,* 1950 Census of Agriculture. Data are based on reports for only a sample of farms)

creased production from doing a superior job of farming. On the other hand, if you rent on the cash basis, you will be incurring more risk than under any other type of lease. In case of a crop failure or a sharp drop in prices, your rental payment will not change.

Some landlords experienced difficulty collecting cash rents during depression years. For this reason there was a shift away from the cash lease during the 1930's. However, it is still the most frequent method of renting in the northeast part of the country. It is also commonly used in the western states and in parts of Minnesota and Wisconsin.

Sliding-scale cash leases

Attempts have been made to reduce the tenant's risk, in renting on a cash basis, by including a clause in the lease whereby the size of the rental payment changes according to shifts in the prices of farm products. This device also decreases the tendency of cash rents remaining high during periods of falling prices and lagging behind when price levels are rising.

Simple methods can be used to make cash-leasing terms flexible. For example, instead of charging $15 cash rent per acre for a farm the landlord and tenant could agree that the rent should be 10 bushels of corn per acre. As a result, when the price of corn increased, rent would go up, and, when the price of corn declined, the cash-rental payment would decrease. Or the arrangement can be broadened to include more farm products. Under one such agreement used successfully on a midwest farm since 1932, the tenant each year pays a cash rent per acre equal to the sum of the value of the following: (1) 3 bushels of no. 2 corn, (2) 3 pounds of 92 score butter, (3) 3 dozen grade-A eggs, and (4) 30 pounds of good to choice hogs, liveweight. Chicago prices on December 15 are used in placing a value on these products each year. Several experiment stations publish an index that takes into consideration changes in the prices of the principal farm commodities produced in their areas. Cash-rental payments can then be varied with changes in the index. This system, like the one described above, relates the rental payment to the prices of a variety of farm products instead of to a single product.

The sliding-scale or flexible-cash lease is not widely used. Some people object to it because of its failure to remove the risk arising out of low yields. They point out that prices, and hence cash rents, are likely to be high during years in which yields are low. To eliminate this hazard, a flexible cash lease should contain a clause providing for a reduction in rent in the event of crop failure.

Crop-share leases

When a farm is rented on the crop-share basis, the tenant gives part of the crop for rent. Typically he also pays a cash rent on the hay and pasture land. In addition, a cash rental on buildings is becoming increasingly common. Under the crop-share arrangement the landlord's principal contribution is land and buildings whereas the tenant contributes labor and machinery. The cost of a number of inputs such as feed and fertilizer are often shared by both. The tenant typically has full responsibility for the livestock program. He furnishes all livestock, pays all livestock expenses, and receives all livestock income.

The crop-share lease is popular among landowners and tenants alike for several reasons. The risk is low for the tenant since the amount of rent moves up and down with changes both in yields and prices. The landlord has a stake in the outcome of the cropping system and hence has an incentive to provide lime, to build terraces, and to furnish cribs and granaries. Landlords also find it easier to collect their rent under the crop-share than under the cash lease.

Figure 11. Under crop-share leases the landowner and the farm operator divide the grain. Hay and pasture land are typically rented for cash. When farms are rented on a livestock-share lease, the landlord also shares in livestock returns. (Courtesy Deere & Co.)

On the other hand, the crop-share lease requires more supervision on the part of the landlord than the cash lease. It also requires a greater outlay of capital for seed, fertilizer and spray materials. Under the crop-share lease the landlord benefits directly from high yields and good prices but also shares the difficulties arising from poor crop yields and low prices.

Livestock-share leases

Although the terms of stock-share leases vary somewhat from one community to another, the tenant customarily furnishes all the labor and crop machinery. The landlord furnishes the land and buildings. Generally the tenant and landlord own the livestock and livestock equipment jointly and share all livestock expenses equally. The landlord and tenant usually share crop and livestock returns on a fifty-fifty basis. As a result livestock share leases are known as 50–50 leases in some communities.

Some tenants like a livestock-share lease because it allows them to start farming on a larger scale with their limited capital than a

Figure 12. Leasing arrangements, especially crop-share and livestock-share leases, require a close working relationship between the landowner and tenant. (Courtesy Soil Conservation Serv.)

cash or crop-share lease. Frequently they can obtain better and larger farms by renting on a stock-share basis. The landlord's direct interest in the livestock program encourages him to make more improvements such as buildings, fences, and feeding floors.

The drawback of the livestock-share lease from the standpoint of the tenant is that he must share returns from livestock production with the landlord. The benefits from any extra effort on his part in both crop and livestock production are shared by the landlord; if he were renting on a cash or crop-share basis, he would get the entire return from livestock. In addition to the sharing of livestock returns, tenants sometimes object to the close working relationship with the landlord that the livestock-share lease requires.

Some landlords prefer the livestock-share lease because it provides them an investment opportunity for more capital. They can also take a more active role in the operation and management of the farm. Many landowners believe that a livestock-share lease leads to better land use since both parties are interested in feeding the crops raised on the farm.

Other landlords find they are not in a position to take the added risk and put into the business the added capital that a livestock-share lease requires. Often farm owners lack the knowledge of livestock farming needed to share intelligently the management responsibility on a stock-share farm. In other cases they may be too far away from the farm, or they may simply prefer not to spend the time necessary to give proper attention to a stock-share operation.

Drawing up the Lease

Terms of the lease

Several questions arise concerning the terms of a lease. What percentage of the crop should the tenant and landlord get? How much cash rent should you pay on hay and pasture land? How should seed and fertilizer expenses be divided?

You will find that leasing terms that are customary in the community influence many landlords and tenants in drawing up a lease. Often both parties use the degree to which a provision is accepted and followed in the community as a test of its fairness. Prevailing rental provisions are a good starting point in drawing up leasing terms, but it may be necessary to modify them for several reasons.

Drawing up leasing terms introduces many of the elements of a bargaining process. If there are few farms to rent and many tenants competing for them, the landlord is in a position to press for more favorable terms than are customary. On the other hand, when tenants are scarce and there are many job alternatives outside of farming, they are in a stronger bargaining position.

Leasing terms should reflect differences in the quality of the resources furnished by each party. This is taken care of in part, at least, by the tendency of a well-improved farm to attract a superior tenant. The share of the crop given as rent under the crop-share lease is established by community custom. Any adjustments for above-average improvements typically are made on the cash-rental payment for hay and pasture land. This has the unfortunate effect of encouraging tenants to reduce the rental payment by cutting down on the acres in meadow. To avoid this difficulty, it is better to put a cash rent on hay and pasture land, in line with its productivity, and arrange a separate building rental that takes into account the quality of the improvements on the farm.

Advantages of a written lease

If you rent a farm, you and the landlord will have to agree on many details of operating the farm and of sharing expenses and income. The contract between the tenant and landlord covering these matters is referred to as a lease. Leases often are verbal contracts. An Iowa study showed that 70 per cent of leases in a north central Iowa area were oral agreements. What are the advantages of having the lease in writing?

1. Preparing a written lease helps insure that the terms will be carefully worked out. One of the dangers of making an oral agreement is that many of the terms will not be discussed and actually agreed upon. However, when the two parties secure one of the recommended leasing forms and go through it together step by step, they can be fairly sure of discussing most of the important points.

2. Misunderstandings are minimized. If you sit down with a land-owner to work out a definite, written agreement, some differences of opinion almost certainly will arise. However, it is better to settle these differences at the start of your working relationship than to be troubled by them later on. Often misunderstandings arise simply because the matter was not discussed at the time the leasing agreement was made. The farming program also may suffer for lack of a definite understanding. A tenant, for example, may object to using fertilizer, because a definite method of sharing the cost has not been worked out. Or weeds may go unsprayed, although the landlord is willing to pay for the spray and the tenant is willing to put it on, simply because the point was not considered in drawing up leasing terms.

3. Difficulties are avoided in the event of the death of either party. Both landlord and tenant may be in good health at the time the rental agreement is made, but an acute illness or an accident may result in the sudden death of either party. If the terms of the lease

have been written out, settling accounts will be easier. This is especially important in livestock- and labor-share leases where the terms of the lease differ from those customarily used in the community.

Provisions to be included

There are a number of leasing forms that you can use as a guide in drawing up a written lease. The lease you use should provide a written agreement on the following points:

1. *Period of Lease and Provisions for Cancelation and Termination.* Although leases may extend for any length of time, they usually are drawn up for a single year. Often it is taken for granted that the lease will continue for a longer period unless one party or the other cancels it. In addition to specifying the length of time of the agreement, the lease should also state when notice of cancelation must be given. In some states the law specifies that, if notice of termination is not given by a certain time, the lease automatically continues.

2. *Kind and Amount of Rental Payment.* Under typical crop-share and livestock-share leases, the proportion of the crop or livestock going to each party should be specified. In addition, the amount of cash rent to be paid on hay and pasture land and on buildings and when it is to be paid should be clearly indicated. In crop-share leases, the responsibility of the tenant in delivering the landlord's share of the grain to him should be stated.

3. *Maintenance of Property.* Although the landlord owns the buildings and fences on the farm, the tenant is usually expected to share in their maintenance. In most communities the tenant is also expected to help repair and construct fences. These responsibilities should be defined in the lease.

4. *Conservation of Land Resources.* As pointed out before, the tenant usually has a shorter-term interest in the farm than the landlord. This arises out of his insecurity of tenure and the fact that the land belongs to someone else. In order to help protect his land, it is wise for the landowner to state in the lease the rotation to be followed and the conservation practices such as contouring and terracing that are to be used.

5. *Other Improved Farming Practices to Be Followed.* Most leases contain a clause indicating that the tenant is expected to employ good husbandry in farming the land. This is hard to define, and the tenant and landlord often do not agree on what is included

under this term. Therefore, it is a good idea to write out in greater detail what is actually expected of the tenant. This includes use to be made of fertilizer and details of the tenant's responsibility in controlling weeds.

6. *How Expenses Are to Be Shared.* Modern farming makes use of many purchased items such as fertilizer, lime, seed, and sprays. The lease should set forth definitely how the cost of these items is to be shared. This not only avoids misunderstandings but also helps to insure that these items will be used when they are needed.

7. *Paying the Tenant for Improvements That Are not Completely Used up When He Moves.* Some farm inputs are not used up in a single year; hence, part of their value frequently remains when the time comes for the tenant to move. If no provision is included in the lease for repaying the tenant for any unused portion, he understandably will hesitate to invest his money in these types of inputs when he rents on a year-to-year lease. Provisions of this type are called compensation for unexhausted improvements clauses.

Improving Farming on Rented Farms

Studies show that rented farms frequently are not farmed so well as owner-operated farms. For example, cropping systems often include a higher proportion of intertilled crops. Fewer conservation measures are used. Buildings and other improvements are not so well cared for.

Of 83 tenants interviewed in a western Iowa area where erosion is a serious hazard, 49 said that difficulties arising out of rental agreements were a major obstacle to improved soil conservation. A Nebraska study showed that houses and other buildings were poorer on rented than on owner-operated farms. Of course, these difficulties do not arise on all rented farms, but they are sufficiently widespread so that anyone looking forward to operating a rented farm should understand why they arise and what can be done to overcome them.

Let us examine the principal causes of these leasing problems:

1. *Tenure is insecure.* Most tenants have less security of tenure than owner operators. This is reflected in part in the short length of time most tenants live on a farm. More than 60 per cent of all tenants in the United States had farmed their current farm for a period of less than 5 years in 1950. The percentage of tenants and owners who had been on their current farm for different numbers of years is shown in Figure 13 by areas of the United States. Ten-

ants who rent from close relatives are usually exceptions; their
security of tenure often approaches that of owner operators.

Insecure tenure interferes with planning and carrying out long-
term farming programs. Tenants hesitate to undertake improvements that will take several years to pay for themselves. For example, they may be reluctant to adopt conservation measures because
they may not be on the farm long enough to get the benefits from
them. For the same reason, tenants sometimes do not keep up
fences and buildings as well as do owner operators.

The fact that a tenant has lived on a farm for a long time does not
necessarily mean that he has felt secure in his tenure. He may have

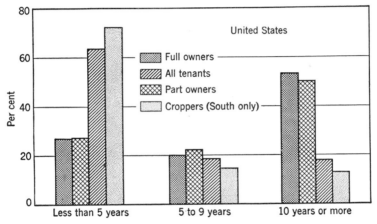

Figure 13. Percentage of owners, part owners, and tenants who had been on
their present farm for various numbers of years. (From *Farm Tenure, a
Graphic Summary*, 1950 Census of Agriculture)

felt that each year likely would be his last on the farm. This attitude could cause him to take a short-run view of his farming operations and to farm poorly as a result, even though he continued to
rent the farm for a long period. I know of one situation in which
the tenant felt over a period of 7 years that each year would be his
last one on the farm. The farm was owned by an estate, and the
heirs planned each year during this period to sell the farm. As a
result, the tenant farmed all through the 7-year period as though
he would not be on the farm the next year. During the seventh year,
the farm was finally purchased by one of the heirs, and the tenant
was given assurance that he could continue to rent it as long as he
did a good job. After the uncertain tenure situation was cleared up,

a long-run cropping program was established, permanent pastures were improved, some badly needed terraces were built, and part of the farm was contoured.

2. *Returns to the landlord for improvements are indirect.* When a farm is rented on a crop-share or cash basis, the landowner benefits only indirectly from good buildings and other livestock facilities. A good set of improvements may help the landlord to attract and keep a better tenant. Providing good livestock facilities may encourage the tenant to raise more livestock. In this way more feed is fed on

Figure 14. One of the disadvantages of renting a farm is that tenure may be insecure. Renters frequently face the prospect of having to move to another farm. Insecurity of tenure often interferes with making and carrying out long-term farm plans. (Courtesy Wallaces' *Farmer and Iowa Homestead*)

the farm and more manure returned to the land, resulting in higher yields in which the landlord shares. These returns are hard to measure in dollars and cents. They may seem insignificant or uncertain to many landlords and cause them to hesitate to make improvements.

Lack of buildings and livestock facilities is one of the principal criticisms that tenants make of rented farms. One crop-share renter complained that the roof of the barn leaked, causing hay to spoil and making it difficult to produce high-quality milk. He called it to the attention of his landlord repeatedly. When a repair crew appeared on the farm, the tenant thought he had at last won his point. Instead, the crew went to work repairing the granary in which the landlord's grain was stored, even though, in the tenant's opinion, the roof of the barn was much more in need of repair. The landlord was investing his money in improvements that would yield a direct return to him.

3. Returns are not shared in same proportion as costs. When an owner operator improves the drainage on his farm by installing tile, he gets all of the added yield that results. But, when an owner who rents his farm on a crop-share basis makes the same improvement, he gets only half or even less of the increased yield, depending on the terms of the lease. Therefore, there is much less incentive for the owner who rents out his land to improve the drainage than for the owner-operator.

Table 2. Effect of Sharing Costs on Number of Tenants Applying Fertilizer and on Rate of Application—Crop-Share Farms*

Item	Farms Where Landlord Shares Costs	Farms Where Landlord Does Not Share Costs
% fertilizing corn	60.0	6.9
% fertilizing oats	42.2	3.4
Lb fertilizer applied on corn per farm†	5104	795
Lb fertilizer applied on oats per farm†	4227	466

* *Iowa Agr. Expt. Sta. Res. Bull.* 386.
† Figure is average for those applying fertilizer.

On the other hand, the landlord may be reluctant to apply fertilizer. If the tenant were to use fertilizer and stand all of the cost, he would get only a share, say one half, of the added return. Suppose putting 40 pounds of nitrogen side dressing on corn would increase the yield 8 bushels per acre. If the price of nitrogen were 14 cents per pound and corn were $1.25 per bushel, the cost of the nitrogen would be $5.60 and the added return from using it $10.00. This would be profitable for an owner operator. But, if the tenant had to stand the full cost but got only half the return, he would be paying out $5.60 to get back $5.00. He obviously could not afford to do this. That failure to share costs results in less fertilizer being used is shown in Table 2. Here the pattern of fertilizer use on crop-share farms where landlords share the cost is compared with the pattern on farms where they do not. A similar problem exists in many other farming practices such as spraying weeds, cultivating corn an added time, using improved seeds, and contour farming.

4. Two parties are involved in the management. Whenever a major change is to be made in the farming program on a crop-share or livestock-share farm, usually both the landlord and the tenant must agree on how to proceed. Often neither one has the final authority to make a decision. Sometimes necessary changes are not made because the two parties fail to agree on a course of action. An example might be the decision to buy feeder cattle under a livestock-share lease. In other instances the decision may not be made soon enough because of the divided responsibility. Lack of agreement on how much or what type of fertilizer to use may result in none being applied. Failure to carry out a profitable farming practice will also result whenever either the tenant or landlord lacks sufficient capital to adopt the improved practice.

Unfortunately, situations sometimes arise in which the two parties grow to distrust or even dislike each other. As a result, they may not evaluate suggestions made by each other objectively. When the landlord and tenant cannot get along, their incentive to give their best thought and effort to the business may be destroyed.

Ways of improving farming on rented farms

Following are a number of ways in which some of the difficulties arising out of leasing arrangements may be overcome:

1. Providing Greater Security of Tenure. Leases that extend for a term of three to five years help to promote security of tenure. Therefore, in renting a farm you may want a long-term lease; you will find, however, that many landlords hesitate to enter into a long-term agreement because they cannot change tenants immediately if they are dissatisfied. In addition, some landowners believe that giving a tenant a long-term lease tends to dull his incentive to do a good job. Only a small percentage of leases are for more than one year.

It is the degree of security that the tenant feels that influences his attitude toward making long-run improvements. For this reason, if you cannot rent a farm on a long-term lease, the next best thing is to get the landlord's assurance that you can continue to stay on the farm as long as you do a good job. One way of making this agreement more definite is to have the landowner include a "continuation clause" in the lease setting forth his intention to retain you as the tenant as long as you continue to perform satisfactorily.

2. Providing Compensation for Unexhausted Improvements. You will be in a better position to make such improvements as liming, fencing, and terracing if the landlord agrees to pay you for any unused benefits when you leave the farm. For example, when you share the cost of lime, the landlord may agree to compensate you if you leave the farm before getting full benefit from it. Suppose you spend $500 for lime and you and the landowner agree that the soil will benefit from the treatment over a five-year period. The landlord would agree to pay you $400 if you left after one year, $300 if you left after two years, and so forth. This is the compensation-for-unexhausted-improvements provision that was mentioned previously as one of the essentials of a good lease.

Several experiment stations have included clauses in leases that provide compensation to tenants for unexhausted conservation work, but these contracts are not in general use. The Nebraska lease contains the following provisions:

> If the tenant has built soil-saving dams, terraces, drainage systems, or other water control structures, he shall be reimbursed for his labor on the following basis:
>
> Four fifths, if the structure has been used not over 1 year.
>
> Three fifths, if it has been used more than 1 year and not more than 2 years.
>
> Two fifths, if it has been used more than 2 years, and not more than 3 years.
>
> One fifth, if it has been used more than 3 years, and not more than 4 years.
>
> No payment for structures used more than 4 years.

The same principle can be used for other types of improvements. Suppose the tenant wants a bathroom in the house. This will not yield any direct returns to the landlord. As a result, he may be reluctant to make the improvement. However, some landlords permit the tenant to go ahead and make and pay for improvements of this type. Then they agree to pay the tenant part of the cost if he moves. If you use this arrangement of paying for an improvement, you should work out a schedule with the landlord showing how the improvement will be depreciated. This arrangement works in much the same way as it would with lime. For example, suppose the cost of installing a bathroom is $1,000 and that it is expected to last 20 years. The improvement would be depreciated at the rate of $50 per year. If you move at the end of 1 year, the landlord will pay you $950. If you move at the end of 10 years, the landlord pays you only $500. Usually the next tenant will continue the arrangement where the last one left off.

3. Greater Use of Special Rents to Encourage Landlords to Improve Buildings. If the landlord receives no direct benefit from an improvement such as a pressure water system or a feeding floor, he may still be encouraged to provide the improvement through the use of a special rent. Often the tenant will profit financially by paying the added yearly rent necessary to encourage the landlord to make the improvement.

Suppose you are a dairy farmer renting a farm on a crop-share basis and want to change from a cream to a grade-A milk market. However, before the change can be made the barn and milkhouse will have to be remodeled to meet sanitary regulations. Let us assume that this change will cost $2,000. As the tenant, you will not be justified in making these improvements because you might have to move in a year or two. The landlord will also hesitate to invest the $2,000 because he will get no direct return from it. However, if you agree to pay an added rent of, say, $200 per year, for these improvements the landlord will get $100 per year to cover depreciation and $100 return on the capital he has invested. Your income might be increased considerably more than $200 per year by being able to sell grade-A milk instead of cream. Hence, you will both profit from the arrangement.

4. A Better Sharing of Costs and Benefits. When both the tenant and landlord benefit from an input or improvement, the cost, if possible, should be shared in the same proportion as the benefits. Where it is not feasible to share costs and returns on an improvement, one party can make an improvement that would be of doubtful profitability from his standpoint alone, and, in return, the other party can stand the full cost of some offsetting improvement. As a tenant you might agree to clear land, fill gullies, build terraces, or do other conservation work during slack periods in return for the landlord's installing a water system.

5. Use of Livestock-Share Lease Where It Is Adaptable. Under the stock-share lease, both landlord and tenant share in benefits from a wider range of improvements than under the crop-share or cash-rental agreement. For example, the landlord will benefit directly from better buildings, watering facilities, feeding floors, and fences. For this reason he will have a greater incentive to make investments of this type.

In addition, the livestock-share lease encourages greater livestock production. As a result, more grain is fed on the farm, and there is an outlet for more grass and legume crops.

6. Greater Control of Cropping Program by Landlord on Farms Where Renter's Tenure Is Insecure. Renters who are uncertain how long they will remain on a farm have a tendency to raise a large acreage of high-income, intertilled crops. Under these circumstances, it is the landowner's responsibility to see that the tenant follows a cropping program that is consistent with good land use and maximum long-run income. By doing so, he not only protects his own financial interest but also maintains the farm in good condition for the next tenant.

Problems

1. The class should be divided into pairs, one member of each pair acting as a landlord and the other as a tenant. With a specific farm such as your home farm in mind, draw up a crop-share leasing arrangement with your partner. Use the standard leasing form most common in your area, and change or add to it as you consider necessary. Now have the other member of the pair serve as landlord, and work out a livestock-share lease.

2. List all of these lease types commonly used in your community. Which is most common in your state. Why do you think this type of lease is so popular?

3. List the farms that border on your home farm. Have other members of the class do the same. Combine the lists into one for the entire class, being careful to eliminate duplication. Divide the list into renter- and owner-operated farms. Then determine how long each farmer has lived on his farm. If you do not know, have your father help you make an estimate. How does the average number of years that the tenants have farmed their present farms compare with the number of years for owner operators? Can you see any indications that short tenure has interfered with good farming practices on the rented farms?

4. Select a crop-share rented farm, and estimate the rent the landlord received last year from it. What rent would he have received had the farm been rented at prevailing cash-rental rates? How do you account for the difference? How has this difference changed during the last 20 years?

5. How would you determine if the rent being charged on a farm was fair?

6. What are the most frequent complaints that you hear from tenants about their leasing arrangement and landlord? What complaints do land-

lords make? What changes in leasing arrangements, if any, would help reduce these difficulties?

References

Bondurant, John, "Land Tenure in Southern Logan County, Kentucky," *Kentucky Agr. Expt. Sta. Bull.* 464, 1944.

Case, H. C. M., and Paul E. Johnston, *Principles of Farm Management,* Chapter 18, J. B. Lippincott Co., Chicago, Philadelphia, New York, 1953.

Efferson, J. Norman, *Principles of Farm Management,* Chapter 20, Mc-Graw-Hill Book Co., New York, 1953.

Farm Tenure; a Graphic Summary, Bur. Census, U.S. Dept. Commerce, and Bur. Agr. Econ., USDA, cooperating, 1950.

Farm Tenure; a Graphic Summary 1950, Cooperative Report, 1950 Census of Agriculture, Vol. V, Part 5, Dec. 1952.

Forster, G. W., *Farm Organization and Management,* 3d Ed., Chapters 15 and 16, Prentice-Hall, New York, 1953.

Frey, John C., "Some Obstacles to Soil Erosion Control in Western Iowa," *Iowa Agr. Expt. Sta. Res. Bull.* 391, 1952.

Headington, R. C., and J. I. Falconer, "Size of Farm Units as Affected by the Farming of Additional Land," *Ohio Agr. Expt. Sta. Bull.* 637, 1942.

Heady, Earl O., and Earl W. Kehrberg, "Relationship of Crop-Share and Cash Leasing Systems to Farming Efficiency," *Iowa Agr. Exp. Sta. Bull.* 386, May 1952.

Hopkins, John A., and William G. Murray, *Elements of Farm Management,* 4th Ed., Chapter 6. Prentice-Hall, New York, 1953.

Lambrecht, George, and Lyman Wallin, "Farm Tenancy in Box Butte County, Nebraska," *Nebraska Agr. Expt. Sta. Bull.* 336, 1942.

Lloyd, O. G., H. S. Moraine and J. R. Hays, "Principal Methods of Share Renting and Cooperation for Unexhausted Improvements in Four Types of Farming Areas in Indiana," *Purdue Agr. Expt. Sta. Bull.* 464, Jan. 1942.

McCoy, John H., "The Stock-Share Lease," *Kansas Agr. Expt. Sta. Circ.* 252, Nov. 1948.

McNall, P. E., "The Farm Lease," *Wisconsin Agr. Ext. Serv. Circ.* 303, May 1940.

North Central Regional Land Tenure Committee, "Improving Farm Tenure in the Midwest," *Illinois Agr. Expt. Sta. Bull.* 502, 1944.

Pond, G. A., "Farm Tenancy in Minnesota," *Minn. Agr. Expt. Sta. Bull.* 353, 1941.

Quackenbush, G. B., and O. G. Lloyd, "Farm Tenure in Indiana by Type of Farming Area," *Indiana Agr. Expt. Sta. Bull.* 488, 1943.

Ratchford, Brice C., "Rental Arrangements for Progressive Farming," *N. Carolina Agr. Ext. Serv. Southern Farm Management Ext. Pub.* 3.

Robertson, Lynn S., and Ralph H. Woods, *Farm Business Management,* Chapter 16, J. B. Lippincott Co., Chicago, Philadelphia, New York, 1950.

Timmons, John F., and Raleigh Barlowe, "Farm Ownership in the Midwest," *North Central Regional Publication* 13, *Iowa Agr. Expt. Sta. Res. Bull.* 361, June 1949.

Buying a Farm

Most farmers want to own the farm they operate. A few are fortunate enough to inherit a farm; however, most must make careful plans in order eventually to buy a farm. The large percentage of farmers who become owners by buying is shown graphically in Figure

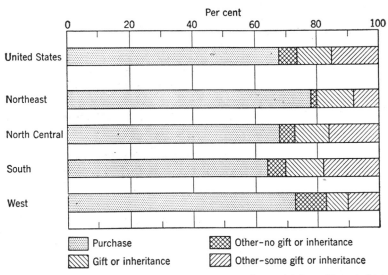

Figure 15. Percentage of owners by method of acquisition, United States and regions, 1946. (Bur. Agr. Econ., USDA)

15. Earning and saving enough money for a down payment, paying off the mortgage, and improving the farm are often a lifetime project. The decisions involved in buying a farm are probably the most important management decisions that farmers must make.

Management Problems

1. Deciding whether to own or rent.
2. Deciding when to buy.
3. Selecting a farm.
4. Determining the value of a farm.
5. Avoiding common mistakes in buying a farm.
6. Closing the transaction.
7. Interpreting the legal description of farms.

Deciding Whether to Own or Rent

Why is owning the farms they operate such a common goal among farm families? What are the advantages of farm ownership that

Figure 16. One of the advantages of farm ownership is that the farm family has a greater incentive to improve the surroundings in which they live. (Courtesy Soil Conservation Serv.)

lead farm people to attach so much importance to achieving this goal? Let us discuss briefly the most important advantages arising out of ownership.

1. Greater Security of Tenure. Once the farm operator owns his farm and has paid for it, he can expect to stay on the farm as long as he likes. On the other hand, most rented farms involve some doubt about future tenure. The landlord may become dissatisfied with the tenant's work, he may sell the farm, or it may be sold as a result of the death of the landowner. The tenant can find himself looking for another farm to rent for any of these reasons.

2. Better Living Conditions. Unlike most other businesses, the farm is also a home for the family. Owning the farm enables the family to add conveniences to the home and landscape, to set out orchard and small fruit crops, and to add other improvements that make the farm a better place to live. Many landowners are unwilling to provide these improvements on rented farms. Although some renters make and pay for improvements of this kind, most of them hesitate to spend money in this way because making an arrangement with the landlord for getting repaid in the event they move is often difficult.

3. Greater Freedom in Management. On rented farms, particularly under crop- and livestock-share leases the landowner must be consulted before major decisions are made. Sometimes the operator and the owner do not see eye to eye. This can interfere with a good job of farming. Even when farm operators find the landowners reasonable to deal with, they often do not like the idea of having to consult them before making decisions. They would much prefer to be independent and be free to exercise their own judgment. We should recognize, however, that the necessity of consulting the landlord is not always a disadvantage. If the tenant is not a skillful manager, the advice given him by the landlord may help him to avoid errors in management. Even good managers occasionally find that "two heads are better than one" in dealing with some of their problems.

4. Pride of Ownership. Aside from the other advantages of owning that we have discussed, some people derive a great deal of pleasure out of being able to call the farm their own. This may be due, to a large extent, to community attitudes toward ownership. There is evidence that owners enjoy more prestige than renters in many communities. Although this factor is difficult to evaluate, it is undoubtedly of importance in encouraging some tenants to buy a farm.

Now let us examine the other side of the picture. What are the disadvantages that go with ownership?

1. Ownership involves more risk than renting when large amounts of credit are used. In the past, many families have lost heavily by attempting farm ownership with a large amount of borrowed money. Farm prices fell, and they found it difficult to meet their mortgage payments. As a result, they lost their farms, the money paid down on them, and the principal payments made on the mortgage.

Although great numbers of farmers have lost their farms in this way during the past, there is reason to believe these dangers have been lessened. As we shall see in Chapter 5, credit arrangements to finance the purchase of farms have been greatly improved. In addition, government price-support measures likely will continue to be used to cushion the impact of falling prices.

2. Owners must frequently farm smaller and poorer farms than renters. Often the prospective farm buyer does not have enough money to buy a sufficiently large or a top-quality farm. For this reason, a farmer who attempts ownership with limited capital frequently buys a farm that is smaller and less productive than the one he was renting. As a result, he may actually decrease his net income. He is justified in doing this, however, if he believes that the nonmonetary advantages of ownership outweigh this loss of income.

3. Attempting ownership sometimes causes a chronic shortage of capital. Meeting payments on the farm must receive top priority from the farm family's income. If ownership it attempted with a small down payment, the family may be under considerable pressure to meet interest and principal obligations. Under these conditions there may not be enough capital to keep an adequate livestock program, to buy fertilizer, or to make needed improvements on the farm. In addition, the level at which the family is able to live may suffer.

Deciding When to Buy

Farm real-estate prices fluctuate widely through the years. The changes that have taken place during the last 40 years are shown in Figure 17. With the exception of the land boom in the '20's, the trend in land prices has followed fairly closely changes in farm prices. The index of value shows the value of land as a percentage of the 1935–39 value. For example, in 1920, land values were 205 per cent of what they were in 1935–39. In 1933, they were only 88 per cent of the 1935–39 values. A farmer who bought his farm in 1920 saw the dollar value of his investment drop sharply. If the farm was mortgaged, the average farm owner experienced great difficulty in meeting interest and principal payments. On the other hand, a farmer who bought his farm in the late '30's or early '40's saw the value of his land increase rapidly. In addition, the rise in farm prices greatly eased the task of paying off the mortgage.

As we look back, it is easy to see that the '20's was a poor time to buy a farm. And it is just as easy to see that the period from 1938 to 1942 was an exceptionally favorable time in which to buy. But farmers must look ahead, not backward, in making this decision. Unfortunately it is impossible for farmers or for anyone else to predict with any degree of accuracy what will happen to the price of farm land in future years. Since they have no control over long-time

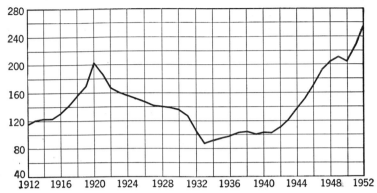

Figure 17. Index numbers of the average value per acre of farm real estate, 1912–52 (1935–39 = 100). (From Bur. Agr. Econ., USDA)

price trends and cannot predict them, most farm families would probably do best to buy when they are in a position to do so. They should concentrate on (1) saving enough money for a sizable down payment, (2) finding the farm that is the right one for them and (3) buying it at a price that is in line with the existing market.

Land booms

The exception to what we have said above is this: Farmers who are interested in buying a farm for a business and a home should avoid buying during a speculative land boom. The symptoms of an increase in land values built on speculation are fairly definite. People become highly optimistic about the future of land values. Land prices rise more rapidly than prospects for future income from land justify. Buyers enter the market with a view to selling when they can make a quick profit. The good fortune of individuals who have made a quick, easy profit encourages others to try it. These buyers, acting on the basis of their optimistic appraisal of future land prices, drive land values up still more by competing to buy the land that is for sale.

The drop in land prices comes suddenly, and the decline is rapid. Those persons who took their profit and stayed out of the market thereafter end up ahead. But many others are left with land for which they have paid too much.

Speculation of this type may be justified for people who are financially in a position to gamble, but it is poor business for the individual who is buying land with the expectation of paying for it out of earnings. Following through the appraisal routine outlined below will help you determine whether land values are actually in line with the earning capacity of the land.

Selecting a Farm

What should you look for in choosing a farm to buy? Of course you will be interested in the farm's capacity for producing income. We will discuss how to determine the value of a farm in terms of its income-producing capacity in the next section. But first we want to look at factors not closely related to this that should be taken into consideration.

Neighborhood and location

When a farm family buys a farm, it is usually buying a home as well as a business. For this reason the type of community in which

Figure 18. Location in a community with good school facilities adds to the value of a farm for a family who are buying a home as well as a business. (Courtesy *Successful Farming*)

the farm is located is important. How good are the schools? Is there a church of your denomination conveniently located? Is the farm on an all-weather road so that the family can take part conveniently in community activities? Is a good shopping center within easy reach of the farm? Is electricity available from a central station? Unless you are unusually fortunate, you will not find a

Figure 19. The type of road should be taken into consideration in putting a value on a farm. Good roads help in getting products to market and make the farm a more pleasant place to live. (Courtesy Barrett division, Allied Chemical & Dye Corp.)

farm that suits you in all these respects. But you should consider all these factors and decide which ones you are most willing to do without where a choice must be made.

Living conditions

If you plan to live on the farm, you will be especially interested in the house; its size, condition, arrangement, and facilities. Is it adequate in its present condition? How costly would the necessary improvements be? In addition to the house itself you should consider the way in which the farmstead is arranged. Is the house far enough away from the lots? Is the farmstead located in a well-drained area? Does the farm have a windbreak?

The size of the farm

Ideally the farm should be large enough to enable you and your family to utilize your combined labor and management efficiently. There are also economies in using machinery on a larger number of acres. However, the amount of the down payment required usually serves as a limit to the size of farm that can be purchased. Should you use the money you have to make a small down payment per acre on a large farm, or should you pay down more per acre

on a small farm? Because of the risk involved in heavy borrowing, most farm families prefer the latter course. Often you can
overcome the disadvantage of having a smaller number of acres to
work, in part at least, by developing an intensive livestock program and buying feed. In other instances you may be able to field-
rent additional land.

The family with only enough money to make a minimum down
payment on a farm too small to make efficient use of their labor and
management is probably attempting ownership prematurely. This
is especially true if making the down payment leaves them too short
on capital to expand through developing a livestock program or
renting additional land.

Determining the Value of a Farm

If you buy a farm to operate rather than as a speculative venture,
you are interested primarily in its capacity to produce income. In
the following sections we will study a commonly used method of
estimating the value of a farm. As will become evident to you, it is
not foolproof, but learning how to apply this procedure should
demonstrate to you how important the productivity of the farm and
future farm prices are in determining how much a farm is worth.
First we will discuss how to determine the value of a farm solely
from the standpoint of its income-producing ability. Then we will
consider how to adjust this value for factors that tend to make the
farm a good home.

Steps in appraising a farm

The value of a farm depends on its capacity to produce income.
Since we are interested here only in the income that the land earns,
we would like to separate it from the income earned by labor and
capital on the farm. In order to do this, we estimate the income
that the farm would earn if it were rented out at prevailing rental
rates. We follow this procedure even though the buyer expects to
operate the farm himself. This amounts to saying that prevailing
rental rates reflect the amount of income on a farm that can be
credited to the land and buildings. If you pay more for a farm than
the rental income would justify, it means that you will be getting a
smaller return for your labor, management, and working capital than
these would earn on a rented farm. Therefore, the central task in
putting a value on a farm is to estimate what the yearly income to
the landlord is likely to be in the future. Once this is done, it is a

simple matter to determine how much you will be justified in paying for the farm, in order to achieve a given rate of return on your investment.

The steps that should be followed in estimating the value of a farm are as follows:

1. Examining the soil to determine the crops that can be grown and what the long-run yields will be.
2. Estimating long-run prices for the crops produced.
3. Determining the landlord's share of the crops.
4. Estimating the landlord's expenses.
5. Capitalizing the landlord's income.
6. Adjusting the value of the farm for special features.

Examining the soil resources

In order to determine what crops can be grown and what future yields you can expect, you must take a careful inventory of the soil resources on the farm. This will mean determining the type of soil,

Figure 20. The cropping pattern followed on similar farms in the community is a good guide to use in determining for appraisal purposes the crops you can grow on a farm. (Courtesy Soil Conservation Serv.)

its texture, and topography. It will also involve being on the lookout for sandy spots and poorly drained areas. The crops being grown on similar soil in the community are good guides to follow in determining what crops can be grown successfully on the farm. Then you must decide what combination of crops (particularly grain and meadow crops) can be grown and still maintain the productivity of the soil. The problem of deciding which rotation will accomplish this is discussed at length in Chapter 6. Before you attempt to make an appraisal yourself, you should study this chapter.

Once you have decided what crops can be produced and in what combination, you should estimate what the yield of the crops will be. Here you are interested in the average yields you can expect over the long run. Past yields on the farm are the best basis for making estimates of future yields. But, since it is usually impossible to get reliable information of this kind, township or county yields often must be used as a starting point. Yields obtained in this way can be adjusted upward or downward, depending on how the farm under study compares with other farms in the community.

It is important to have some actual yield history covering at least a ten-year period on which to base your estimate of future yields. Guesses are likely to miss the mark widely. Many persons have a tendency to remember only the good years and to forget the poor ones in estimating long-run averages. Doing this causes one to overestimate the value of the farm he is appraising.

Estimating long-run prices

In making a systematic appraisal, it is necessary to estimate the prices that will be received in the future for the crops to be raised on the land. Whenever a prospective buyer puts a price on a farm that he expects to buy as an investment, he cannot escape making at least a roundabout prediction of future prices. You will be justified in paying a great deal more for a farm if you expect prices to be high than if you think they will be low. There is no foolproof way of arriving at the right prices to use in making an appraisal. A convenient method is to take average prices for the last 15 or 20 years.

Determining the landlord's share of the crops

As was pointed out before, we are interested in estimating the landlord's return rather than returns to the whole farm. In order to do this, it is usually best to use the crop-share lease, although the procedure can also be followed with the cash lease. Here again you must decide what the rental terms are likely to be over a long-run future period. Usually rental shares change slowly. Therefore it is a common practice to use the prevailing division of crops. Where hay and pasture land are rented for cash, it is usually best to use the average cash rent that was received during the last fifteen or twenty year period.

Estimating landlord's net income

Thus far we have discussed the problems of estimating future yields and prices and the share of the crop going to the landlord. By multiplying the yield times the price and figuring the landlord's share of the crop plus any cash rent, we can arrive at the landlord's gross income. But we are interested in his net income. Therefore we must estimate what the landlord's expenses on the farm will be and deduct them from his gross. These expenses will be taxes, insurance, seed and fertilizer, and improvement upkeep and repair. Taxes and insurance can be estimated on the basis of what they have been in past years. A charge for fertilizer and grass seed should be included only if they are furnished by the landlord. If a charge for fertilizer is included, this should be taken into account in estimating future yields. Estimating depreciation and repair on property presents a more difficult problem. The proper figure to use is the amount of money that it would take each year to maintain the buildings in a usable condition. No allowance should be made for buildings that are obsolete or unnecessary on the farm.

Applying the appraisal procedure

Let us now illustrate our steps by an example. First we will show how the landlord's net income can be estimated. Then we can estimate the value of the farm based on its earning capacity. We will use a 160-acre central Iowa farm consisting of Clarion and Webster soils in our example. Soil productivity can be maintained on this farm by following a corn-corn-oats-meadow rotation.

An estimate of the landlord's long-run gross income and the manner in which it was calculated are shown in Table 3.

In order to convert the $3,077 gross income arrived at in Table 3 to net income, we must deduct the following expenses: taxes $310, insurance $40, fertilizer and seed $230, and building upkeep $300, or a total of $880. The expected net income therefore would be $2,197.

Next is the crucial step of moving from income to value. You

Table 3. Long-Run Cropping System, Expected Yields and Production, and Landlord's Gross Income on a 160-Acre Central Iowa Farm

Crops	Acres	Expected Yield per acre, bu	Total Expected Production	Land- lord's Share	Price	Landlord's Gross Income
Corn	76	56	4,256	2,128	$ 1.04	$2,213
Oats	38	44	1,672	669	0.61	408
Hay	19	Cash rent	...		12.00	228
Rotated pasture	19	Cash rent	...		12.00	228
Roads, farmstead lots, and waste	8					
Total	160	...	...	...	...	$3,077

must first ask yourself this question: What rate of return would I be willing to accept from a farm investment? If you are borrowing part of the money, you will want to get at least as much as the interest you will be paying on the mortgage. This typically would range from 4 to 5 per cent. In our example, we will use 4½ per cent per year. We are saying, in effect, that our $2,197 yearly income equals 4½ per cent of the value of the farm. The relationship between income and the value of the farm can be expressed as follows:

$$\text{Value of farm} = \frac{\text{expected landlord net income}}{\text{rate of return}}$$

In our example the figures would be $2,197/0.045 = $48,822, the capitalized value of the 160-acre farm. This would be a value of $305 per acre based on the earning capacity of the farm. By using the landlord's returns, we have based our value on the production of the land and not on the labor and capital supplied by the operator and his family.

Other factors to consider

Once you have placed a tentative value on the farm based on its earning capacity, there are several adjustments you should consider. The $305 figure we arrived at above assumed that there is an average set of buildings on the farm. If the buildings are above average and are the type of buildings you can make use of, you will be justified in placing an increased value on the farm. If you expect to live on the farm and the house is above average, you may also be justified in paying more for the farm than the $305 per acre figure. Other factors that might justify paying a higher price are (1) an

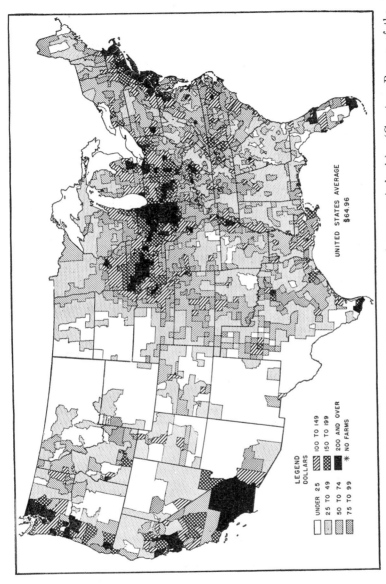

Figure 21. Average value of land and buildings per acre (county unit basis). (Courtesy Bureau of the Census)

exceptionally good location and (2) community advantages such as good schools, roads, and churches.

On the other hand, if the buildings and fences are particularly poor and in need of immediate repair, you will not be justified in paying the amount arrived at on the basis of the farm's earning capacity. You should subtract enough from this figure to pay for putting the buildings and fences in reasonably good shape. The fact that a farm is located on poor roads will also decrease its value.

How different factors affect value

Following through a systematic appraisal procedure centers our attention on the factors that are important in determining what price we can afford to pay for a farm. Let us examine how the following four factors affect the amount we would be justified in paying for a farm: (1) yields, (2) expected prices, (3) expenses, and (4) rate of interest. If yields on the farm referred to in Table 3 were 50 bushels for corn and 40 bushels for oats instead of 56 and 44, the landlord's expected net income would be $1,923 and the estimated value $267 per acre. Thus, farms on which we expect lower yields are worth less. On the other hand, higher yields result in a higher income and hence a higher value.

If we were pessimistic about the future of farm prices and expected them to be, say, 80 cents for corn and 45 cents for oats instead of the $1.04 and 61 cents used in the example, the estimated value would drop to $219 per acre, owing to a decline in expected income. Or, if expenses were increased, say, by one dollar per acre because of an increase in taxes, the estimated value would drop by $22 per acre. The influence of yields, prices, and expenses on the value of the farm is not difficult to understand, since they affect directly the amount of income we can expect from the farm. However, the influence of the level of interest rates is not so evident. As the interest rate increases, the amount you can afford to pay for a farm decreases. Let us see why this is true. Suppose we estimate the landlord's income on a farm at $2,000. If we use 4 per cent as the capitalization rate, we would arrive at the following value:

$$\frac{\$2,000 \text{ (expected income)}}{0.04 \text{ (capitalization rate)}} = \$50,000$$

How would the value be affected by an increase in the capitalization rate to 5 per cent?

$$\frac{\$2{,}000 \ \text{(expected income)}}{0.05 \ \text{(capitalization rate)}} = \$40{,}000$$

Thus you must take the rate of interest you would have to pay on borrowed money into consideration in determining how much to pay for a farm. If interest rates are low, you can afford to pay more, since a given amount of income will meet the interest payment on a larger mortgage. Higher interest rates have the opposite effect.

The large changes in value that result from altering expected yields, prices, costs, and interest rates suggest the complexity of farm valuation. The fact that it is difficult to make these estimates does not mean that following through the appraisal process is of no value. Approaching the appraisal systematically helps you focus attention on the important factors that enter into an over-all estimate of value. This is better than making an uninformed guess.

Comparing values

Prospective buyers frequently consider several farms before making a final choice. How can the appraisal procedure be used to decide which farm is the best buy? In order to make comparisons, the estimated value should be computed for each farm being considered, as shown in the example above. The yields used in each case should reflect the productivity of the land on the farm. However, the same prices and the same capitalization rate should be employed for the two or more farms being compared. After the values of the farms have been compared on the basis of their income-producing ability, nonincome factors such as location, the house, and community advantages should be considered.

Appraising cash-rented farms

In our illustration of how to estimate the value of a farm, we calculated the landlord's income on the basis of crop-share rent. In some areas where few farms are crop-share-rented, determining going rental rates may be a problem. If cash renting is common in the area, the landlord's net income may be estimated by subtracting the landlord's expenses under a cash lease from the rent he can expect. From this point the procedure followed is exactly the same as when income is estimated from crop-share rent.

Avoiding Common Mistakes in Buying a Farm

Failure to recognize problem soil areas

In determining the productivity of a farm, you must be on the lookout particularly for farms that have areas of poor drainage and sandy spots. Both these soil conditions can be deceptive. Farms that have drainage problems are often offered for sale during a comparatively dry year in which they show up well. Buyers who see these farms during favorable years are likely to get a distorted impression since they can raise excellent crops when the rainfall is properly distributed during the season.

Sandy spots can cause the same kind of difficulty. Sandy farms look the best during years of above average rainfall. They also look best in May and June when moisture is more abundant and the land is covered with vegetation.

In order to guard against these difficulties and to do the best job of evaluating the soil resources on a farm, it is well to see the farm during several different seasons of the year. Being familiar with the farm over a period of years is also an advantage.

When both of these safeguards are impossible, an experienced appraiser usually can detect the presence of soil problems. If you are not sure about the soil on a farm and are an inexperienced buyer, you should seek advice from a disinterested and qualified appraiser. Buying land that you are not sure about involves more risk than the average buyer is in a position to take.

Overvaluing poor land

Experience has shown that buyers are more likely to pay too much for poor land than for good land. This is particularly true in good land areas. The price of poor land often sounds reasonable in comparison with prices of the better-quality land in the area. The price of one farm that yields 10 per cent less than another should be more than 10 per cent lower in order to be in line. Generally the cost of producing an acre of crop on poor land is as great as or even greater than on good land. For this reason the difference in net income between a good and a poor farm will be greater than the difference in yield. Suppose, for example, that the expected gross income, based on expected yields and prices, were $50 per acre on one farm and $35 per acre on a second farm. If the cost of producing the crop were $20 per acre on both farms, the first farm would return a net of $30 per acre, or twice as much as the $15 return per acre on the second farm.

Paying too much for buildings

Valuing buildings on a farm is a difficult job. Many people are impressed by a well-kept, expensive set of buildings. They apparently consider that such buildings are a mark of success. Hence there is a great temptation to pay more for buildings than they are worth.

You should guard against using the cost of constructing a building as a measure of its worth. The real question you must answer if you are buying the farm to operate is: How useful will the building be in your farming operation? A large, elaborately equipped dairy barn, for example, will be worth little to you if you plan to keep a beef cow herd.

Even though a building can be put to use on the farm, it may be more elaborate than is necessary. You are not justified in paying more for an extravagant building than for a cheaper one that will serve the same purpose adequately. Indeed, too expensive a set of improvements may decrease income by keeping repairs and maintenance costs at a high level. Taxes may be higher too.

Placing too much emphasis on temporary soil conditions

Low crop yields may be due to the soil being basically poor and low in productivity: Regardless of the treatment given, it does not produce well. On the other hand, low crop yields may be due to poor management and overcropping on a basically good soil. Many buyers fail to make a distinction between these two classes of farms. You can afford to pay much more for the basically good but run-down farm than for the farm that is fundamentally poor in soil.

In purchasing a run-down farm that has good possibilities for being restored to a high state of productivity, you should realize that the building-up process requires time and takes capital. You should be in a position to put money into lime, fertilizer, and grass seed and be able to wait several years for yields to increase.

Some buyers also place too heavy a discount on a farm that is weedy. In most cases this is a temporary problem. Improved tillage tools and weed sprays have made the weed problem much easier to deal with than 20 or 30 years ago.

Closing the Transaction

Once you have found a farm and have agreed with the seller on the price, your next problem is to close the transaction and get possession of the farm. The first step in closing the transaction is to draw up "an agreement to purchase" or a contract of sale. At the time this is done, you usually advance a small down payment as assurance to the seller that you will keep the agreement. The contract of sale should indicate the purchase price of the farm and the date or dates at which additional payments will be made. In addition, the sale contract should specify when you will take possession and who will get the growing crops and who will pay the taxes and insurance until you take possession.

The seller must furnish an abstract. This is a document that shows all the legal transactions that have taken place previously involving the farm being sold. You can then have the abstract examined by a qualified person to see if the seller clearly owns the farm. He will also ascertain whether there are any mortgages against the farm and whether all taxes have been paid. This step is important since you want to be sure that the seller is actually in a position to sell the farm and that there will be no claims against it once you have purchased it. If there appear to be any defects in the seller's title (or ownership) to the farm, you should require that they be cleared up before you make final payment.

In most land transactions, the seller gives title to the land through a warranty deed. This is a legal instrument on which the consideration (amount of money) being given to the seller is specified and the farm is described. In addition, it states that the seller relinquishes all claims to the property and agrees to compensate the buyer for any loss that may arise out of the seller's failure to furnish a clear title.

Interpreting the Legal Description of Farms

Each farm in the United States has a legal description. If you know how to interpret this description, you can tell exactly the location of a farm.

Here is a typical legal description:

E½ of the SW¼ and the NW¼ of the SE¼ of Sec. 16,— T 84N, R 25W of the 5th P.M.

In reading the description, it is best to start at the end and read backward toward the beginning. The last part of the description, T 84N, R 25W of the 5th P.M. describes the location of the township. It is read as follows: Township 84 north and range 25 west of the 5th principal meridian. There is only one township with this description. Since you ordinarily will experience no difficulty in locating the township in which a farm is located, we will not discuss further the meaning of the last terms of the description.

In order to grasp the meaning of the first term an understanding of how sections are laid out within townships is necessary. Each township is approximately 6 miles square and consists of 36 sections,

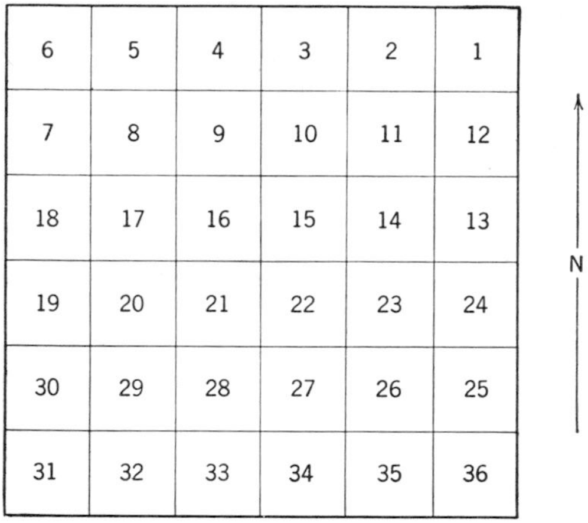

6	5	4	3	2	1
7	8	9	10	11	12
18	17	16	15	14	13
19	20	21	22	23	24
30	29	28	27	26	25
31	32	33	34	35	36

N

Figure 22. How sections are numbered in a township.

each containing 640 acres. Sections are always numbered as indicated in Figure 22 with section 1 in the northeast corner and section 6 in the northwest corner.

Returning now to the legal description given above, we can determine that the farm being described is located in section 16. The next problem is to determine where within the section it is located. In order to get a clearer picture of this, let us take section 16 out of Figure 22 and show it separately in Figure 23. The section is first divided into quarters. When this has been done, the E½ of the SW¼ can be easily located. The SE¼ is again divided into quarters, each quarter containing 40 acres. Once this has been done the location of the NW¼ of the SE¼ also becomes clear. The shaded area in Figure 23 shows how this 120-acre farm is located within section 16.

Because of the curvature of the earth, it is impossible to have every section contain exactly 640 acres. Corrections are made along the north and west boundaries of the township. Therefore sections 1 through 6 and sections 7, 18, 19, 30, and 31 usually do not contain exactly 640 acres. The correction is made in each of the quarter-section tracts along the north and the west sides of the townships.

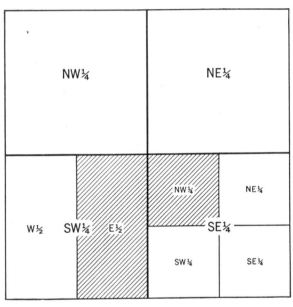

Figure 23. Diagram showing location of the farm within section 16.

These quarters are referred to as "fractional" quarters. They are described as follows: NW fractional ¼ of Sec. 5, T 84N, R 25W of the 5th P.M.

Areas in the eastern part of the United States are not laid out on the basis of a rectangular survey, the system we have just described. In this area a system of metes and bounds is used. Under this procedure, an attempt is made to describe the farm by describing its boundaries. A typical description of this type is as follows:

It being part of a hundred-acre lot numbered 187 in the second division of land in said town, bounded by beginning at a pitch pine now or formerly standing and being numbered 187; then West 25 degrees North 61 rods to a black ash tree now or formerly standing, marked 187; thence South 25 degrees West 32 rods 12½ feet to a stake and stones; then East 25 degrees South 61 rods to a stake and stones; thence North 25 degrees East 32 rods 12½ feet to the first mentioned bound. Said tract lying in the Northwest corner of said hundred-acre lot and containing about 12½ acres.

One of the chief difficulties in following this description is that it often depends on stones, stakes, or trees, all of which may be temporary.

Use of maps

Maps can be highly useful in locating farms. They are usually available for each county, showing the townships and sections within the county. In addition, the location of roads, railroads, ditches, and often farmsteads are indicated on these maps. Plat books are also available in most counties. These books show all the tracts of land in the county and indicate who owns each one.

Problems

1. Plot on a graph the trend in land values for the last 10 years in your area. Next extend the line in the direction in which you think land values will change in the next 10 years.
2. Look up in the latest U.S. Census the value of the land in your own county. In addition, look up the value of land in each county bordering on the county in which you live, and make comparisons. How do you account for the differences that exist?
3. Find out the legal description of your home farm. Then see if you can locate it on the county map, using the legal description as a guide.
4. Have all members of the class estimate what the average yield per acre has been during the last 8 years for the major crops in the townships in which they live. Then compare this information with the estimates published by the crop-reporting service. Do you think farmers are more likely to underestimate or overestimate yields? How do you account for the differences that exist? What effect would these errors have if you were to make them while appraising a farm?
5. Follow through the appraisal procedure outlined in this chapter either on your home farm or some other farm in your community. Do you think the farm would sell for more or less than the figure you arrived at?
6. Obtain a copy of an abstract of title for a farm with which you are familiar. How many different owners has the farm had? How many times has it been mortgaged?

References

Hopkins, J. A., and W. G. Murray, *Elements of Farm Management,* 4th Ed., Chapter 5, Prentice-Hall, New York, 1953.

How Much Can I Afford to Pay for a Farm, *Iowa Agr. Ext. Serv. Pamphlet* 94, 1946.

Lundy, Gabriel, and Ray F. Pengra, "Land Market Trends in South Dakota, 1941–1950," *S. Dakota Agr. Expt. Sta. Bull.* 413, 1951.

Moore, H. R., and R. A. Bailey, "Ohio Farm Real Estate Prices," *Ohio Agr. Expt. Sta. Res. Bull.* 711, 1951.

Murray, W. G., *Farm Appraisal*, Iowa State College Press, Ames, 1951.

Robertson, Lynn S., and Ralph H. Woods, *Farm Business Management*, Chapter 17, J. B. Lippincott Co., Chicago, Philadelphia, New York, 1950.

Scofield, W. H., and R. D. Davidson, "The Farm Real Estate Situation," *USDA Circ.* 823, 1949.

CHAPTER

5

Using Credit in
the Farm Business

Few farmers can become farm owners without borrowing a considerable portion of the purchase price. Even farmers who rent farms frequently must use some credit in order to have enough livestock, machinery, and equipment to do a good job of farming. Farmers in the United States in 1952 were using more than $6 billion to finance the purchase of farm real estate and more than $7 billion to finance livestock, machinery, and supplies.

Under what circumstances should you use credit? From whom should you borrow? What are the characteristics of a desirable loan? What factors does a creditor consider in deciding about a loan? These are some of the questions we will consider in this chapter.

No doubt you have found that many people regard the use of credit as bad. This is understandable, in view of the unfortunate experiences some farmers have had borrowing money in the past. However, lending practices have been improved greatly during the last 20 years. As a result, some of the hazard of using credit has been removed. Failure to use credit can be just as serious a mistake as using it carelessly or too liberally. You should not try to do without this important tool for increasing farm income, but you should learn how to use it as safely and profitably as possible.

Management Problems

1. Understanding credit terms and instruments.
2. Choosing a source of long-term credit.
3. Determining the provisions of a long-term loan.
4. Choosing a source of short-term credit.
5. Budgeting short-term loans.
6. Using credit productively.

7. Recognizing the risk in heavy borrowing.

8. Establishing a good credit rating.

Understanding Credit Terms and Instruments

Following are some of the principal instruments that are used in the farm credit field.

Mortgages

A mortgage is an instrument that gives the holder a legal claim against property as security for the payment of a debt. The mortgage provides that the holder can force payment of the loan or acquire title to the property through a legal process known as "foreclosure" if the loan is not paid. The property may be sold at public auction. If any money remains after the creditor has been satisfied, it is turned over to the debtor. Mortgages on such items as machinery and livestock are known as chattel mortgages. Mortgages on the farm are called real-estate mortgages or simply farm mortgages.

Mortgages are recorded at the county courthouse. This makes it possible for persons taking a mortgage on property to check to see whether anyone else has a prior mortgage. More than one mortgage may be filed against a piece of property. The mortgage filed first is called a first mortgage. A mortgage filed against property already covered by a first mortgage is called a second mortgage. The holder of the first mortgage has first claim on the property if foreclosure is necessary to force payment of the loan. When there is no money left after the first mortgage has been satisfied, the lender holding the second mortgage often finds it impossible to obtain payment on his loan. This is the reason why second mortgages are usually less desirable security than first mortgages.

Promissory note

A note is a written promise on the part of the maker to pay a certain sum of money on demand or more often on some specified date to the bearer of the note. The note may or may not be secured by a mortgage. The amount of interest to be paid is also shown on the note. Lenders sometimes require a cosigner on a note. For example, a farm operator may wish to borrow money but is not considered a good credit risk by the lender. This often happens when the borrower lacks collateral. Collateral is an asset such as land, livestock, or machinery that may be mortgaged by the lender to assure repay-

Figure 24. A typical promissory note.

ment of the loan. When collateral is lacking, the lender may require the borrower to get someone who is a good credit risk to sign the note with him. The cosigner then becomes liable along with the maker of the note for its repayment. Consequently, cosigning a note is not a good practice unless you have complete confidence in the ability and intentions of the borrower to repay the note.

Sales contract

The sales contract has been widely employed during recent years as a credit instrument in land transactions. It is used in this way: If you have only enough money to make a small down payment, you may buy a farm on the basis of a sales contract. The seller does not convey title to the land to you but agrees to do so when you have paid a specified amount. Usually this arrangement continues only until you have paid enough so that you are able to finance the remainder through a farm mortgage loan. This involves less risk to the seller since he has not given you title to the land. He can regain possession much more simply, in the event you fail to meet your payments, than if he had taken a first mortgage. On the other hand, buying on contract gives you an opportunity to secure control of land even though you can make only a small down payment.

Choosing a Source of Long-Term Credit

The major purposes for which farmers use long-term credit include (1) loans to buy land and (2) loans for improvements. Such loans are referred to as long-term credit because they are repaid over an extended period of time. They usually are secured by a mortgage on the farm.

Sources of long-term credit

Most farm mortgage loans are made when farmers or investors buy land. But they also may be used to finance new buildings or land improvements and to refinance short-term loans in periods of financial stress. The principal sources of farm mortgage loans are:

1. Insurance companies.
2. Federal Land Banks.
3. Farmers Home Administration.
4. Individuals.
5. Commercial banks.

The changing importance of these sources over the last forty years is shown in Figure 25.

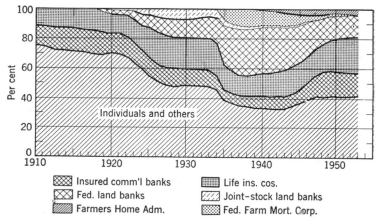

Figure 25. Percentage of outstanding farm mortgage loans held by principal lenders, United States, January 1, 1910–48.

Insurance companies

Insurance companies are a good source of farm mortgage credit. Their commitments to their policy holders are of a long-term character. This permits them to offer long-term loans that provide for gradual repayment of the debt. Insurance companies compete actively for farm loan business in the better farming areas of the country. Typically they have local agents such as bankers, real estate brokers, or lawyers whom the prospective borrower can contact. In addition, they have trained personnel who appraise the property to be mortgaged and close the loan.

Federal Land Banks

The Federal Land Bank system was created in 1916. It is a semi-public organization sponsored by the federal government. However, the funds that the land banks lend are not supplied by the government but are raised through sale of bonds to individuals and private financial institutions.

The Federal Land Banks were created as a result of agitation to improve the long-term credit situation in agriculture. Many farmers and farm leaders thought that existing credit institutions were not adequately serving the needs of farmers. The principal criticisms made of lending practices at that time were as follows:

1. Too many loans were for too short a period.
2. The commissions and other expenses involved in obtaining a loan were excessive.
3. Interest rates were too high.

The Federal Land Banks were organized to improve these conditions by (1) channeling funds more directly from investment centers to farms and (2) introducing better lending practices.

The Federal Land Bank system is organized partly on a cooperative basis. Farmers borrowing from the bank are organized into local units called National Farm Loan Associations. Each borrower must buy stock in the cooperative association equal to 5 per cent of the amount of his loan. The local cooperative associations own stock in the land banks and secure funds through them. These associations have been the weakest part of the land bank system. In many cases they lack sufficient financial resources to hire a capable manager. Most borrowers take little interest in them once they have obtained their loan.

Some farmers prefer not to borrow from the Federal Land Banks because of the capital stock requirement. In recent years, others have found that the land banks have been unable to lend as much money on a farm as private institutions. The reason is that federal legislation limits the size of the loan to 65 per cent of the "normal" value of the farm.

In spite of their curtailed activity during recent years, the Federal Land Bank system has served a useful purpose. Many farmers were able to avoid foreclosure by refinancing their loan with a land bank during the depression. In addition, the land banks have been an important influence in improving lending practices in the farm loan field.

In a Pennsylvania study, farmers were asked for their opinions on the advantages and disadvantages of different sources of long-term credit. Their answers are summarized in Table 4.

Table 4. Advantages and Disadvantages in Obtaining Long-Term Credit from Various Sources as Mentioned by 399 Commercial Farmers in Pennsylvania, 1947*

Source	Advantages	No. Times Mentioned	Disadvantages	No. Times Mentioned
Bank	Knows lender, favorable attitude toward lender	58	High interest	92
			Not lenient and understanding	43
	Convenience in obtaining	43	Inconvenience in repaying	19
	Convenience in repaying	23		
	Understanding and lenient	20		
National Farm Loan Association	Cheaper interest	75	Source not familiar	125
	Convenience in repaying and longer terms	54	Inconvenience in obtaining	28
	Understanding and lenient	28		
	Knows lender, favorable attitude toward lender	20		
Individual	Cheaper interest	44	Insecure and unreliable	55
	Understanding and lenient	33	Not lenient and understanding	52
	Convenience in obtaining and repaying	26	High interest	29

* From *Penn. Agr. Expt. Sta. Res. Bull.* 514.

Farmers Home Administration

This agency developed out of several agencies created by the federal government during the depression to aid farmers. One of the chief functions of the agencies that were the forerunners of the Farmers Home Administration was to help tenant operators become owners. The Farmers Home Administration still extends some credit for this purpose. Farmers who wish to buy a farm through this agency must make application to a local committee. This group screens the applicants carefully. One of the advantages of securing a tenant purchase loan from the Farmers Home Administration is that a larger proportion of the purchase price of the farm can be borrowed. In addition, the loan is geared to the new owner's ability to repay. Supervision and counsel are provided for the borrower while the loan is being repaid.

The number of loans available from the Farmers Home Administration is dependent on the amount of money appropriated by Congress for this purpose. Since World War II, comparatively few loans of this type have been available.

Individuals

Often when farms are sold the seller agrees to keep part of his money in the farm. Typically, he makes the loan secure through a mortgage. Whether this is a good source of credit depends on the individual seller involved and the terms of the loan. Individuals usually have had less experience in farm lending than other credit agencies. As a result, the terms of the loan often are not so carefully drawn up as those of loans arranged through an established credit institution.

Banks

Commercial banks have several distinct advantages over other agencies as a source of farm mortgage credit. They are readily accessible to the borrower. In addition, the banker often knows the borrower well and is in an excellent position to supervise the loan. On the other hand, banks are handicapped in the farm loan field because their loans typically must be made for short periods. A large proportion of the deposits in most commercial banks are demand deposits. This means that the depositor can call for his money at any time he chooses. As a result, banks cannot tie up too large a proportion of their assets in long-term loans.

Under existing laws, national banks may now lend up to 60 per cent of the value of a farm for a period of 10 years if the terms of the loan provide that 40 per cent of the principal will be repaid during this period. If no provision is made for payments on the principal during the course of the loan, the latter must be limited to 50 per cent of the value of the property and cannot run for a period of more than 5 years. Sometimes banks enter into agreements with other lending agencies whereby they can make loans that extend over a period longer than 5 or 10 years in length.

In borrowing from a bank to buy land, you must keep in mind the short-term character of the loan. If the loan is large, repaying it during the 5- or 10-year lending period is usually impossible. Although banks will usually refinance the loan at the end of the period, they may not be in a position to do so if funds are tight. Under these circumstances, you may be forced to turn to some other lending institution at a time when obtaining a loan on favorable terms is difficult.

Determining Provisions of the Long-Term Loan

In addition to the size of the loan and the rate of interest, you should give careful thought to the repayment schedule in planning a farm mortgage loan. What are some of the characteristics of a desirable repayment program?

The repayment schedule should be geared to ability to pay

Despite the experience of some borrowers during the 1940's, paying for a farm is typically a long-time job. When large proportions of the purchase price must be borrowed, the borrower should not count on paying for the farm in less than 20 to 40 years. The repayment schedule should be planned accordingly. If the borrower obligates himself to make principal payments that are too large, he is likely to be chronically short of capital for operating and maintaining the farm. In addition, the level of living of the family may be lowered unnecessarily.

If only a small amount is borrowed, having the loan extend over a long period is usually unnecessary. Under these circumstances, the 5- or 10-year loan available from commercial banks is satisfactory.

The loan should be amortized

An amortization plan is a system whereby the principal on the loan is repaid through a series of payments during the course of the loan. At the termination date of an amortized loan, all of the interest and the principal has been paid. This is in contrast to the arrangement typical in the past in which no principal was paid during the course of the loan and the entire principal became due when the loan expired.

There are a number of different amortization plans. One such plan used by the Federal Land Banks is called the standard plan. Under this arrangement equal payments are made semiannually over the entire period of the loan. This plan, applied to a $14,000 loan with interest rates at 4 per cent, extending over a period of 34½ years, is illustrated in Table 5. Here the semiannual payment is $378. Of the first payment, $280 goes to pay the interest and $98 is applied to the principal. With each payment, the amount of inter-

Table 5. Payments under a Standard Amortization Payment Plan*

34½ Years—Semiannual Installments
Principal $14,000.00, Interest Rate 4%

Install-ment Number	Total Install-ment	Interest	Principal	Unpaid Balance
1	$378.00	$280.00	$ 98.00	$13,902.00
2	378.00	278.04	99.96	13,802.04
3	378.00	276.04	101.96	13,700.08
4	378.00	274.00	104.00	13,596.08
5	378.00	271.92	106.08	13,490.00
6	378.00	269.80	108.20	13,381.80
7	378.00	267.64	110.36	13,271.44
8	378.00	265.43	112.57	13,158.87
9	378.00	263.18	114.82	13,044.05
10	378.00	260.88	117.12	12,926.93
11	378.00	258.54	119.46	12,807.47
12	378.00	256.15	121.85	12,685.62
13	378.00	253.71	124.29	12,561.33
14	378.00	251.22	126.78	12,434.55
15	378.00	248.70	129.30	12,305.25
16	378.00	246.10	131.90	12,173.35
17	378.00	243.47	134.53	12,038.82
18	378.00	240.77	137.23	11,901.59
19	378.00	238.04	139.96	11,761.63
20	378.00	235.23	142.77	11,618.86
..	......	......	......	....
60	378.00	62.76	315.24	2,822.95
61	378.00	56.46	321.54	2,501.41
62	378.00	50.03	327.97	2,173.44
63	378.00	43.47	334.53	1,838.91
64	378.00	36.77	341.23	1,497.68
65	378.00	29.96	348.04	1,149.64
66	378.00	22.99	355.01	794.63
67	378.00	15.89	362.11	432.52
68	378.00	8.65	369.35	63.17
69	64.43	1.26	63.17	–0–

*From *Financing Farm and Ranch Activities*. Farm Credit Administration.

est decreases and the amount applied on the principal increases. By the time the 68th payment is made, only $8.65 is needed to pay the interest and $369.35 is applied to the principal.

The size of these payments should be no larger than can be earned by the land itself under the level of management the borrower can supply. If the loan cannot be amortized on this basis over a 30-to-40-year period, the down payment made on the farm is not sufficiently large for a sound attempt at ownership.

The loan should contain prepayment privileges

The repayment schedule should be extended over a long period so that the payments will not be burdensome. But provisions should be arranged for making payments ahead of schedule, should the borrower find himself in a position to do so. Most lending institutions will permit the borrower to pay ahead without imposing a penalty on the principal paid in advance. This enables him to reduce the proportion of future payments that must be applied to interest and permits the loan to be paid up much sooner. Notice in Table 5 that an extra payment made early during the loan period will reduce the total number of payments necessary to repay the loan by three to four. This is true because all of the extra payment can be applied to reducing the principal.

Ideally the repayment schedule on long-term loans would be geared to the amount of income earned on the farm during each year. If this plan were used, farmers would increase the size of their payment after a good year and reduce the amount paid after a poor year. Loans of this type are not yet available through established lending agencies. Some lenders permit the borrower to establish a reserve account with them that can be applied to the payment of the loan in the event of a bad year. Usually the reserve account earns interest. This is really no great advantage since the borrower could maintain a liquid reserve such as war bonds on his own. It should be pointed out that prepayments ordinarily do not serve as a reserve to draw on in low income years. Under the typical prepayment plan a delinquency would result if the borrower could not meet a regular payment in spite of the fact he had paid ahead on the loan. This is usually true, regardless of the number of prepayments that have been made on the loan.

Choosing a Source of Short-Term Credit

Credit used to finance the purchase of such items as livestock, machinery, feed, seed, and fertilizer is called short-term or production credit. We use this term to describe loans for these purposes because the periods over which the loans extend usually are short compared to those for farm mortgage loans. The principal sources of short-term loans are:

1. Merchants and dealers.
2. Individuals.
3. Banks.
4. Production Credit Associations.
5. Farmers Home Administration.

Merchants and dealers

It is a common practice among farmers to buy supplies and then to pay the merchant at some later date. Often this practice is a convenience to both the farm operator and the dealer. Sometimes the money owed will be carried on the books with no arrangement made for paying interest. However, if a dealer follows this practice consistently, he must charge enough more for the product he sells to cover the interest charge. In other instances the dealer will require that the buyer give a promissory note. Usually the time of repayment and the rate of interest are specified on the note. In addition, the dealer will often secure his loan by taking a chattel mortgage on the item he has sold or on crops and livestock on the farm. Machinery and commercial feed in particular are sold under these arrangements.

Generally, it is not a good practice to depend on merchants and dealers for credit. If interest is charged, it is usually higher than that charged by specialized credit agencies. In addition, if you obtain credit elsewhere and pay the dealer cash, you are in a position to do a better job of buying. You can buy where you get the most for your money instead of from the dealer willing to advance you credit.

Individuals

Borrowing from individuals is still a common practice among farmers. Often these transactions take place between relatives. In other cases the loan results from one individual's selling some item to another on credit. Whether an individual is a desirable source of short-term credit depends on the situation surrounding the loan. Difficulties sometimes arise in credit transactions between individuals because the terms of the loan are not definitely written down. Individuals are a somewhat less dependable source of credit than established agencies because death or a change in the financial position of the lender may lead to a demand for a premature repayment of the loan.   The advantages and disadvantages of different sources of production or short-term credit given by the farmers in the Pennsylvania study mentioned above are shown in Table 6.

Table 6.   Advantages and Disadvantages in Obtaining Production Credit from Various Sources as Mentioned by 399 Commercial Farmers in Pennsylvania, 1947 *

Source	Advantages	No. Times Mentioned	Disadvantages	No. Times Mentioned
Bank	Convenience in obtaining	107	High interest	34
	Knows lender and has confidence in him	48	Not lenient and understanding	17
	Convenience in repaying	21		
Individual	Cheaper interest	15	Insecure and unreliable	53
	Convenience in obtaining and repaying	14	Not lenient and understanding	28
	Lenient and understanding	13		
Production Credit Association	Cheaper interest	26	Source not familiar	147
	Convenience in repaying	20	Inconvenience in obtaining	34
Merchant or dealer	Convenience in obtaining	10	High interest	23

* From *Penn. Agr. Expt. Sta. Bull.* 514.

Commercial banks

Commercial banks are in a much better position to extend short-term than long-term credit.   Historically, most of their lending has been for a short period.   They enjoy several advantages over most other credit agencies that offer short-term loans.   They are close to the needs of the farmer and are readily accessible.   Loans from them usually can be arranged conveniently.

Some banks have been criticized for failure to lend money to buy feed and fertilizer, and for conservation measures.   This reluctance is usually due to a belief on the part of the bankers that obtaining repayment of loans of this type is difficult.   Adverse weather can reduce the returns from money spent on fertilizer. With money spent for conservation the returns may be indirect and several years in coming. However, banks are increasingly recognizing the desirability of lending for these purposes. Many have added trained specialists to supervise their farm lending activity. These men are in an excellent position to recognize the types of loans that are pro-

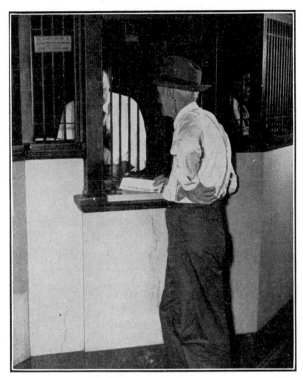

Figure 26. Banks are an excellent source of short-term credit for farmers. They usually are conveniently located and are in a position to know the needs and capabilities of the borrower. (Courtesy Soil Conservation Serv.)

ductive and to give proper supervision to the loans after they are made.

Production Credit Association

As it had done earlier with long-term credit, the federal government in 1933 took steps to make short-term credit available to farmers on more satisfactory terms. Among the measures taken to ease the short-term credit situation was the establishment of Production Credit Associations. These associations are organized as cooperatives, similar to the National Farm Loan Associations of the Federal Land Banks. Their purpose is to advance credit to farmers for crop and livestock production.

If you wish to borrow from such an organization you must buy $5 worth of stock in the association for every $100 that you borrow. The local Production Credit Associations, working through a government-created organization known as the Federal Intermediate Credit Bank, are able to channel funds from the centers where money is available to farmers seeking credit. Because they are backed by the Federal Government and have a reputation for being financially sound, the Federal Intermediate Credit Banks are able to furnish money to the cooperative Production Credit Associations on reasonable terms. It should be emphasized that the money borrowed from the Production Credit Associations does not come from federal funds but is borrowed from private lenders through the Federal Intermediate Credit Banks described previously.

The Production Credit Association satisfied a real need in many areas, particularly in the years immediately after they were organized. Since World War II the credit situation has eased considerably, and most farmers find borrowing from their local bank more convenient. Since Production Credit Associations are not located in every county, some farmers are forced to drive several miles to transact business with their local association. In addition, some borrowers do not like to buy the stock in the association that is required of all borrowers.

The Production Credit Associations pioneered several improved lending practices. They set the pattern for making a careful analysis of the uses to be made of the loan and the probable outcome of the venture. Many commercial banks have followed their example. In addition, they popularized the use of the budgeted loan in the short-term credit field. We will discuss this lending procedure in a later section.

Farmers Home Administration

In addition to making loans to tenants to purchase farms of their own, the Farmers Home Administration also lends money for crop and livestock production. However, only low-income farmers who cannot obtain credit from some other source are permitted to borrow through this agency. All loan applications are investigated by a local committee to be sure that the farm family needs the loan and will put it to good use. Once the loan is made, farm and home management counsel is provided the borrower. Production loans extend for a period of 5 years.

Like tenant purchase loans, all of the money the Farmers Home Administration lends for production purposes is provided by Congress through a special appropriation each year. Since the early 1940's the activity of this agency in both the farm mortgage and production credit fields has been greatly curtailed.

Budgeting Short-Term Loans

Under a budget plan of extending short-term credit, the lending agency and the borrower periodically decide what credit will be needed in the farming operation and when repayments can be made. An example of how this system of lending works is shown in Table 7. Here borrower and lender studied the farmer's credit needs

Table 7. **Example Illustrating the Budget Plan for the Use of Short-Term Credit**

Month	Purpose for Which Loan Was Made or Source of Money for Repayment	Bor- rowed	Repaid	Balance Out- standing at End of Month	Interest Charge for Month at 6% per Annum
February	20 tons hay	$400		$ 400	$2.00
March	10 brood sows	500		900	4.50
April	5 tons fertilizer	450		1,350	6.75
May	300 bu corn	435		1,785	8.93
June				1,785	8.93
July	Cattle sales (July 15)		$1,000	785	6.42
August	300 bu corn	450		1,235	6.18
September	Hog sales (Sept. 15)		1,000	235	3.68
October	Hog sales (Oct. 15)			0	0.59

early in the year and decided how much money he would need during the year and when he would need it. They also decided which months of the year income from the farm would be heavy and therefore when the borrower could make payments on the loan. The lender then agreed to make a specified amount of credit available to the borrower on the dates they had decided he would need it. Under this arrangement, the borrower pays interest on the money only for the time he actually uses it.

This plan has several advantages over the methods typically used.

If credit is arranged ahead of the time it will be needed, farm operators can count on its being available and can make their plans accordingly. In addition, the amount of interest to be paid is reduced. In the example shown in Table 7, the operator actually borrowed a total of $2,235 during the year. His interest bill was only $47.98. If he had borrowed the entire $2,235 for the full 8½-month period, the interest charge would have been $94.99.

The fact that a budget plan is used does not alter the lending agency's procedure in arranging security for the loan. The borrower must still sign a promissory note on which the amounts and dates of advancements and repayments are stated. In addition, the lending agency will usually require collateral for the loan.

Using Credit Productively

For what purposes should credit be used? Generally it should be confined primarily to purposes that are productive. This means that the added income resulting from the loan each year should be enough to pay the interest plus part of the principal. If you borrow money to buy a television set, to take a vacation trip, or to buy a new car, the investment you have made will return no income, but the interest and principal will have to be paid. Obviously transactions of this type do not contribute to financial progress. These are often called consumption loans. We cannot make the rule that credit should never be used for family living purposes. Sometimes it cannot be avoided because of unforeseen emergencies. In other cases it may be the only means of obtaining improved housing or other conveniences that are costly but last a long time. But credit for consumption purposes can lead to financial troubles and should be employed sparingly.

On the other hand, if you borrow money to buy fertilizer, add more brood sows, or buy better dairy cows, you can reasonably expect to pay the interest on the loan and eventually the loan itself from increased earnings. Credit used for these purposes is typically highly productive and increases income unless some misfortune arises. The best way to estimate the probable return from use of credit is to work out a budget. Methods of budgeting are discussed in Chapter 14.

There are many other uses for credit on the farm that are not easy to evaluate. Will buying new machinery increase income enough to cover interest charges and eventually pay the principal? If it allows the operator to farm more acres, it may be a highly productive use of credit. If it does not, then returns must come through saving labor or doing a better job. It is often difficult to justify buying new machinery on credit under these circumstances. Similarly, deciding whether to borrow to add new buildings or to paint or improve existing structures is a difficult problem. Sometimes investments to protect an existing improvement add to income over a long period, by extending the life of a building or reducing maintenance costs. In other cases, expenditures for these purposes may improve the appearance of the farm or make the work more convenient. But improved appearance and greater convenience will not provide added income to meet principal and interest payments.

Before using credit for any of these borderline investments, you should analyze them carefully. If they do not promise a fairly certain and direct return, they should be postponed until they can be financed without the use of credit.

Recognizing the Risks in Heavy Borrowing

Effect of falling prices on net worth

Why do experienced farmers and lenders place so much emphasis on using credit conservatively? The amount of risk involved in borrowing money becomes greater as the ratio of debt to the borrower's net worth increases. If farmers could always count on increasing or at least stable farm prices, this risk would not exist. But future prices are highly uncertain and, if we can judge from the past, are subject to sharp declines.

Let us examine what happens to a farm operator's net worth when the prices of the things he owns drop sharply. This will help to explain why persons who have had long experience with credit urge young farmers to use it moderately. Following is a simplified net worth statement of a farm operator making fairly heavy use of credit. He is borrowing one dollar for every dollar of his net worth.

You will notice that the net worth statement lists assets on one side and liabilities on the other. Assets are the items of value that are owned by the farm operator or are owed to him by someone else. Liabilities are claims against the business such as mortgages or notes owed by him to others. Net worth is the amount by which assets exceed liabilities.

Assets		Liabilities	
160 acres of land	$50,000	Mortgage on land	$25,000
Livestock	7,500	Loan at bank	10,000
Machinery	7,500		
Feed on hand	5,000		
Total assets	$70,000	Total liabilities	$35,000
		Net worth	35,000

Now let us assume that a 33 per cent drop in the value of the things he owns occurs before he has had an opportunity to pay off any more of his debt. His net worth statement after the price drop would be as follows:

Assets		Liabilities	
160 acres of land	$33,333	Mortgage on land	$25,000
Livestock	5,000	Loan at bank	10,000
Machinery	5,000		
Feed on hand	3,333		
Total assets	$46,666	Total liabilities	$35,000
		Net worth	11,666

As a result of the 33 per cent decline in prices of the things he owns, his net worth has been reduced from $35,000 to $11,600.

Let us carry our example one step further. Instead of borrowing one dollar for every dollar of net worth, let us assume that the farm operator borrows two dollars for every dollar of his net worth. He invests the added capital he has borrowed in more land, livestock, machinery, and feed. Under these conditions his net worth statement would be as follows:

Assets		Liabilities	
240 acres of land	$ 75,000	Mortgage on land	$50,000
Livestock	11,250	Loan at the bank	20,000
Machinery	11,250		
Feed on hand	7,500		
Total assets	$105,000	Total liabilities	$70,000
		Net worth	35,000

Again let us assume a 33 per cent decline in the prices of the things the farm operator owned took place. After the price drop his net worth statement would look like this:

Assets		Liabilities	
240 acres of land	$50,000	Mortgage on land	$50,000
Livestock	7,500	Loan at the bank	20,000
Machinery	7,500		
Feed on hand	5,000		
Total assets	$70,000	Total liabilities	$70,000
		Net worth	–0–

The drop in the price level of 33 per cent in this case has caused the net worth of the borrower to drop from $35,000 to zero. This is a much sharper decline than in the previous example where he had borrowed less.

A decline in farm prices always causes the net worth of the farm operator to decrease. But the effect is magnified when he is in debt. This is true because the size of the debt remains fixed in terms of dollars in spite of the decrease in prices. This tendency for the risk arising out of borrowing to increase with the amount of credit used is called the principle of increasing risk. It may be stated as follows: As the ratio of debt to net worth increases, the decrease in net worth arising out of a decline of a given magnitude in the value of farm assets becomes greater.

There is, of course, another side to this picture. The heavy borrower makes out well during periods of rising prices. The value of his assets increase sharply, but the size of his debt stays the same in terms of dollars. As a result his net worth increases much more rapidly than if he had borrowed conservatively or not at all. Many young farmers who had borrowed heavily were able to make rapid financial progress during the 1940's and early 1950's because of the rising price level.

Difficulties in meeting payments

Falling prices also work a hardship on the heavy borrower by making it more difficult for him to meet interest and principal payments. The farm borrower typically must meet his payments from the farm products he sells. When prices decline, it takes more of what he sells to make the payments on his loan. The amount of farm products necessary to make a $500 payment on a loan during different years is shown in Table 8. A farmer who borrowed in 1918

Table 8. Quantities of Farm Products Needed to Make a $500 Payment on a Loan, 1913–1952

Year	Units	1913	1918	1923	1928	1933	1938	1943	1948	1952
Corn	Bushels	720	360	690	600	1,390	1,020	450	380	320
Wheat	Bushels	620	240	520	440	760	890	370	250	240
Hogs	230-lb hogs	30	14	34	25½	55	31½	16	9½	12
Cattle	1,000-lb steers	84	54	95	36	92	53	42	23	19½
Butterfat	Lb of butterfat	1,720	920	1,080	1,080	2,620	1,920	1,000	620	680
Eggs	Dozen of eggs	1,500	840	1,080	1,770	3,570	2,490	1,350	1,050	1,200

saw his principal and interest payments magnified many times in terms of farm products between the time he borrowed the money and 1933. On the other hand, farmers who borrowed during the 1930's had to sell much smaller amounts of farm products to meet payments on their loan during and after World War II.

Establishing a Good Credit Rating

It is not unusual to find that one farmer in a community has no trouble getting credit while his neighbor finds it impossible. The reason for this situation is evident when one considers that lending agencies are primarily business establishments. They make their income by lending money at interest. This money usually belongs to someone else. When they lend money, they must take precautions to assure that the borrower will meet his principal and interest obligations. If creditors were often wrong in evaluating the borrower's willingness and capacity to repay his loan, they soon would fail financially.

Following are some of the most important factors that lenders take into consideration in deciding whether or not to grant a loan:

1. *Financial Position of the Borrower.* The lender's primary interest is the amount of collateral that the borrower has with which to back up the loan. In addition, he will be interested in any other debts the prospective borrower has. Creditors sometimes are willing to lend money to good credit risks without formally securing the loan with a mortgage, but they are willing to do this only if the borrower is in a strong financial position and has a good reputation for paying his debts.

2. *Borrower's Ability to Repay the Loan.* Even though the borrower may have sufficient security, the credit agency may prefer not to make a loan if there are likely to be difficulties over its repayment. Collecting through foreclosure is an unpleasant and time-consuming procedure which lenders prefer to avoid. Nearly every farm loan must be repaid out of income earned on the farm. Therefore, the lender is interested in the borrower's ability to make money. This means that he will be particularly concerned about the size of the business, the machinery and livestock the farm operator has to work with, and the borrower's ability to manage his farm business.

3. *Purpose of the Loan.* It is easiest to secure credit to finance ventures that will increase income. Creditors usually are also willing to refinance loans that are scattered among a number of different creditors. Such a procedure may enable the borrower to obtain a more favorable interest rate and to work out an orderly plan for repaying the loan.

Many lenders are reluctant to advance credit for family living purposes. Money invested in this way is used up and does not produce income to repay the loan. Creditors require more collateral on loans of this type than on those where the money is to be used for productive purposes.

4. Character and Reputation of the Borrower. The lender is interested in the character of the prospective borrower and especially in anything in his past record that suggests he might attempt to avoid repayment of the loan.

The lender will investigate the following matters in judging the borrower's character:

(*a*) His past record of repaying loans and the number and the size of his debts presently outstanding.

(*b*) Any inaccurate or false statements concerning his financial position and his income-earning capacity.

(*c*) Whether he has ever used bankruptcy or compromise of debts or other legal means to avoid repayment of debts.

Summary

In the previous pages we have discussed a number of factors that you should consider in using credit. We may summarize the most important of these factors as follows:

1. Credit usually should be confined to uses that promise enough return to pay the interest plus part of the principal each year.

2. Long-term loans should be amortized over the term of the loan.

3. The repayment schedule, and hence the length of term of the loan, should be arranged so that the loan can be repaid from income.

4. Established credit institutions are generally a more economical source of short-term credit than merchants and dealers.

5. Long-term loans should include provisions that permit prepayments on the loan without an excessive penalty.

6. Increasing the amount of money borrowed increases the risk of financial difficulties arising from falling farm prices.

7. Lenders consider the purpose of the loan, the financial position of the prospective borrower, his ability as a manager, and his charter in deciding how much money, if any, to lend.

Problems

1. Many people regard the use of credit as "bad." How do you account for this attitude? Under what circumstances do you think that the use of credit is bad? When is it a good practice?

2. Mr. Duncan owns 160 acres which is paid for. In addition he has $10,000 cash and wants to buy another 160-acre farm adjoining his farm which is for sale. It can be bought for $43,000. By mortgaging both farms he can borrow enough money to finance the transaction. He can obtain a loan from the following sources:

(a) Federal Land Bank. This loan will run for 34 years and require a payment of $810 each year.

(b) An insurance company on the same basis.

(c) The local bank. This loan from the bank runs for 10 years and requires only that he pay $1,350 a year interest. The entire $30,000 principal would come due at the end of the 10-year period.

The interest on the loans from all three sources would be 4½ per cent. From which of the three sources would you recommend that he obtain the loan?

3. Mr. Benton is in the process of buying a 160-acre farm. Its purchase price is $50,000, and he has $25,000 available for down payment. In addition, he has a good set of farm machinery and a dairy herd, both of which are paid for. By selling some of the machinery and part of his dairy herd, he can pay $30,000 down on the farm. He can get along by hiring a baler, combine, and cornpicker. Would you recommend that he sell his baler, combine, and cornpicker and half of his dairy herd and make as large a down payment as possible?

4. You have $1,000 which you are going to lend to a neighbor to buy brood sows. You have known him for several years and know that he is honest. However, he also has borrowed some money from the bank. What steps should you take to see that the $1,000 will be repaid?

5. Investigate the lending policies of the banks in your local community. What interest rates do they charge? What procedure do they follow in making a loan? Under what circumstances will they lend money for the purchase of fertilizer and for soil conservation practices?

6. How far is it to your nearest Production Credit Association? Compare it as a source of short-term credit with your local banks.

References

Berg, Sherwood O., E. Fred Koller, and O. B. Jesness, "Loans of Production Credit Associations to Minnesota Farmers," *Minn. Agr. Expt. Sta. Bull.* 410, Mar. 1952.

Case, H. C. M., and Paul E. Johnston, *Principles of Farm Management*, Chapter 17, J. B. Lippincott Co., Chicago, Philadelphia, New York, 1953.

Dougherty, L. A., "Agricultural Credit for New Hampshire," *New Hampshire Ext. Circ.* 304, Dec. 1951.

Diesslin, H. G., "Short-Term Agricultural Loans of Selected Indiana Banks," *Purdue Agr. Expt. Sta. Bull.* 558, Nov. 1950.

Diesslin, H. G., and G. E. Heitz, "Budgeting Farm Production Loans of Production Credit Association," *Purdue Agr. Expt. Sta. Bull.* 557, Nov. 1950.

Efferson, J. Norman, *Principles of Farm Management*, Chapter 19, Mc-Graw-Hill Book Co., New York, 1953.

Financing Farm and Ranch Activities, Farm Credit Administration, Omaha, Neb. 1951.

Forster, G. W., *Farm Organization and Management*, 3d Ed., Chapter 25, Prentice-Hall, New York, 1953.

Hopkins, John A., and William G. Murray, *Elements of Farm Management*, 4th Ed., Chapter 26, Prentice-Hall, New York, 1953.

"Improving Land Credit Arrangements in the Midwest," *Purdue Agr. Expt. Sta. Bull.* 551, June 1950.

Larsen, Harald C., and Neil W. John, Managing Farm Finances, *USDA Misc. Pub.* 652.

Miller, L. F., and F. A. Hughes, "Credit Sources, Practices, and Opinions of Pennsylvania Farmers," *Penn. Agr. Expt. Sta. Bull.* 514, June 1949.

Murray, William G., *Agricultural Finance*, Iowa State College Press, Ames, 1941.

Robertson, Lynn S., and Ralph H. Woods, *Farm Business Management*, Chapter 13, J. B. Lippincott Co., Chicago, Philadelphia, New York, 1950.

The Balance Sheet of Agriculture (published annually), Bur. Agr. Econ., USDA.

CHAPTER

6

Planning the Cropping Program

To simplify our approach to the problems of planning a cropping program, we will consider cropping systems for level farms with little or no erosion hazard in this chapter. Then in the next chapter we will discuss the additional problems that are encountered on farms where soil erosion is a hazard. Even though you are interested only in cropping programs for hilly land, you should study this chapter thoroughly. Most of the principles discussed here apply on both hilly and level land.

Management Problems

1. Selecting high-income crops.
2. Choosing a crop rotation.
3. Planning the field layout.
4. Managing pastures.
5. Planning the fertilizer program.

Selecting High-Income Crops

Estimating the gross income per acre that each crop will produce should be your first step in deciding how well different crops are fitted to your area and your farm. Yield averages over a period of several years from the farm being studied are the best basis for making this comparison. But past yields from a single farm are seldom available for all the crops that you might wish to compare. For this reason it usually is necessary to refer to township or county yield estimates in analyzing different crops. In order to even out the effect of variations in the weather, income from the different crops over a span of 5 to 10 years should be compared.

The gross income produced by the major crops in three midwest counties is compared in Table 9. This comparison emphasizes the outstanding ability of corn to produce a high gross income in areas to which it is adapted. However, there are marked differences in

102

Table 9. Gross Income-Producing Ability of Major Crops in Three
Cornbelt Counties*

Crop	Story County, Ia.			Franklin County, Mo.			Stark County, Ohio		
	Long-Time Yield per acre, bu	Price per bu	Gross Value per acre	Long-Time Yield per acre, bu	Price per bu	Gross Value per acre	Long-Time Yield per acre, bu	Price per bu	Gross Value per acre
Corn	57	$1.26	$71.82	33	$1.36	$44.88	46	$1.37	$63.02
Oats	38	0.73	27.74	22	0.78	17.16	41	0.80	32.80
Soybeans	23	2.35	54.05	11	2.37	26.07	18	2.40	43.20
Winter wheat	20	1.78	35.60	17	1.80	30.60	26	1.87	48.62

* Based on 1939 to 1948 yields and 1942 to 1951 prices.

Figure 27. Corn produces a high gross income per acre. However, on most
farms it is necessary to include some grass and legume crops in the rotation
to maintain total corn production on the farm at a high level over a period
of years. (Courtesy Deere & Co.)

the competitive position of the other crops among the three counties compared. Although corn outyields soybeans in Story County, Ia., the income advantage of corn over beans is not so great in this county as in Franklin County, Mo., or Stark County, Ohio. On the other hand, winter wheat compares much more favorably with the other crops in Ohio than in Missouri or Iowa.

Costs of production

In the previous section we compared the gross income per acre produced by different crops. Another factor that should be considered in deciding how well the different crops fit on a farm is their cost of production. A Minnesota study indicates that the costs of producing the major crops are not greatly different from each other. According to this study, soybeans were the least costly and alfalfa and corn silage were the most costly to produce. These comparisons are given in Table 10. The only costs included in the table were the

Table 10.   Cash Costs of Producing Major Crops per Acre on
32 Southern Minnesota Farms, 1951*

	Oats	Soy-beans	Corn Husked	Corn for Silage	Alfalfa Hay and Silage
Preharvest Costs					
Power	$ 1.45	$ 3.10	$ 3.50	$ 3.61	$ ...
Seed	3.27	4.55	1.70	1.75	6.06
Commercial fertilizer	1.34	...	3.12	0.95	0.25
Machinery	3.39	2.31	3.33	3.66	...
Other	0.04	...	0.29	...	1.52
Total preharvest costs	$ 9.49	$ 9.96	$11.94	$ 9.97	$ 7.83
Harvest Costs					
Power	$ 2.01	$ 0.60	$ 1.61	$ 2.82	$ 4.18
Machinery	3.20	2.26	2.56	5.51	8.16
Other	0.84	...	0.32	0.74	...
Total harvest cost	$ 6.05	$ 2.86	$ 4.49	$ 9.07	$12.34
Total cash cost	15.54	12.82	16.43	19.04	20.17

* Adapted from *Univ. Minn. Div. Agr. Econ. Rept.* 203.

direct outlays that the farmer had to make in order to produce the crops. In addition to these costs, land and labor were also used in raising the crops.

The labor required on the 32 Minnesota farms to produce and harvest an acre of each crop is shown in Table 11. Ensiling corn in

**Table 11.   Hours of Labor Required to Produce Major Crops per Acre
on 32 Southern Minnesota Farms, 1951***

	Oats	Soy-beans	Corn Husked	Corn for Silage	Alfalfa Hay and Silage
Preharvest	1.7	3.2	3.9	4.0	...
Harvest	3.9	1.0	2.5	5.6	6.6
Total	5.6	4.2	6.4	9.6	6.6

* Adapted from *Univ. Minn. Div. Agr. Econ. Rept.* 203.

particular takes a great deal of labor.   The differences in the total
amount of labor required for the other crops, are not so great, rang-
ing from a low of 4.2 hours per acre for soybeans to 6.6 hours per
acre for alfalfa.   These comparisons do not reflect all the differences
in labor requirements among the crops.   Putting up hay or grass
and corn silage usually involves heavy physical labor.   On the other
hand corn, soybean and small grain production, are almost entirely
mechanized on most farms.

The time at which each crop requires labor is also important in
planning the cropping program.   For example, alfalfa hay and corn
often compete for labor in June.   But oats and corn seldom demand
attention at the same time of the year.

Figure 28.   Harvesting corn as silage requires more labor than harvesting it
for grain.   This is true even though the ensiling operation is mechanized.
(Courtesy Monsanto Chemical Co.)

Although these labor requirements for the different crops are typical for many farms, they will not be the same on all farms. Differences in the texture of the soil and differences in the machinery and other equipment available for planting, cultivating, and harvesting crops will cause them to vary from one farm to another.

Other factors

When production costs are subtracted from gross income, it is evident that some crops do not produce so high a net income as others. Why do farmers continue to raise these crops? Often they serve a special function in the cropping system and are grown for this reason. The grass and legume crops are outstanding examples. We will consider their role in the cropping system at greater length in a later section. Oats and soybeans also often serve special purposes in the cropping program. In spite of their low income-producing ability, oats may be raised for any one of the following reasons:

1. To help distribute labor and machinery requirements when the oats are raised with other crops. They fit particularly well with corn because they can be planted before corn and harvested after the corn is cultivated but before it is picked. This is an important factor on farms with a short supply of labor.

2. To serve as a nurse crop for grass and legume crops. Grasses and legumes are usually sown with a companion crop to protect them while they are in the seedling stage. Oats serve this purpose well in areas where they are adapted to it.

3. To provide a source of bedding on livestock farms. In making our earlier comparison of the income-producing ability of the major crops, we did not include the value of the straw from oats. The value of bedding varies greatly from one farm to another. On cash-grain farms the straw is often left in the field, but on farms with a sizable livestock program it is a valuable by-product of the oats crop.

If oats do not serve one or more of these three purposes, they should not be included in the cropping system, because they return a low dollar income. Some farmers argue that they should be raised because they are a good feed for dairy cows, poultry, and young pigs. Although oats are an excellent feed for some types of livestock, you should not overlook the possibility of raising a more profitable crop and then buying oats or some high-protein feed that will replace oats in the ration.

Soybeans sometimes can be included profitably in the cropping pattern to serve one or more of the following purposes:

1. To Replace Corn When Adverse Weather Delays Planting. Soybeans planted after the first week or two of June often will yield a greater return than corn planted on the same date. Using soybeans instead of corn where planting is seriously delayed also serves as insurance against getting an immature corn crop.

Figure 29. Although soybeans typically do not yield so high a gross return as corn in most of the cornbelt, they often can be fitted profitably into the cropping system. They help distribute labor requirements more evenly and often take the place of oats or second or third-yar corn in the rotation. Soybeans are also an excellent emergency crop when wet weather delays planting corn. (Courtesy International Harvester Co.)

2. To Replace Third- or Fourth-Year Corn in the Cropping Plan. Sometimes the cropping system is not well organized or gets off schedule. When this happens, it is often necessary to raise an inter-tilled crop 3 or 4 years in succession on the same land. In areas where they are well adapted, planting soybeans instead of third- or fourth-year corn may result in a higher income.

3. To Help Distribute the Work Load. In most areas, soybeans can be planted later and harvested earlier than corn. In addition, in areas where fall plowing is feasible, growing soybeans instead of corn makes it possible to do more of the plowing in the fall.

4. To Reduce Risk through Increasing Diversification. Soybeans are a relatively certain crop. In addition, they may do well during years in which corn yields poorly. Planting part of the acreage to beans helps to insure against having a year of very low crop income.

People sometimes attribute soil-building properties to soybeans because they are a legume, and include them in the cropping plan for this reason. Experimental studies indicate that soybeans do not add nitrogen to the soil when harvested for grain even though they are a legume. They make heavy demands on other soil nutrients such as phosphorus and potassium. Only where soil texture is "heavy," do they have a beneficial effect and then only through loosening the soil.

Farmers sometimes replace corn with soybeans because they think soybeans are a good cash crop. This is not a sound basis for including them in the cropping system. Corn also can be readily marketed for cash, and an acre of corn will usually yield a higher cash return than an acre of beans. The only advantage that soybeans enjoy over corn, in most cases, as a cash crop is that they can be sold several weeks earlier in the fall.

Choosing a Crop Rotation

Advantages of a systematic rotation

What are the advantages of a systematic rotation? When the crops grown on a field are changed from year to year, weeds, insects, and poor soil structure are less of a problem. In addition, rotation enables meadow or pasture crops to furnish organic matter and add nitrogen for succeeding crops. Although practically all farmers change crops from field to field, many do not follow a systematic rotation.

Under a systematic rotation program, some of each of the crops included in the rotation would be raised every year. Rotations are often referred to by the number of years it takes them to make a complete cycle on the farm. For example, 3 years would be required for a 3-year rotation to complete the sequence of crops in all fields on a farm. An example of the way in which a 4-year rotation plan would work is shown in Figure 30. Here the sequence of crops being grown is corn–corn–oats–clover. The 160-acre farm is divided into four equal fields. With 8 acres out for farmstead and roads, 76 acres of corn, 38 acres of oats, and 38 acres of clover are raised each year.

Aside from beneficial effects of the grass and legumes, the advantages of following a systematic crop rotation plan are:

1. The demands on labor and machinery are distributed more evenly through the cropping season. Where the changing of crops is not well planned, acreages of each crop often will vary considerably from year to year. As a result, peaks in the labor load develop.

2. The feed supply is more stable from year to year. There always will be some year-to-year fluctuation in the amount of feed produced, due to variations in the weather. But a well-planned ro-

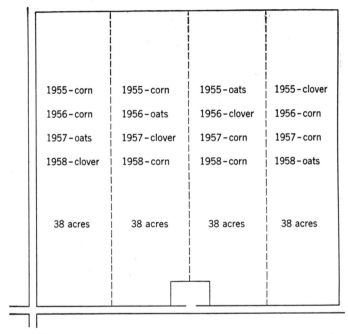

1955 - corn	1955 - corn	1955 - oats	1955 - clover
1956 - corn	1956 - oats	1956 - clover	1956 - corn
1957 - oats	1957 - clover	1957 - corn	1957 - corn
1958 - clover	1958 - corn	1958 - corn	1958 - oats
38 acres	38 acres	38 acres	38 acres

Figure 30.   Example showing a well-organized corn–corn–oats–clover rotation on a level 160-acre farm.

tation system with fields of even size is a big help in providing a balanced and stable feed supply.

3. The amount of risk is reduced. When a large proportion of the crop land is in a single crop, the amount of risk is great. If the weather or prices are unfavorable for this one crop, farm income will be low. But, when several crops are raised, the risk of having a very low income is reduced. This is true because both weather and prices will not often be unfavorable in any one year for all the crops that are included in the rotation.

4. The amount of storage space needed for crops is not so great. Because the acreage of each crop remains approximately the same from year to year in a well-planned rotation system, less total storage space is required. When a large acreage of one crop is raised one year and a small acreage the following year, part of the storage space will stand idle during some years.

Comparing returns from rotations

Even though you have narrowed down the number of crops you wish to produce, there are many combinations or rotations in which they can be put together. How should you go about selecting the most profitable one? Returns that can be expected from alternative crop rotation should be estimated by the use of a budget. In order to budget the income or the value of the feed that will be produced under each rotations, you must have estimates of (1) the yields that can be expected from each crop and (2) the price you can expect to get for each crop. The market value should be figured as a first approximation, even though the crop will be fed to livestock. In the preliminary budget, prevailing rental rates can be used to estimate the return to land in pasture.

The budget for each rotation should be worked out in terms of total production for the farm as a whole. Attempting to work out the budget on a per-acre basis is confusing and often leads to errors. It was shown in Table 10 that the differences in the cost of producing the major crops are not great. Therefore working out the gross returns that can be expected from each rotation gives a fairly accurate picture of how the rotations compare on a net income basis. If you want the budget to be more accurate than this, you can make the comparisons on a net income basis by subtracting direct production costs from gross income.

Highest yields per acre not the goal

Average yields per acre and the total amount of each crop that would be produced on 100 acres of crop land are compared for six different rotations in Table 12. These yields are based on a crop rotation experiment that was carried on for a long period of years on the Wooster and Canfield soils in Ohio. You should notice that the first two "rotations" contain no forage. But, as we move down the column, the percentage of forage increases until it reaches 60 per cent in the last rotation. As a rule, the average yields of grain per acre increases as the proportion of grasses and legumes in the rotation

Table 12. Average Yield per Acre and Total Production from 100 Acres of Soils with Different Cropping Systems on Ohio Soils*

Cropping System	Total Acres of Each Crop			Yield per Acre			Total Production		
	Corn	Wheat	Alfalfa	Corn, bu	Wheat, bu	Alfalfa, tons	Corn, bu	Wheat, bu	Alfalfa, tons
Continuous corn	100	0	0	35	...	...	3,500	...	...
Corn-wheat	50	50	0	47	24	...	2,350	1,200	...
Corn-wheat-alfalfa	33.3	33.3	33.3	67	41	2.7	2,231	1,365	90
Corn-corn-wheat- alfalfa-alfalfa	40	20	40	65	32	3.5	2,600	640	140
Corn-wheat-alfalfa- alfalfa	25	25	50	68	42	3.2	1,700	1,050	160
Corn-wheat-alfalfa- alfalfa-alfalfa	20	20	60	72	44	3.2	1,440	880	192

* Adapted from *Handbook of Ohio Experiments In Agronomy*, Ohio Agr. Expt. Sta., Wooster, Ohio.

becomes greater. This relationship is followed fairly closely by the Ohio yield estimates shown in Table 12. If your goal were to get as high a yield per acre as possible, you would always choose a rotation that contains a large proportion of forages. But the rotation that gives the highest yield of grain per acre rarely gives the greatest income from the cropping system as a whole.

Table 13. Total Value of Production from 100 Acres under the Six Rotations with Hay at Two Different Prices*

			Total Value of Production	
Cropping System	Value of Grain Production	Total Tons of Hay	Hay Priced at $10 per ton	Hay Priced at $20 per ton
Continuous corn	$4,795	...	$4,795	$4,795
Corn-wheat	5,463	...	5,463	5,463
Corn-wheat-alfalfa	5,595	90	6,495	7,395
Corn-corn-wheat- alfalfa-alfalfa	4,759	140	6,159	7,559
Corn-wheat-alfalfa- alfalfa	4,292	160	5,892	7,492
Corn-wheat-alfalfa- alfalfa-alfalfa	3,618	192	5,538	7,458

* The prices used are the average prices received by Ohio farmers during the period 1942-51.

Complementary relationship

The total value of the grain production in each of the six rotations is given in the second column of Table 13. An important relationship is illustrated by what happens to grain production as the crop land seeded to alfalfa is increased from zero to one third of the acreage. Even though the acreage in grain is decreased from 100 to 67, the total value of grain production increases. When increasing the proportion of acres of forage in the rotation increases the total grain production, even though the number of acres of grain are decreased, forage is complementary with grain.

The yields given in the table are long-run yields. If you know that you are going to be on the farm only a year or two and will

Figure 31. Forage may be either complementary or competitive with grain production. When raising forage results in a long-run increase in total grain production, the relationship is said to be complementary. When the forage in the rotation reduces the total amount of grain produced, the relationship is said to be competitive. (Courtesy Deere & Co.)

not have an opportunity to raise corn on any of the land put to grass, this complementary relationship between the grass and grain crops is of no advantage to you. Under these circumstances, you would profit by raising forage crops only if the output from an acre of forage is worth more to you than the return from an acre of corn. In planning a short-run cropping program the average yield of each crop during the last 2 or 3 years should be used instead of long-run rotation yields. Of what importance is this complementary relationship between forage and grain if you are planning a long-run cropping program? You will want to include at least enough forage to give you the greatest total production of grain. In doing so, you will not only get more grain but will have the added forage as well. Even if you have no use for the forage and plow it under, raising the complementary forage would be profitable.

Competitive relationship

Looking again at Table 13, we see that increasing the proportion of forage in the rotation from 33 to 40 per cent by changing from a corn–wheat–alfalfa to a corn–corn–wheat–alfalfa–alfalfa rotation

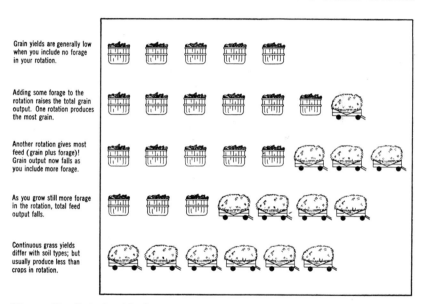

Figure 32. Relationship between total grain and forage production in the rotation. (From "The Right Rotation for Your Farm," *Iowa Farm Science,* Nov. 1948)

would decrease the total value of grain raised. However, it would increase the total amount of hay harvested each year from the 100 acres of crop land from 90 to 140 tons. When increasing the amount of forage in the rotation decreases the total amount of grain produced, the relationship between grain and forage is said to be competitive.

The typical relationship existing between grain and forage in the rotation is illustrated in Figure 32. Here forage is first complementary and then competitive with grain as the amount of forage in the rotation increases.

Is the 50 tons of added hay gained worth more than the $836 worth of grain given up? This is the decision that a farmer on soil of this type must make in choosing between a corn–wheat–alfalfa and a corn–corn–wheat–alfalfa–alfalfa rotation.

Problems in budgeting

Students often are inclined to look for a simple method of selecting a cropping system. But there is no such method. Using rules of thumb such as choosing the rotation that gives the highest corn yield per acre or the most total digestible feed nutrients generally leads to the wrong answer. The best approach to the decision is to use a preliminary budget as shown in Tables 12 and 13. The tentative cropping plan or plans selected in this way can be fitted to the livestock program by the procedure explained in Chapter 14. The two most difficult problems in working out a crop budget are (1) to obtain long-run yield estimates and (2) to estimate the value of additional acres of pasture or tons of hay. Even though knowledge of these two factors is imperfect, working out a budget is better than guessing or following some faulty rule of thumb.

The prices that you should use in estimating returns from different cropping programs depend on the length of the time period in which you are interested. If you are making plans for only a year or two, present prices adjusted to conform to the price outlook immediately ahead should be used. If you are making long-run plans, average prices over the last 5 to 10 years are better, since they are more likely to reflect accurately the long-run price relationships among crops. You should bear in mind, however, that you are interested in past prices only as guides to the future. If you have a good basis for believing that future prices relationships will differ from those prevailing in the past, you should adjust the prices you use in your budget accordingly.

Differences among farms

The yield and production figures given in Table 12 show the relationship between rotations and production on Canfield and Wooster soils in Ohio only. Yield responses to rotations will be different on other soil types. On some soil types, it may be necessary to keep more than a third of the land in grasses and legumes in order to get the most total grain production over a long period. On other soils such as the Muscatine soils of north central Illinois, total grain production can be maintained with only 20 or 25 per cent of the land in grass. If heavy applications of fertilizer are used, there is growing evidence that the most profitable rotation on some soils may be one containing little or no forage, such as a rotation consisting of corn–corn–oats with a crop of legumes seeded with the oats.

The same principles of choosing a rotation apply on hilly land as on level land. However, more grass must be included in the rotation in order to get the largest total grain production over a long-run period on hilly land. The grasses and legumes are necessary in order to control erosion; erosion losses must be cut down to maintain production over an extended period. If the land varies a great deal from one part of the farm to another, it is often necessary to fit two or even three different rotations to the farm. This problem is discussed more fully in the next chapter.

Most farm land now has been mapped and classified. On the basis of this information plus rotation experiments, agronomists have made estimates of yield responses with different rotations on many soils. Although these estimates are not always entirely accurate, they are the best data available for planning the cropping program.

Influence of the livestock program

You may be troubled by the fact that we have estimated the cash value of crop production in our preliminary budget, even though part or all of the crop may be fed to livestock. This procedure, however, gives us useful approximations even for livestock farms because the relative prices of feed crops tend to reflect their relative value as feeds. Usually, you can narrow down the choice of a rotation to two or three promising alternatives by using this procedure.

In the example cited above, the two most promising rotations appear to be corn–wheat–alfalfa and corn–corn–wheat–alfalfa–alfalfa. The final choice between the two should be made by the use of a budget of the entire farming program in which one or more alternative livestock programs are fitted to the cropping system. This procedure will aid in deciding whether the 50 tons of added forage is worth more than the $836 worth of grain given up in choosing between the corn–wheat–alfalfa and a corn–corn–wheat–alfalfa–alfalfa rotations in the example above. The problems involved in making complete farm budgets are discussed in Chapter 14.

Under what circumstances are you justified in sacrificing grain production in order to produce more forage? Farmers usually find that using forage profitably becomes more difficult as they raise large amounts. The amount of grain given up per acre of added forage raised also increases as more and more forage is included in the rotation. On most farms these two factors combine to place a limit on the amount of forage that can be included profitably in the rotation.

Forage-grain combinations on dairy farms

In areas located near large population centers, dairying often has a wide advantage over other livestock products because of a favorable milk price. Many of these farms must depend partly on

Figure 33. When producing forage results in sacrificing grain production, forage is said to be competitive with grain. To be justified in giving up grain to raise more forage, farmers must have a profitable outlet for the forage. On most farms this means feeding it to livestock. (Courtesy Union Pacific Railroad)

purchased feed in order to maintain a herd large enough for economical production. It is more economical to purchase grains than forages because of the lower cost of transporting grain for long distances. As a result the size of the dairy operation is often limited by the volume of forage produced.

On these farms it is often a good goal to organize the cropping system to maximize the total production of forage instead of grain. But raising the greatest output of forage does not mean having the entire acreage in grass and legume crops. Where the land can be cultivated, the total production of forage from a given acreage is usually increased by raising some grain to serve as a nurse crop for new seedings. Used in this way, grain is complementary with forage, just as forage is complementary with grain at the other end of the range. A Michigan study indicates that, when an alfalfa–bromegrass combination is used, the maximum acreage that can be kept in hay and pasture is about 70 to 80 per cent. However, this same study showed that few farmers find it profitable to have more than 60 per cent of their tillable acres in alfalfa and bromegrass. Seeding failures sometimes make it necessary to re-establish the stand. If left too long, the alfalfa in the stand tends to thin out, thus reducing the quality of the forage. This same problem

Table 14.   Average Yields from Forage Crops

Yield per acre, pounds

Crop	Hay Equivalent	Digestible Protein	Total Digestible Nutrients
Alfalfa (2 cuttings)	6,050	635	3,040
Red clover (2 cuttings)	3,640	258	1,900
Orchard grass, Ladino clover (4 cuttings)	4,070	452	2,170
Timothy	3,190	93	1,560
Oats	3,190	156	1,500
Millet (Japanese)	6,610	337	3,130
Corn silage	9,800	355	5,360
Permanent pasture (improved)	2,700	310	1,610

arises when stands of forages of other types are left down too long.

In the New England states where the land and climate is not well adapted to producing corn for grain, part of the acreage not in grass and legume crops is typically planted to corn for ensiling. Corn used in this way returns a high yield of total digestible nutrients per acre compared with forage crops (Table 14). The acreage of corn silage that can be raised is limited, however, since yields decline when the proportion of land in row crops is increased. In addition, raising a large acreage of silage results in a higher labor peak during the harvesting season.

Planning the Field Layout

A carefully planned field layout makes it easier to follow a systematic crop rotation and to do the field work efficiently. The shape of the farm and the lay of the land determine how much of a problem planning the field layout will be. Square or rectangular farms that have level topography and are free of obstructions such as ditches, rock piles, or timber are the easiest to plan. On these farms, fields usually can be laid out so that they are equal or nearly equal in size. The same number of fields ordinarily should be provided as the number of years or multiple of the number of years in the rotation. For example four (or eight) should be used if the farm is to be put under a 4-year corn–corn–oats–clover rotation.

Odd-shaped or triangular fields should be avoided where possible. They result in point rows, more turning with machinery, and more waste land. Having long narrow fields is a disadvantage where corn is checked and cultivated crosswise. In spite of the greater amount of fencing and the disadvantage during corn cultivation, most farmers prefer the rectangular-shaped fields.

Where the farm is rough and has a serious erosion hazard, fields should be laid out so that the land can be farmed on the contour and in accord with its capability. Often on farms of this type the soil varies considerably from one part of the farm to another, and two or even more different rotations must be followed on the same farm. As a result there often are many small fields; it is difficult to make them of equal size. Either two different rotations on the same farm or fields of unequal size will cause the acres in each crop to vary from one year to the next. It would be more convenient to have fewer and larger fields and the same acreage of each crop every year. However, it usually is better to sacrifice these conveniences in order to reduce erosion losses. Laying out fields on rough land is discussed more fully in the next chapter.

Attention must also be given to the livestock program in planning the field arrangement. It is advantageous from the standpoint of livestock production to have rotation pastures located near the farmstead and the water supply. This is especially true of hog pastures. If pastures are located a long distance from the farmstead, providing adequate water often becomes time-consuming and costly.

Usually it is necessary to provide lanes so that livestock can move to and from pasture. Because land in lanes is wasted except as a place on which to travel, there is a temptation to make lanes too narrow. Narrow lanes are inconvenient for moving machinery to and from the fields. In addition, where they are heavily traveled by livestock, lanes have a tendency to become muddy. If they are made wider these difficulties are minimized.

Farm management specialists have observed that a farmer frequently is handicapped in rearranging his farms because he is not critical enough of his present plan. Fences that have been located in one place for a number of years are frequently regarded as permanent. Similarly, a farmer who has been farming around rock piles, ditches, or trees often comes to regard them as permanent fixtures. You should not overlook opportunities for improving the field arrangement. Often someone not so well acquainted with your farm as you are can make helpful suggestions on the field layout.

Type of fences

Should temporary or permanent fences be used? It is becoming increasingly common for farmers to fence permanently only lots and the outside boundary of the farm. Within the farm, only those fields that will be pastured are fenced each year and then only with temporary fences. Using this system reduces the number of internal fences on the farm and does away with the wasteland and weeds associated with fence rows. During some years, two fields can be put together and farmed as one field where the rotation includes two or more years of the same crop. The disadvantage of using temporary fences is that they must be moved every year or two as the pasture is rotated from one field to another. The labor involved in changing fences can be reduced by using the improved fencing materials and tools now on the market.

Establishing a rotation

Establishing a rotation on a piecemeal basis is difficult. Working out a new rotation and field arrangement can be accomplished best by planning the entire farm at once. Changing from the existing cropping pattern to a new rotation may require several years. Fences must be changed and new seedings established. The field layout and cropping pattern should be planned carefully for each year during the shift.

Even after the rotation is well established, it is often difficult to follow it exactly. Rotations may be disrupted by failure to get a stand of new seeding or by winter killing of the existing stand. When this happens, temporary forage crops can be used if forage is needed for livestock. In other cases, the best method for getting back into the rotation is to include an extra year of corn.

You should look upon the crop rotation system as a master plan. It should be returned to as quickly as possible when disrupted. Even though following it exactly may be difficult, having a master plan has many advantages over cropping the land haphazardly.

Managing Pastures

Pasture programs on dairy farms

When a large proportion of the farm is in forage and the livestock program is built around it, selecting the best combination of legumes and grasses is fully as important as deciding the best balance between grain and forage crops. Because forages are particularly important on specialized dairy farms, we will discuss the pasture program primarily from the dairyman's standpoint. However, the same principles apply to planning pastures for other types of livestock.

In planning his feed supply, the dairy farmer should try to select the most economical sources of feed. Almost always pasture is the cheapest source of forages during the pasture season. For this reason dairymen should extend the time that cows can obtain a high-quality feed supply from pasture. This extending process usually involves some expense in the form of fertilizer, improved grasses, and mowing. These costs must be weighed against the cost of obtaining added forage in other ways, such as feeding hay or silage.

Two problems are of primary importance in planning the pasture program: (1) providing adequate pasture during the summer and fall months and (2) providing high-quality pasture. The two are closely related. Usually steps that result in an improved seasonal distribution of pasture also improve the quality.

The sources of pasture on a typical farm include (1) permanent pastures, (2) rotation pastures, (3) hay aftermath, and (4) new seedings. Farmers can choose from many kinds and varieties of forage plants in planning pastures. Each crop has a seasonal production pattern that differs from others. Permanent pastures typically produce abundantly in the spring and then drop off sharply during the summer and fall. Pasture studies at the Storrs Experiment Station in Connecticut showed that 72 per cent of the annual production of untreated permanent pastures occurred before mid-July. Usually applications of lime and fertilizer to pasture crops increase the yield per acre but do not greatly alter the seasonal production pattern.

The seasonal patterns from the major pasture crops in southern New England are shown in Table 15. The unit used to measure the pasture supply is cow-days. One cow-day of pasture is enough to graze one cow or her equivalent in young stock for one day.

Table 15. Seasonal Growth Pattern of Specified Crops When Used for Pasture in Southern New England*

Cow-days per acre

Kind of Pasture	May	June	July	Aug.	Sept.	Oct.	Total
Permanent (with no brush and few trees)							
1. Not fertilized	12	10	6	3	2	1	34
2. Lime and superphosphate	28	21	13	7	4	2	75
3. Lime and complete fertilizer	48	31	15	8	5	3	110
Ladino–Grass Mixtures							
1. Grazed entire season	40	40	34	26	14	6	160
2. Mowed June 1	—	40	34	26	14	6	120
3. Mowed June 10	—	20	34	26	14	6	100
4. Mowed June 20	—	—	34	26	14	6	80
5. Mowed June 30	—	—	14	26	14	6	60
6. Mowed June 1 and July 10	—	—	—	30	20	10	60
Small Grains							
Oats and Ladino. Seeded in April	—	40	40	20	5	—	105
Oats and Ladino. Seeded in May	—	20	40	—	20	—	80
Rye or wheat and Ladino. Rye seeded in Oct. Ladino seeded in Mar.	60	—	20	15	5	—	100
Barley or oats. Seeded Aug. 1	—	—	—	—	26	16	42
Barley or oats. Seeded Sept. 1	—	—	—	—	—	22	22
Rye or wheat. Seeded Sept. 1	—	—	—	—	—	16	16
Rye or wheat. Seeded in corn in July	—	—	—	—	—	10	10
Alfalfa (a total of three grazings)	—	100	40	30	—	30	200
Other Grasses							
Timothy. Cut June 15	—	—	—	30	5	—	35
Red clover and timothy. Cut June 15	—	—	10	25	10	—	45
Red clover–grass mixtures	45	45	10	25	10	—	135
Millet or Sudan grass. Seeded June 5	—	—	40	60	20	—	120
Millet or Sudan grass. Seeded July 5	—	—	—	40	40	—	80

* From *Storrs* (Connecticut) *Agr. Expt. Sta. Bull.* 283.

Notice that the Ladino–grass mixtures yield much better during summer and fall months than other crops.

Regardless of how the pasture program is arranged, more pasture will be available during the spring and early summer than in July, August, and September. One of the best methods of dealing with this problem is to mow hay from part of the forage acreage when the growth is abundant. In this way, more acres are available for pasture during August and September. Ladino–clover–grass mixtures are particularly well adapted to this practice. The first cutting can be made into hay or grass silage in June when permanent pastures are producing well. Later growth can be pastured when permanent pastures become short.

Controlled grazing

The yields of both permanent and rotation pastures can be increased by careful attention to the time and intensity of grazing. Grazing pastures either too early in the spring or too late in the fall will reduce the production from them. It usually is more economical to supplement pastures during these periods than to overgraze them. Where rotation pasture is to be plowed and put to an intertilled crop the next year, heavy grazing in the fall generally does no damage.

Some farmers prefer to follow a system of rotational grazing. In this system, pastures are fenced into several small areas and the animals shifted from one area to another during the pasture season. In this way, each area is rested part of the time. There is evidence that this practice may increase the total pasture yield somewhat. However, the worth of the added pasture must be weighed against the cost of the extra fencing involved.

Permanent pastures

In some areas the number of acres in permanent pasture on many farms exceeds the acres in crop land. What management program should be followed on land in permanent pasture? Under what circumstances should such land be put into rotation? When does pasture improvement pay?

The first step in managing permanent pastures is to put as much of the land in rotation as can be farmed safely and profitably. This will increase the acreage of grain crops as well as the total amount of pasture nutrients produced. Rotated pastures commonly have a carrying capacity two to three times greater than permanent blue grass pastures. Contouring and terracing for controlling erosion have made it possible to farm land that was formerly left in permanent pasture without excessive erosion. In other cases putting permanent pastures into rotation can be made practical by improving drainage. Although a rotation in which corn is grown only once in 4 or 5 years may be necessary on land now in permanent pasture, income on most farms may be increased by bringing such land into rotation.

You should not make the mistake of assuming that all land in permanent pasture should be cultivated. Some of it may be too low in fertility or drained too poorly to farm profitably. It is difficult to decide which land can and cannot be profitably cultivated. Where drainage or excessive erosion are hazards, trained soil and engineering specialists can give you valuable aid in making this decision.

A second way of increasing returns from permanent pastures is to improve them by reseeding and applying lime and fertilizer. This process is commonly known as pasture renovation. Research studies and the experience of many farmers have shown that the carrying capacity of run-down pastures can be greatly increased through renovation. The initial cost of the improvement varies from farm to farm and may run as high as $40 to $50 per acre. Even though the benefits of this process last for a number of years, the cost per acre may be as much as $10 per year.

In deciding whether to improve permanent pastures you should first decide if you can use added forage profitably. If you can, then you must decide if improving pastures is the most economical way of obtaining it. The following are some ways other than improving pastures by which the supply of forage can be increased:

1. Including more rotation pasture in the rotation. In this case, the cost of the added pasture is the grain that must be sacrificed in the rotation plus the cost of establishing the stand.

2. Renting additional pasture land.

3. Purchasing hay, thus freeing some of the present hay acreage for use as pasture.

Some farmers make the mistake of spending money for improving pastures when they do not have sufficient livestock to make use of more pasture. On cornbelt farms it usually is best to give priority to establishing a good rotation system on the tillable land first. This is particularly important on farms with limited capital. Once this has been accomplished, the farm operator often finds that he has enough rotated pasture to meet his needs without spending money to improve permanent pastures.

Planning the Fertilizer Program

In this section we are primarily interested in the dollar and cents side of using fertilizer. If you have not already done so, you should study the technical characteristics of the different types of fertilizer. This will help you understand the management problems involved in their use.

In planning the fertilizer program, it is important that you look on fertilizer as another tool to help increase farm income. Although we often speak of soil needing fertilizer, our basic interest is in the increase in yield we get from using it. We often hear people express the view that they hesitate to begin using fertilizer because once they start they cannot stop. There is no scientific basis for this idea. A farmer can stop using fertilizer anytime he finds that it does not pay. However, most farmers continue to use it once they have started because they find it profitable.

In spite of the fact that fertilizers have been utilized in limited quantities for many years, there still is much that we do not know about their use. The manager planning a fertilizer program must make many decisions on the basis of very little information. Agronomists in experiment stations all over the United States are hard at work determining the yield responses that we can get from different types and amounts of fertilizer on different soil types. The work that already has been done by these research workers can serve as a general guide. But the manager should approach the development of a fertilizer program with an attitude of experimentation. He should be ready to alter methods and rates of application as he learns more about fertilizers and the response he gets from them on his farm.

Fertilizer analysis

Commercial fertilizers usually contain nitrogen, phosphorus, or potash, or some combination of these three plant nutrients. In addition, they sometimes contain small amounts of trace elements. The contents of fertilizer are described by a formula containing three numbers such as 16-20-0. The first number gives the pounds of nitrogen (N) in each 100 pounds of fertilizer; the second indicates the pounds of available phosphorus (P_2O_5), and the third the pounds of available potash (K_2O). Thus, 100 pounds of a 16-20-0 fertilizer would contain 16 pounds of nitrogen, 20 pounds of phosphorus, and no potash.

Fertilizers of many different analyses are available on the market. If you are buying fertilizer, you are interested in the pounds of actual plant nutrients you are getting and not the total pounds of fertilizer. Suppose you plan to apply superphosphate on new seeding. You could buy 0-45-0 or 0-20-0. The first fertilizer contains $2\frac{1}{4}$ times as much phosphorus as the second. Buying 0-45-0 would be the cheaper source of phosphorus whenever it could be bought for less than $2\frac{1}{4}$ times as much as 0-20-0.

Usually plant nutrients can be purchased more economically in the form of high-analysis fertilizers (those containing a high proportion of plant nutrients) because the cost of handling and transporting each 100 pounds of actual plant nutrients is less. In addition, high-analysis fertilizers are more convenient for the farm operator to store and apply than low-analysis materials, since fewer pounds must be handled.

Determining most profitable rate of application

Farm operators who have enough capital so that they can buy all the fertilizer they can profitably use are interested in the answer to this question: What rate of fertilizer use will result in the greatest increase in net income? To show the principle that should be followed in making this decision, we will study the most profitable rate of applying nitrogen to corn. To answer this question we need to know three things: (1) the yield responses we can expect from different amounts of fertilizer, (2) the price we can expect to get for the corn, and (3) the cost of the fertilizer.

Table 16 shows the increases in the yield of corn that result from increasing amounts of nitrogen fertilizer on Iowa soils. This table illustrates a typical response of crop yields to added amounts of fertilizer; the yield per acre continues to increase as more fertilizer is added. But each additional 20 pounds of nitrogen that are added give smaller and smaller increases in yields. In the example given in the table, the first 20 pounds of added nitrogen increased corn yields 10 bushels per acre; the second 20 pounds added 5 more bushels to the yield. However, as we continue to the last 20-pound addition, we find that this added only 2 more bushels of corn. This tendency of an input to yield successively smaller increases in output as more and more of it is applied is called the principle of diminishing returns.

Table 16. Example Showing How to Determine the Most Profitable Amount of Nitrogen Fertilizer to Apply to Corn*

Total Nitrogen Applied per acre, lb	Yield of Corn, bu per acre	Cost of Added Fertilizer	Added Corn, bu	Value of Added Bushels of Corn	Total Profit per acre, from Fertilizer
0	70				
20	80	1st 20 lb—$3	1st 20 lb—10	$12.50	$ 9.50
40	85	2nd 20 lb—$3	2nd 20 lb—5	6.25	12.75
60	88	3rd 20 lb—$3	3rd 20 lb—3	3.75	13.50
80	90	4th 20 lb—$3	4th 20 lb—2	2.50	13.00

* Adapted from *Iowa Agr. Expt. Sta. and Ext. Serv. Bull.* P114, cooperating. Pounds of nitrogen refers to pounds of elemental nitrogen.

It may be stated as follows: When one input is increased in proportion to the other inputs in a production process, the output resulting from each added input of the variable factor tends to decline either immediately or after an initial stage of increasing returns. In the example of the fertilizer, the variable factor is the fertilizer itself. The other factors that tend to remain fixed are the land, machine costs, and the work that goes into producing an acre of crop. The diminishing returns relationship is fundamentally a physical one. However, when we apply a price to the variable input and a price to the output or product, we can use the principle as a guide in making economic decisions.

The principle of diminishing returns applies to a great many other decisions that must be made on the farm beside the most profitable amount of fertilizer to use. For example, it enters into deciding how much grain to feed dairy cows, how many hens to put in the laying house, how many times to cultivate corn, and how much labor to spend on any livestock enterprise.

Balancing added costs and added returns

In the example shown in Table 16, the cost of each added 20 pounds of nitrogen is $3 when the price of nitrogen is 15 cents per pound. The value of the bushels of corn added by each 20 pounds of fertilizer when the price of corn is $1.25 per bushel are shown in the fifth column in the table. The greatest possible increase in net income per acre will be achieved when the cost of the last 20 pounds of nitrogen added is just less than the value of the increased yield it produces. In the example shown in Table 16, the cost of the third 20 pounds is $3 and the return from it is $3.75. Hence, it is still profitable to apply this third 20 pounds of nitrogen. But the cost of the fourth 20 pounds of nitrogen is $3, whereas the value of the added return is only $2.50. Therefore, it is not profitable to add the fourth 20 pounds. The labor used in applying the fertilizer has not been considered in this example because very little extra labor is required to put on heavier applications.

How does the price of corn in relationship to the cost of fertilizer influence the most profitable rate of application? If the price of corn changes very much from $1.25, the price used in the example, the rate of application at which returns are just greater than the added costs will also change. For example, if the price of corn goes up to $1.60 per bushel and the price of fertilizer remains unchanged, adding the fourth 20 pounds of fertilizer becomes profitable. Under these price relationships, the fourth 20 pounds of fertilizer would still cost $3 while the return from the added yield would be $3.20. On the other hand, if the price of corn dropped to $0.75 per bushel, the return from the third 20 pounds would be only $2.25. Therefore, applying more than 40 pounds of nitrogen would not be profitable.

These relationships are illustrated graphically in Figure 34. Here the solid black bars in the graph at the top indicate the return that would be realized from each 20 pounds of nitrogen fertilizer when corn is $1.60 per bushel. The other two graphs are the same except that corn is assumed to be worth $1.25 in the middle graph and $0.75 in the bottom one. The cost line in all three graphs shows the cost of 20 pounds of nitrogen when the price of nitrogen is 15 cents per pound. With corn at $1.60 per bushel, the added return even for the fourth 20-pound unit does not drop below the cost line; therefore adding 80 pounds of nitrogen per acre is profitable.

However, adding the fourth 20 pounds is not profitable when the price of corn drops to $1.25 per bushel. This is illustrated in the middle graph where the return from the fourth 20 pounds drops below the cost line. Therefore, the most profitable rate of application under these price relationships is 60 pounds per acre.

The bottom graph shows the relationship between cost and re-

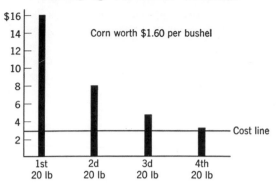

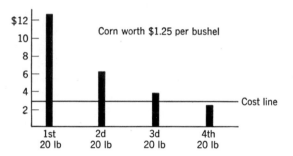

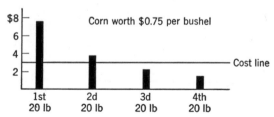

Figure 34. Balancing added cost and added returns from fertilizer use.

turns when corn is 75 cents per bushel and nitrogen is 15 cents per pound. Returns stay above the cost line only for the first and second 20-pound applications; hence, it is profitable to add only 40 pounds of nitrogen.

The principle of balancing added costs and added returns explains why it is good business to limit the use of fertilizer during periods of unfavorable farm prices and to step up fertilizer use when prices

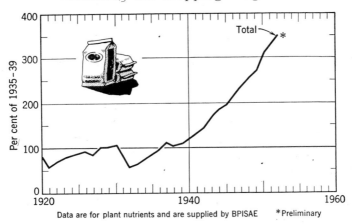

Data are for plant nutrients and are supplied by BPISAE   *Preliminary

Figure 35. Fertilizer consumption: Fertilizer use increased sharply during and after World War II. The improved capital position of farmers and the favorable relationship between farm prices and fertilizer costs encouraged greater use of fertilizer during this period. (Bur. Agr. Econ., USDA)

are high. The price of fertilizer like that of many other farm inputs tends to change more slowly than farm product prices, dropping more slowly when farm prices fall but also going up more slowly when farm prices rise.

Figure 36. It is profitable to use fertilizer at higher rates when the price of the product being grown is high relative to the cost of the fertilizer. The return from each dollar invested in fertilizer decreases as it is applied at heavier rates. Therefore, farmers who have only a limited amount of money to invest in fertilizer will get a higher return by putting their limited supply on more acres at lower rates of application. (Courtesy Deere & Co.)

Other applications of balancing added costs with added returns

The principle of balancing added costs with added returns applies to the use of any variable input on the farm where the amount of the variable input is not limited. For example, a fourth cultivation of corn is profitable if the value of the added yield of corn just exceeds the cost of the added cultivation. Or it is profitable to continue feeding more grain to a dairy cow as long as the value of the added milk exceeds the cost of the added feed.

The principle also applies to broader management decisions. For example, putting more money into improvements such as a new machine shed will increase farm income only if the return in terms of reducing machinery costs each year exceeds the annual use cost of the shed. Or improving the drainage system is profitable only if the value of the added yields each year exceeds the annual cost of the additional tiling.

Fertilizer decisions where capital is limited

We have seen how the principle of balancing added costs and added returns applies where sufficient capital is available to make maximum use of fertilizer. What principle should guide the farmer who has only a limited amount of money to put into fertilizer? In this case a different but related principle, that of alternative returns, should be applied. This is the same principle we applied to the allocation of limited capital among competing uses when we were discussing the investment problem faced by many beginning farmers. Let us restate the principle: When a resource is limited, all possible alternative uses for it should be examined and any added quantities should be used where they will yield the greatest return. Therefore, if you have a limited amount of capital to put into your farm business, you must first of all decide whether money invested for fertilizer will produce more than if it were invested somewhere else in the business. You must also estimate the return that you can expect from fertilizer used at different rates and on different crops and must put your fertilizer dollar to work where it will bring in the greatest return.

Let us examine what happens to the return per dollar invested in each 20 pounds of fertilizer as the rate of application increases. We will use the same yield relationships shown in Table 16 when nitrogen was applied to corn. In the example we assume that the price of corn is $1.25 per bushel and the price of nitrogen fertilizer 15 cents per pound.

You will notice that the return per dollar invested is greater at the lower rates of application (Table 17). Therefore, if you have only a limited amount of money to invest in fertilizer, you will get a larger return if you use your small fertilizer supply at lower rates on more acres.

Table 17. Example Showing How the Return per Dollar Invested in Fertilizer Decreases as the Rate of Application Increases

Total Nitrogen Applied per acre, lb	Cost of Added Fertilizer	Value of Added Bushels of Corn	Return per dollar Invested in Fertilizer
0			
20	1st 20 lb—$3	$12.50	1st 20 lb—$4.17
40	2nd 20 lb—$3	6.25	2nd 20 lb—$2.08
60	3rd 20 lb—$3	3.75	3rd 30 lb—$1.25
80	4th 20 lb—$3	2.50	4th 20 lb—$ .83

In allocating his fertilizer money, the farm operator with a limited budget also must decide how much to spend on lime and on fertilizer for the new seeding, on starter fertilizer and on nitrogen for side dressing the corn. Sometimes the highest return might result from spending a part of the limited fertilizer budget on all four uses. After you have made this decision, you must also choose the fields that will give the greatest response. For example, if you decide that starter fertilizer is the best investment, you must decide how much to put on first-year corn and how much to put on second-year corn.

Rate of planting and fertilizing use

How does the thickness of stands of corn and other crops affect the most profitable level of fertilizer application? Unfortunately, relatively little experimental work has been carried on in this area. As a result, farmers must depend to a large degree on their own observations and a knowledge of the basic principles involved to lead them to a reasonably accurate answer.

We will approach the problem of the best combination of plants and fertilizer to use by first looking at the factors determining the best rate of planting at any one level of fertility. In its simplest form the rate of planting problem is one of combining a variable input (seed) with a fixed resource (land). When we continue to add more seed to each acre, the added bushels of product we get from each added input of seed declines. This is the same diminishing-returns relationship that we observed previously as more and more inputs of fertilizer were added to a given land area (Table 16). If we continue to increase the rate of planting, we eventually come to a point where yield per acre reaches a maximum and then begins to decline. The relationship between different levels of plant population and corn yield is illustrated in Table 18. This experiment was

Table 18. Relationship between Fertilizer Response and Level of Plant Population*

Average No. of Plants per Acre	Bushels per Acre		Increase from Fertilizer, Bushels per Acre
	Low Fertility	High Fertility	
7,450	47.8	63.4	15.6
10,900	54.1	84.3	30.2
14,300	58.6	95.0	36.4
17,550	64.0	100.9	36.9
21,050	64.5	117.1	52.6

* From Iowa Agr. Expt. Sta.

conducted on Fayette soils, soils that are found in parts of Minnesota, Wisconsin, Iowa, and Illinois. The yields in the low-fertility column were obtained from land that had no fertilizer; those in the high-fertility column were obtained from the same land on which 1,000 pounds of 10-10-10 fertilizer had been applied.

Notice in the table that plant population increases by steps of 3,000 to 4,000 plants per acre. Yields increase rapidly at first from heavier rates of planting on both low- and high-fertility land. However, the added output from added seed drops off much more sharply on land low in fertility than on land where fertility is high. The rate of planting has not been carried to a high enough level on either the low- or high-fertility soils to cause total yield per acre to decline. To arrive at the most profitable rate of planting for any one level of fertility, we would apply the principle of balancing added cost with added returns; we would increase the rate of planting until the value of the added yield just exceeded the cost of the added seed. As a practical matter, however, we can greatly simplify our search for the best combination of plant population and fertilizer by ignoring the cost of any added seed since it is so small. When we do this, our problem becomes one of determining which level of planting will allow us to use fertilizer most profitably.

Now let us return to the other part of the problem: the increases in yield that result from fertilizer as the plant population increases.

Notice in the table that the 1,000 pounds of fertilizer increased yields by 15.6 bushels per acre on land with 7,450 plants per acre. As the rate of planting was stepped up, the response from fertilizer increased also, until, with 21,050 plants per acre, the 1,000 pounds of fertilizer had increased corn yields by 52.6 bushels. This is the rate of planting that gives us the most profitable response from fertilizer under the conditions represented in Table 18.

Notice that Table 18 does not provide enough information for us to make an accurate decision on the most profitable rate of fertilizer use at each level of planting. In order to do this, we would need to know how much the yield increased for, say, each 100 pounds of fertilizer that was added. Then we could apply the rule of adding fertilizer until the added return was equal to the added cost as we did in Table 16 for each level of planting. The final step would be to determine at which rate of planting fertilizer added the most profit when used at the best level. Or, if we had a limited amount of money to invest in fertilizer, we would select the rate of planting and level of fertilizer application that would give us the greatest return for our fertilizer money.

Before we leave the problem of the best combination of plant population and fertilizer to use, we should add a note of caution. The data shown in Table 18 apply to only one soil type. On soils of lower fertility, yields may actually begin to decrease before the 21,050 plant population is reached. Similarly, the response from higher levels of plant population will be lower during dry years. Although we do not possess enough basic information to adjust plant population to fertility levels accurately, we do have enough information to indicate that a proper balance is highly important from a dollar and cents standpoint. Furthermore, we know that we cannot expect the full income-increasing effect from fertilizer unless we step up planting rates as we increase fertility.

Balancing fertilizer

In order to be used most economically, fertilizer nutrients must be applied in the proper combination. Increasing the amount of one plant nutrients applied frequently increases the yield response that we get from another, in much the same way that heavier rates of planting increases the response from fertilizer (Table 18). Lack of lime may limit the return from nitrogen or phosphorus. Or lack of phosphorus may result in little or no response from potash. The importance of achieving the proper balance between plant nutrients

Figure 37. In addition to the amount of fertilizer to use, farmers must decide what type of fertilizer to use and how it should be applied. (Reprinted courtesy of Wallaces' *Farmer and Iowa Homestead*)

Figure 38. Soil tests can help the farm manager in estimating where he is likely to get the greatest response from fertilizer. (Courtesy Wallaces' *Farmer and Iowa Homestead*)

Table 19. **Yield Responses from Phosphate and Potash When Used in Different Combinations***

Yield, bu per acre

	No Potash	40 lb Potash	80 lb Potash
No phosphate	55	94	90
40 lb phosphate	54	96	108

* From Iowa Agr. Expt. Sta.

is illustrated in Table 19. Here adding 40 pounds of phosphorus gave little or no response when no potash or even 40 pounds of potash was applied. But, when the rate of potash application was stepped up to 80 pounds, the 40-pound application of phosphorus increased the yield 18 bushels per acre. Similarly, increasing the amount of potash from 40 to 80 pounds gave no response without phosphate. But, when 40 pounds of phosphate were added along with the potash, the added 40 pounds of potash resulted in a 12-bushel yield increase. The information given in the table apply only to Floyd silt loam, a soil that typically responds to potash. However, similar relationships involving nitrogen as well as phosphorus, potash, and lime exist on other soils.

Soil tests are the best guide to getting the proper combination of plant nutrients. In addition, the alert farm operator can tell which nutrients are in short supply by learning the "hunger signs" for each nutrient and then observing growing crops closely.

Estimating fertilizer response

You should not conclude from the examples shown above that the yield increase from fertilizer would be the same under all weather conditions and on all soils. Actually the response to fertilizer differs greatly among farms. Estimating the yield increases that can be expected from different amounts and types of fertilizer presents a difficult problem for the farmer. The fact that yield responses vary from one year to another makes the problem all the more difficult. However, soil tests can be of help in estimating fertilizer responses and in making fertilizer decisions.

Recommended rates of fertilizer application usually accompany the soil test report from the state soil testing laboratory. These recommendations are, of necessity, oversimplified. They cannot take into account the individual farmer's financial position. Often they must also be given so far in advance that they cannot be based on the price outlook for the crop for the year in which the fertilizer will be applied. If the price outlook is unusually favorable and funds are available, profits can generally be increased by exceeding the recommended rates. If you have limited capital, soil tests can help you decide where you will get the greatest returns from your fertilizer dollar. In addition to using soil tests, you should form the habit of observing growing plants for symptoms of nutrient deficiencies and leaving check rows on which no fertilizer is used. You can then use fertilizer at several different rates in order to compare the increases in yields that result.

Problems

1. Compare the gross income-producing ability of crops in your area for the last 5 years. Use township or county yield estimates.

2. If soybeans are raised in your community, explain the role they play in the cropping system.

3. The following are some yield estimates from different rotations on some Ohio soils.

		Average Yield per acre			
		Corn, bu	Wheat, bu	Clover, tons	Timothy, tons
Rotation I	Continuous corn	29	. . .	. .	. .
Rotation II	Corn–corn–wheat–clover	61	33.5	1.8	. .
Rotation III	Corn–wheat–clover	66	38.0	1.9	. .
Rotation IV	Corn–corn–wheat–clover–timothy	67	31.0	1.9	2.1
Rotation V	Corn–wheat–clover–timothy–timothy	77	37.0	2.1	1.9

(a) Estimate the total production of each crop per year on 100 acres.

(b) Prepare a budget of the gross value of grain production and grain plus hay production, using current prices.

(c) Show the range where forage and grain are complementary and where they are competitive.

4. Select a rotation for your home farm. Prepare a budget, showing an estimate of the amount and value of each crop that would be produced.

5. Make a list of decisions on the farm, in addition to the use of fertilizer, where the principle of diminishing returns applies.

References

Brown, Marian E., "Good Pastures Pay," *Missouri Agr. Expt. Sta. Bull.* 547, 1951.

Case, H. C. M., and Paul E. Johnston, *Principles of Farm Management,*

Chapters 4 and 5, J. B. Lippincott Co., Chicago, Philadelphia, New York, 1953.

Efferson, J. Norman, *Principles of Farm Management,* Chapter 14, Mc-Graw-Hill Book Co., New York, 1953.

Forster, G. W., *Farm Organization and Management,* Chapter 6, Prentice-Hall, New York, Sept. 1953.

Heady, Earl O., and Harald R. Jensen, "The Economics of Crop Rotations and Land Use," *Iowa Agr. Expt. Sta. Bull.* 383.

Hopkins, John A., and William G. Murray, *Elements of Farm Management,* Chapters 12, 13, and 14, Prentice-Hall, New York, 1953.

Malone, Carl C., *How to Make Your Farm Pay,* Chapter 6, Iowa State College Press, Ames, 1950.

Robertson, Lynn S., and Ralph H. Woods, *Farm Business Management,* Chapter 8, J. B. Lippincott Co., Chicago, Philadelphia, New York, 1946.

Scarseth, George D., Harry L. Cook, Bert A. Krants, and Alvin J. Ohlrogge, "How to Fertilize Corn Effectively in Indiana," *Purdue Agr. Expt. Sta. Bull.* 482, 1943.

Stalder, W. D., L. S. Robertson, and G. L. Richardson, "Pasture Improvement Costs in Southern Indiana," *Purdue Agr. Expt. Sta. Bull.* 579, 1952.

7

Fitting Soil Conservation Measures to the Farm

In the previous chapter we discussed the problem of planning a cropping system for a level farm. Now we will consider the special problems that arise on rolling and hilly land. Cropping problems on hilly land differ from those on level land in two important respects: (1) Erosion of top soil and gullying occur, and (2) the productivity of the land often differs widely from one area of the

Figure 39. Planning cropping systems for hilly land is more difficult than for level land. It is frequently necessary to use several rotations on hilly farms where the land varies greatly from one part of the farm to another. (Courtesy Allis-Chalmers Mfg. Co.)

farm to another. For these reasons, it is sometimes necessary to fit several different cropping systems to the same farm.

Farmers should be interested in developing systems of farming that control erosion for the same reason that they adopt any other improved farming method, to increase long-run income. Fitting soil conservation measures to your farm does not present you with a choice of conserving or not conserving the soil. You can conserve soil at many different levels, depending on the type and combinations

Figure 40. In deciding what use to make of soil conservation measures, the farm operator must consider the effect they will have on income just as he would with any other farm practices. (Courtesy Soil Conservation Serv.)

of conservation measures you adopt. In deciding how far to go, you should consider how your net income will be affected, just as you would in weighing the use of any other farming practice. Will the added returns be greater than the added costs? Can limited labor and capital be used more profitably to increase the level of conservation than for other purposes on the farm?

It is a growing national ideal that we should pass our land on to the next generation in as good a condition as we received it. The public at large thus has an interest in the way in which soil resources are managed. Fortunately, on many farms, there is no conflict between organizing the farm to achieve maximum long-run income and conserving soil at a level consistent with public ideals. However, there are some important exceptions. Some of the factors that make it difficult for farmers to conserve their soil at a socially desirable level will become clear to you when we discuss the adjustments in the farming program that conservation involves.

Our task in this chapter is to learn how to use soil conservation measures so that they will make the maximum contribution to farm income. We will assume in our discussion that you are familiar with the technical aspects of conservation measures. If this is not true, you should review them.

Management Problems

1. Utilizing land use capability maps.
2. Fitting rotations to the soil map.
3. Using supporting practices.
4. Adjusting the organization of the farm to the soil conservation plan.
5. Estimating costs and returns.

Utilizing Land-Use Capability Maps

A first step in working out a conservation program is to map the land. The Soil Conservation Service has trained soil technicians who will help you prepare a soils map for your farm if they have not already done so. Although the mapping procedure varies somewhat from state to state, most soil maps contain information on soil type, slope, erosion, and land use capability. An example of a land use map for a 262-acre McLean County, Illinois, farm is shown in Figure 41. You will notice that each of the areas delineated contains four symbols. Although the exact meaning of these symbols varies somewhat from one area to another, the general system used to describe the land is similar. We will study the meaning of the symbols used on the map in Figure 41. You should check to see whether the notations used in your area have the same meaning.

In the notation 22-B-1-II, taken from the map in Figure 41, the first symbol classifies the soil on the basis of its underlying or parent material, its inherent fertility, and the dominant soil series. The meaning of the four notations on soil groupings found in Figure 41 are as follows:

Number	Soil Groups
7	Sable-Drummer silty clay loam
9	Muscatine silt loam
22	Saybrook silt loam
29	Elliot silt loam

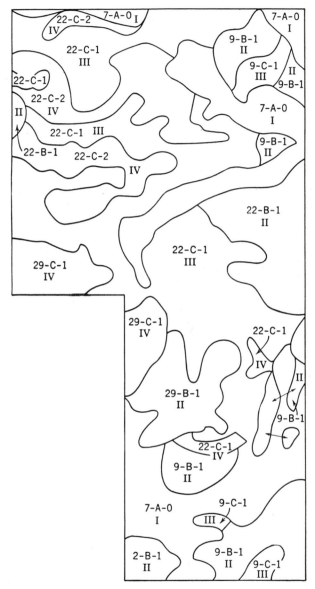

Figure 41.   Land use capability map of McLean County, Illinois, beef cattle
and hog farm. (*Ohio Agr. Expt. Sta. Spec. Circ.* 86)

The second symbol, the letter, indicates the predominant slope of the area. Slope is measured in vertical height per 100 feet of horizontal distance. A one per cent slope means that the land surface rises one foot for every 100 feet of horizontal distance. The meaning of the slope symbols used in Figure 41 are as follows:

$$
\begin{array}{lll}
A & 0 \text{ to } & 2\% \\
B & 2 \text{ to } & 5 \\
C & 5 \text{ to } & 10 \\
D & 10 \text{ to } & 15 \\
\end{array}
$$

The third symbol in the notation indicates the degree of erosion that has taken place. These erosion groups have the following meaning:

0 No apparent erosion
1 Slight to moderate erosion, over 6 inches of topsoil remaining
2 Moderately severe erosion, 2 to 6 inches of topsoil remaining.

On the basis of the soil grouping into which a soil area falls, its topography, and the extent to which it has been eroded, each soil area is placed in a land-use capability class. This is the last symbol in the notation, the Roman numeral, shown in each of the soil areas in Figure 41. The soils on the farm mapped in Figure 41 were classified as follows:

Class   I   Soils that can be cultivated safely with ordinary farming methods.
Class   II   Soils that can be cultivated safely with such practices as contouring, using cover crops, and drainage. Moderate erosion is common.
Class III   Soils that can be cultivated safely with such intensive treatments as terracing and strip cropping. Usually subject to moderate to severe erosion.
Class IV   Soil that is best suited to pasture and hay. When it is plowed, careful erosion prevention practices must be used.

Fitting Rotations to the Soil Map

The next step, once you have prepared a land capability map, is to fit a cropping program to the land. Usually there are several rotations that can be used without excessive erosion taking place. You will also have some latitude in the supporting practices that are used. On some soils, contouring and terracing will permit using a cropping system with a larger percentage of intertilled crops. Where a choice among rotations is possible, the procedure discussed in the

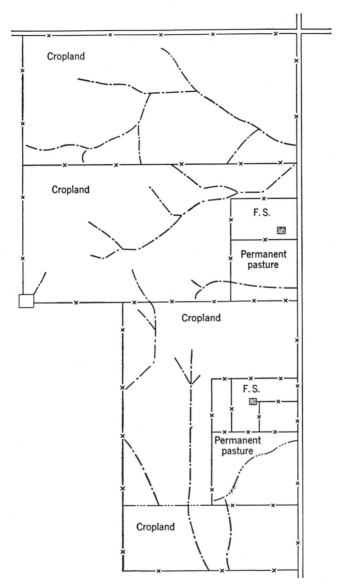

Figure 42. Farm layout and land use on McLean County, Illinois, farm before conservation plan was started. (*Ohio Agr. Expt. Sta. Spec. Circ.* 86)

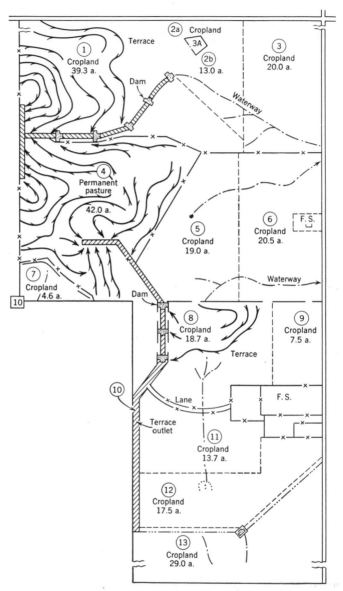

Figure 43. Farm layout and land use on McLean County, Illinois, farm under conservation plan. (*Ohio Agr. Expt. Sta. Spec. Circ.* 86)

previous chapter should be followed in order to select the most profitable plan.

What use can be made of the land capability map shown in Figure 41? The field layout on the farm before the conservation plan was started is shown in Figure 42. It completely ignored erosion problems. The field layout after the conservation program had been established is shown in Figure 43. The conservation plan, in addition to revising all field boundaries called for retiring 26 acres of the land in class IV to permanent pasture. In addition, some terraces were constructed and the entire acreage in intertilled crops was contoured.

Once the principal areas of class-IV land were put into permanent pasture, the rest of the farm could be cropped under a corn–corn–oats–meadow–meadow rotation. There are several advantages to cropping the farm under a single rotation. The cropping system is less complicated, and the acreage of each crop remains more nearly stable from year to year. However, there often is a larger difference in the productivity of the tillable land than is found on the farm mapped in Figure 41. Where this is true, it is usually desirable to give up the convenience of cropping the farm under a single rotation and crop each soil area with the rotation that fits it best. Often this means dividing the farm into many small, irregularly shaped fields.

Fitting a conservation plan to a farm and cropping each soil area according to its characteristics do not always reduce the proportion of intertilled crops. The intensity of the cropping program may be increased on the broad level ridges or on bottom land. In some cases, ridges or level areas that were included in permanent pastures when fields were laid out on a rectangular basis may be put into rotation and cropped heavily. On the other hand, the proportion of intertilled crops on land that has been cropped too heavily can be reduced. The results of this shifting of land use on many farms is a decrease in soil erosion but an increase in total grain production.

Using Supporting Practices

In addition to fitting cropping systems to soil areas, planning a conservation program involves deciding what use, if any, should be made of supporting practices.

Contouring and terracing

Contouring and terracing may be looked on as partial substitutes for grasses and legumes in the rotation. If either contouring or a

Figure 44. This picture shows the soil loss that can result where conservation needs are ignored in planning the cropping system. Farming this land on the contour would have greatly reduced the soil loss and gullying that has taken place. (Courtesy Soil Conservation Serv.)

combination of contouring and terracing is used, the same amount of erosion control can be achieved with a smaller percentage of sod crops in the rotation.

There is evidence suggesting that contouring increases yields significantly. The Illinois study reported in Table 20 indicated that corn yields were increased nearly 7 bushels per acre over a 6-year period. Sizable increases were also reported for soybeans, oats, and

Table 20. Increased Yields and Returns from Contour Farming, Illinois, 1939–45 *

Crop	Average Yield Increase		Increased Returns per acre at 1945 Prices
	Bushels	Per cent	
Corn	6.9	12	$7.38
Soybeans	2.7	13	5.64
Oats	6.9	16	4.69
Wheat	3.4	17	5.37

* E. L. Sauer, "Contouring Produces and Conserves," *Illinois Farm Economics*, April–May 1946, p. 353.

wheat. Similar increases from contouring have been reported in other states.

Changing from up-and-downhill farming to contouring usually necessitates re-arranging fields and fences. This results in more work during the first year or two. However, a Minnesota study found that contouring does not increase labor significantly, once the change-over from up-and-down-the-hill farming has been completed.*

Power requirements are also changed very little. Because fairly substantial yield increases result from contouring at only a small

Figure 45. Contour farming where needed is almost always profitable. Yields are increased through reducing soil loss and conserving moisture. Once fields have been rearranged and fences changed, costs are increased little, if at all. (Courtesy Soil Conservation Serv.)

added cost, contour farming is profitable on all land that needs it. However, contouring does require that farmers develop new skills. As a result, some farmers find adjusting to around-the-hill farming difficult after having farmed up and down the hill for many years.

Terraces also tend to increase yields over a period of years. Yields on terraced fields at a Soil Conservation Experiment Station located on Fayette soils in Wisconsin were 7 per cent higher over a 9-year period than on unterraced land near by. Other studies have demonstrated that, when terraces are properly constructed, they are highly effective in reducing soil losses. For example, it is estimated that the soil loss per acre on Marshall soils with predominant slopes of about 9 per cent would be 19.6 tons with contouring under a

* From *Minn. Agr. Expt. Sta. Bull.* 395.

CCOM rotation. If the land were well terraced, the loss could be reduced to 2.0 tons per acre. Because of its ability to cut soil losses, the greatest contribution that terracing can make to farm income is to permit more land to be kept in high-income row crops and enable some areas to be kept in rotation that otherwise could not be farmed.

The cost of terracing depends on the size of the terrace, the type of soil, moisture conditions, and the amount of filling required. In addition, costs will vary with the amount of work done by the farm operator and the amount custom-hired.

Some estimates of the cost of terrace construction in three mid-western states, using different methods are given in Table 21. Notice

Table 21. Terracing Costs for Different Types of Equipment, 1951*

Type of Equipment	Cost per 100 linear feet			Feet per hour
	Indiana	Iowa	Wisconsin	
Farm tractor and moldboard plow	$1.81	$1.40	$1.45	100–175
Farm tractor and disk plow	1.48	1.84	1.53	100–175
Tractor and disk terracer	1.19	1.90	1.37	100–200
Tractor and disk terracer (custom)	2.00	—	—	—
Whirlwind terracer (farmer-owned)	1.31	1.08	—	—
Whirlwind terracer (custom)	2.15	2.72	2.08	180–340
Motor patrol	2.02	3.00	1.36	300–450
Bulldozers	5.08	3.70	2.08	200–300

* The cost estimates are from *Indiana Agr. Expt. Sta. Bull.* 583 and from work at the Iowa and Wisconsin Agr. Expt. Sta. and Soil Conservation Serv. as reported in *Iowa Agr. Expt. Sta. Bull.* 403.

that the estimates are given on the basis of cost per 100 linear feet. The costs shown do not include moving fences, leveling, filling, and other work that goes along with terracing. The Indiana study found that about ½ hour of work per 100 feet of terraces was required, on the average, to change fences, prepare terrace sites, and build or improve outlets. Other costs not shown in Table 21 such as planning and laying out the terraces ran to 15 cents per 100 linear feet in 1951.

How much is the cost per acre of protecting land with terraces? This question is not answered in Table 21. Per-acre costs depend on the spacing of the terraces and the topography of the land. A Wisconsin study showed that farmers who used their own equipment could terrace fields at a cost of a little over $4 per acre. In addition to the original cost, terraces involve some maintenance costs. Unusually heavy rains occasionally cause the water to break over and cut a channel through the terrace. These break-

throughs must be repaired or gullies will form. However, the cost
per year of protecting land with terraces is very low because they
will last almost indefinitely if properly maintained.

Other supporting measures

In addition to contouring and terracing, grassed waterways, strip
cropping, and buffer strips may be used in the conservation program.
Grassed waterways consist of grassed channels provided to discharge
runoff without causing gullying. Frequently grassed waterways are

Figure 46. Strip cropping is a commonly used method of controlling erosion.
Intertilled crops such as corn are alternated with small grain and sod crops.
This results in small fields or strips of crops, making it difficult to pasture
the grass and legume crops. (Courtesy Soil Conservation Serv.)

established by reshaping old gullies and getting a stand of grass
established in the new channel.

Strip cropping may also be used. This is a system whereby sod
crops are alternated with small grain and intertilled crops on sloping
land. The sod crops tend to break up the length of the slope and to
reduce the rate at which water runs off. Strip cropping has the disadvantage of dividing up each crop into a large number of small
fields. This fragmentation of fields is particularly troublesome with
the sod crops that are to be pastured.

Some farmers follow a modified strip-cropping plan, leaving a buffer strip of grass and legume crops 10 to 20 feet wide. These strips tend to slow down the water coming from the areas above them. Buffer strips are not widely used on cornbelt farms.

Adjusting the Organization of the Farm to the Conservation Program

Using technical assistance

Few farmers have sufficient technical skill to lay out a conservation plan of their own. However, technical assistance is available through the Soil Conservation Service at no charge to the farmer. If

Figure 47. Farm operators should make use of the technical assistance provided by the Soil Conservation Service. They can help the technician prepare the realistic plan that fits the resources of the farm by telling him about their labor and capital position. On most farms a conservation plan must include plans for a livestock program as well as a cropping system to be successful. (Courtesy Soil Conservation Serv.)

you are developing a conservation program, you should make use of this advice in mapping the farm, building terraces, and laying out contours.

Your conservation plan should be planned to fit your financial position and labor situation. The SCS technician cannot do this without your help. It is your responsibility to work closely with him and to help him understand your needs and limitations.

Why must factors other than the soil be considered in planning a conservation program? The reasons will become clearer after you have studied the changes in the organization of the farm resulting from a conservation plan.

Changes in feed supply

Most shifts to a conservation program result in more forage being produced in relation to grain. The changes in the acreage of the different crops that would result from establishing a conservation

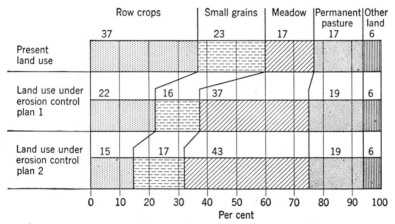

Figure 48. Present and recommended land use on 144 farms in the Ida-Monona Soil Association Area. (*Iowa Agr. Expt. Sta. Bull.* 391)

program on 144 western Iowa farms are shown in Figure 48. You will notice that the present land use on these farms is compared with the recommended land use under two different erosion control plans. In the first plan, maximum use is made of contouring and terracing. In the second plan, greater dependence is placed on sod crops in the rotation. For this reason the increase in meadow crops required to control erosion is not so large under the first plan.

The major changes in the cropping pattern that result from both plan one and plan two are the same; a sharp increase in meadow crops and a large decrease in row crops. However, the change in the total supply of feed does not necessarily follow this same pattern. Although the total output of forage usually increases sharply, total grain production sometimes also increases, in spite of the smaller acreage in grain crops because of higher per-acre yields.

The effect of a change to an erosion control system of farming on the make-up of the feed supply on two western Iowa farms is shown in Table 22. The cropping pattern and production before and after the change are given in the table. The estimates of production after the change assume sufficient time for major effects of the revised cropping systems to be reflected in yields.

Table 22. Estimated Changes in Crop Production That Would Accompany Shifts to Erosion Control Systems of Farming on Two 160-Acre Iowa Farms in the Ida-Monona Soil Area

	Crop Production before Change*			Crop Production after Change in Rotation and Addition of Contouring, Terracing, and Fertilizer†			
Land Use	Acres	Average Yield per acre	Total Production	Land Use	Acres	Average Yield per acre	Total Production
			Farm A				
Corn	93.5	33.5 bu	3,132 bu	Corn	67.1	60.0 bu	4,026 bu
Oats	15.9	22.2 bu	354 bu	Oats	37.7	40.6 bu	1,532 bu
Soybeans	7.0	10.0 bu	70 bu	Alfalfa brome			
Alfalfa brome				pasture	26.3		
pasture	11.0			Alfalfa brome			
Alfalfa hay	8.2	1.6 tons	13.1 tons	hay	26.4	2.0 tons	53.3 tons
Permanent pas-				Other	2.5		
ture waste	20.4						
Other	4.0						
Total	160.0			Total	160.0		
			Farm B				
Corn	70.0	45.1 bu	3,157 bu	Corn	52.6	55.8 bu	2,935 bu
Oats	47.0	39.0 bu	1,833 bu	Oats	35.0	37.6 bu	1,318 bu
Alfalfa hay	20.0	1.4 tons	28 tons	Alfalfa brome			
Permanent pas-				hay	31.4	1.6 tons	50 tons
ture	12.0			Alfalfa brome			
Other	7.0			pasture	31.4		
				Other	5.6		
Total	156.0			Total	156.0		

* Based on 1948 yields adjusted by 10-year county average. The 1948 oat yield on farm *B* appeared to be abnormally high.

† Production estimates allow sufficient time for major effects of revised cropping systems to be reflected in yields.

On farm *A*, both grain production and forage output would be increased over the long run. Therefore, a change to conservation would be advantageous even if there were no profitable outlet for the added forage. This is true because costs would be increased very little if at all over the long run. The increase in total grain production on this farm would be achieved by increasing yields since the

acreage of grain crops would be reduced greatly. Some permanent
pasture also would be brought into rotation. Income would be increased still more by finding a profitable outlet for the added forage.

By contrast, total grain production would be decreased on farm
B. Twelve acres of permanent pasture would be put into rotation
and the acreage of both pasture and hay increased. As a result,
there would be a sharp increase in total forage production. Unlike
the situation found on farm *A,* the profitability of the change is
dependent on finding a way to utilize at least part of the increased
forage. In this case the added forage must provide an additional
source of income to make up for the grain production sacrificed if
income is to be maintained or increased by the change to conservation.

Changes in livestock program and in capital requirements

The changes in crop production described above should make
clear to you that a change to conservation farming does not guaran-

Figure 49. Developing a conservation plan usually results in a large increase
in forage production. As a result more livestock must be kept to make
profitable use of the forage. (Courtesy Allis-Chalmers Mfg. Co.)

tee an increase in income. Often major changes in the organization
of the farm are required.

Many farmers find themselves in the position of the operator of
the second farm shown in Table 22. What does finding a profitable
outlet for the added output of forage involve? First, it means providing a way to harvest and store more hay. This usually requires

an added investment in hay harvesting equipment unless the farm already has this machinery. Forage generally must be fed on the farm to be used profitably because there is no dependable market for it in most areas. Therefore, additional forage-consuming livestock must be purchased or raised on the farm.

Large quantities of forage can be utilized best through dairy or beef cattle, although some farmers have been successful in developing extensive sheep programs for this purpose. Capital must be available to buy the livestock. Or, if you are expanding livestock numbers by saving more breeding stock from an existing herd, you must be willing to sacrifice income from the sale of young stock while the herd is being built up. In addition to the cost of the livestock, most farmers also must provide more housing and livestock equipment.

Nor should you overlook the added labor and new management skill that goes with an expanded livestock program. If you are going into dairying on a large scale for the first time, you must learn how to feed and how to select high producing cows. In addition, you must find a dependable market for your product. If you choose feeder cattle, you must learn to use outlook and market news information in buying and selling. You must also learn how to select animals that will do well in the feed lot and how to feed the cattle efficiently once you have purchased them.

Table 23. Some Characteristics of the Organization of Two Groups of Farms Where Different Levels of Erosion Control Had Been Attained on Marshall Soils in Western Iowa*

	Farms with Low Rate of Erosion	Farms with High Rate of Erosion
Gross profits	$7,058†	$6,056
Net sales of crops	258	1,348
Net production of livestock	6,773	4,708
Livestock investment	4,552	3,850
Per cent feed fed in grain	69	68
Months labor used	16.7	15.8

* Carl W. Allen and Earl O. Heady, "Erosion Control Can Pay Off," *Iowa Farm Science*, Oct. 1948.

† All prices are in terms of the 1945 level.

Some of the changes in organization that arise out of conservation farming are illustrated by the differences between high- and low-conservation farms found in a study of 90 farms in the Marshall soils area of western Iowa. All of these farms contained approximately 160 acres. They were selected in such a way that the soil resources were as nearly similar on all farms as possible. After the farms had been studied with the help of soil scientists to determine the level of con-

Table 24. Estimated Cash Cost of Making All Farming Adjustments Needed in a Conservation Program on Slowly Permeable Soils in Northeastern Illinois

Based on Opinions of Operators of 69 Farms Totaling 18,815 Acres and Averaging 273 Acres per Farm, 1948*

	Cost per Farm	Cost per acre	Per cent of Total
Fertility Costs			
Limestone	$ 809	$ 2.96	12.2
Rock phosphate	1,443	5.29	21.7
Potash	132	0.48	2.0
Total	$2,384	$ 8.73	35.9
Water-Disposal Costs			
Tiling	$ 512	$ 1.88	7.8
Grass waterways:			
Seed	9	0.03	0.1
Construction	49	0.18	0.7
Erosion-control structures	109	0.40	2.1
Total	$ 679	$ 2.49	10.7
Building, Fencing, and Equipment Costs			
Fencing:			
Woven wire	$ 310	$ 1.14	4.7
Barbed wire	119	0.44	1.8
Water supply	123	0.45	1.8
Repair or remodel buildings	702	2.57	10.5
New buildings	394	1.44	5.9
Livestock equipment	39	0.14	0.6
Machinery	449	1.64	6.7
Total	$2,136	$ 7.82	32.0
Livestock Costs			
Dairy cattle	$ 576	$ 2.11	8.7
Beef cattle	305	1.12	4.6
Feeder cattle	466	1.71	7.0
Sheep	41	0.15	0.6
Hogs	1,036	0.13	0.5
Total	$1,424	$ 5.22	21.4
Total costs	$6,623	$24.26	100.0

* E. L. Sauer, J. L. McGurk, and L. J. Norton, "Costs and Benefits from Soil Conservation in Northeastern Illinois," Univ. Illinois Agr. Expt. Sta. in cooperation with Soil Conservation Serv., *USDA Bull.* 540.

servation being achieved on each farm, they were classified into high- and low-conservation farms.

Some of the characteristics of these two groups of farms are shown in Table 23. The high-conservation farms had the highest income. However, to get this added income, their operators (1) fed more of the feed raised on the farm to livestock, (2) had a higher investment in livestock, and (3) used more labor.

The cost of making all the farming adjustments needed in a conservation program on a group of Illinois farms is shown in Table 24. You should recognize, however, that most of these costs represent an investment that will contribute to farm income over a long period of years.

Timing of costs and returns

We have shown one estimate of the costs of developing a conservation plan (Table 24). How soon do these added costs come? When can the increased returns be expected? Most of the added expense comes within the first year or two after the program is initiated. But the added returns are much slower in coming. As a result, the income available to meet living expenses and to pay debts may be less for the first 3 or 4 years after the plan is started than it was before.

An estimate of the pattern of cost and returns in the years after a conservation plan was adopted on two Illinois farms is shown in Table 25. Estimates for all 10 years are based on 1946 costs and 1936–42 prices. This procedure eliminates the effect of variations in the price level from the income estimates. Thus, all of the changes in costs and income are due to changes in the amounts of inputs used and changes in production.

On both farms, income after costs were deducted would be lower during the first 3 years than before the start of the plan. However, from the fourth year on, incomes would be greater as a result of the plan. Over the entire 10-year period, the plan would have been highly profitable on these two farms. The conclusions reached in this study have been substantiated by similar studies in other states. However, the year in which income over costs becomes greater than the preplan income varies somewhat, depending on the severity of the erosion problem and the response of the soil to treatment.

What are the reasons for the pattern of costs and returns shown in the table? During the first year, corn acreage is typically reduced and the oat acreage increased, to establish stands of grasses and legumes. As we have seen from the previous chapter, a low-income crop is substituted for a high-income crop in shifting from corn to oats. In the short-run period, the added forage output may be in direct competition with grain production. During the first year, fences must be changed; lime, seed and fertilizer purchased; and terraces constructed. As a result, costs are increased. The only increase in yields are those due to the use of fertilizer and contouring.

It usually takes several years for the yield-increasing effects of the increased forage in the rotation to be reflected in higher yields. In addition, organizing the livestock program requires a year or two. Once that corn can be raised on land plowed up from meadow and the livestock program has been adjusted to utilize the added forage, income begins to increase.

Length of transition period

There are several advantages in establishing a conservation plan step by step over a period of years. In this way you can acquire

Figure 50. Developing a conservation program requires new skills of the farm operator. Learning how to build and maintain terraces is an example. (Courtesy Soil Conservation Serv.)

the necessary new skills gradually. For example, you will not be farming the entire acreage on the contour during the first year. You can gain experience in working with terraces by starting with only one or two during the first year.

Table 25. Probable Increase in Income and Capital Requirements in Changing to a Conservation Plan on Two Farms Located on Slowly Permeable Soils in Northeastern Illinois*

	1946	1947	1948	1949	1950	1951	1952	1953	1954	1955
Farm no. 1, 160 acres										
Increase in income	$ −73	$ 276	$ 558	$ 673	$ 765	$ 676	$ 567	$ 609	$ 782	$ 653
Cost of plan	893	671	608	563	481	193	193	193	193	193
Increase in income above costs	$−966	$ −395	$ −50	$ 110	$ 248	$ 483	$ 374	$ 416	$ 589	$ 460
Farm no. 2, 168 acres										
Increase in income	$ 757	$ −61	$ 653	$1,050	$1,132	$ 979	$1,157	$ 916	$1,132	$ 979
Cost of plan	823	1,121	1,017	176	210	210	210	210	210	210
Increase in income above costs	$ −66	$−1,182	$−364	$ 874	$ 922	$ 769	$ 947	$ 706	$ 922	$ 769

* Adapted from *Illinois Agr. Expt. Sta. Bull.* 540.

Stretching out the transition period also permits you to do more of the work yourself. Where fences must be changed, grassed waterways established, and terraces constructed, a great deal of work is involved. Attempting to do all of this in a year or two may interfere with getting the other work on the farm done well and on time. But, if conservation work can be done during slack seasons over a period of several years, interference with other work on the farm as well as out-of-pocket costs can be kept at a minimum.

Problems

1. Secure a land use map of a farm in your community, preferably your home farm. Find out what the symbols on the map mean. Then visit the farm, and see if you can recognize the land areas shown on the map.

2. Obtain a soil conservation plan that has recently been made for a farm with which you are familiar. Estimate the amount of forage produced on the farm after the plan is in effect. How many (1) beef cows, (2) dairy cows, and (3) feeder calves would be required to utilize this forage? If you cannot obtain a conservation plan, use the changes in feed output on farm *B* in Table 22, and make these estimates.

3. How many of the farms that surround your home farm (1) are contouring land that should be contoured, (2) are using grassed waterways, (3) have constructed terraces, and (4) are following a rotation that helps to control erosion? What reasons can you give why these practices are not being followed on all the farms where they are needed?

4. Suppose you were attempting to convince the operator of farm *A* in Table 22 that he should change from his present farming plan that does not control erosion to a plan that does. What arguments would you use? How would the arguments you would use with farmer *B* differ from those you would use with farmer *A*? Assume in both cases that the farmer could

expect the production that is indicated in the right half of the table, after the conservation plan is put into use.

5. Studies show that not so many renters as owners of farms have taken steps to control erosion. How do you account for this difference? Why do owners of rented farms sometimes fail to encourage their tenants to follow a conservation system of farming?

References

Anderson, H. O., *Effects of Specified Soil Conservation Practices on Yields and Costs*, Soil Conservation Serv. and Wisconsin Agr. Expt. Sta. (mimeo.), La Crosse, Wis., Jan. 1948.

Atkinson, H. B., and Orville E. Hays, "Erosion Controlled by Terraces," *Wisconsin Agr. Expt. Sta. Bull.* 494, June 1951.

Blosser, R. H., "Farm Organization and Income in Relation to Soil Conservation, Coshocton County, Ohio," *Dept. Rural Econ. and Rural Sociology Mimeo. Bull.* 214, Mar. 1950.

Burson, Paul J., C. O. Rost, and E. R. Duncan, "Soil Fertility and Conservation," *Minn. Agr. Ext. Serv. Bull.* 254, Mar. 1947.

Case, H. C. M., and Paul E. Johnston, *Principles of Farm Management*, Chapter 6, J. B. Lippincott Co., Chicago, Philadelphia, New York, 1953.

Clark, M. W., and J. C. Worley, "Water Management for the Farm; Conserving Soil and Water for Efficient Production of Crops and Livestock." *Missouri Agr. Ext. Serv. Circ.* 557, Apr. 1948.

Cole, R. O., "Soil Conservation in Indiana," *Purdue Agr. Ext. Serv. Bull.* 228, 1950.

"Conservation Problems and Achievements on Selected Midwestern Farm," *North Central Regional Pub.* 23, *Ohio Agr. Expt. Sta. Spec. Circ.* 86, July 1951.

Efferson, J. Norman, *Principles of Farm Management*, Chapter 18, McGraw-Hill Book Co., New York, 1953.

Engene, S. A., and A. W. Anderson, "Effect of an Erosion Control Program on Labor and Power Requirements," *Minn. Agr. Ext. Serv. Bull.* 396, June 1947.

Forster, G. W., *Farm Organization and Management*, 3d Ed., Chapter 20, Prentice-Hall, New York, 1953.

Frey, John C., "Some Obstacles to Soil Erosion Control in Western Iowa," *Iowa Agr. Expt. Sta. Rev. Bull.* 391, 1952.

Heady, Earl O., and Carl W. Allen, "Returns from and Capital Required for Soil Conservation Farming Systems," *Iowa Agr. Expt. Sta. Res. Bull.* 381, May 1951.

Hopkin, John A., and William G. Murray, *Elements of Farm Management*, 4th Ed., Chapter 13, Prentice-Hall, New York, 1953.

Ottoson, Howard W., "Economics of Forage Production and Use in Dakota and Dixon Counties, Nebraska," *Nebraska Agr. Expt. Sta. Res. Bull.* 173, 1953.

Pine, W. H., and Merton L., Otto, "A Study of Selected Conservation Practices in North Central Kansas," *Kansas Agr. Expt. Sta., Agr. Econ. Rept.* 40 (mimeo.), Nov. 1949.

Robertson, Lynn S., and Ralph H. Woods, *Farm Business Management.* Chapter 10, J. B. Lippincott Co., Chicago, Philadelphia, New York, 1950.

Sauer, E. L., J. L. McGurk, and L. J. Norton, "Costs and Benefits from Soil Conservation in Northeastern Illinois," *Illinois Agr. Expt. Sta. Bull.* 540, June 1950.

"Will More Forage Pay?" *USDA Misc. Pub.* 702, Nov. 1949.

CHAPTER
8

Planning the Livestock Program

Livestock products are a major source of farm income in the United States. The value of livestock products marketed typically exceeds the value of crops sold. The heaviest concentrations of livestock production are in the Midwest and in the dairy sections of the northeastern states (Figure 51). It is not uncommon for farm operators in these areas to spend more time working with livestock than with crops.

Livestock increase income in the following ways:

1. By Providing an Outlet for Products That Could not Otherwise Be Marketed. Many farms have some land that is not suited to crop production but does provide pasture. In addition, on most land some grass and legumes must be included in the rotation in order to maintain grain yields at a high level. Most farms also produce straw from the small grain crops and have cornstalks that provide roughage for cattle. All these products would go unused if they were not fed to livestock.

2. By Making Fuller Use of the Labor Supply on the Farm. The crop production season in most areas lasts about six months. Without livestock, the farm operator would be unemployed during much of the remaining 6 months of the year unless he found employment off the farm. Livestock enterprises, if properly managed, also provide profitable employment during slack periods of the cropping season. Furthermore, they may furnish a profitable outlet for family labor that has no alternative use. Farm housewives and children often take the responsibility of caring for the poultry flock, and children too young to do field work may help with other livestock chores.

3. By Keeping Fertility on the Farm. When crops are processed through livestock and fed on the farm, fewer plant nutrients are sold from the farm.

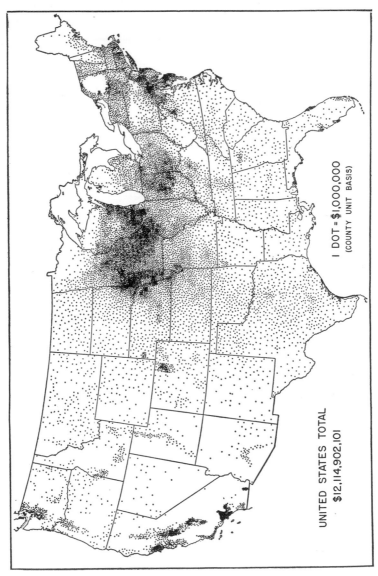

UNITED STATES TOTAL
$12,114,902,101

I DOT = $1,000,000
(COUNTY UNIT BASIS)

Figure 51. Livestock production is concentrated in the cornbelt and in the northeastern states. (Courtesy Bureau of the Census)

Management Problems

1. Analyzing the farm and the operator.
2. Analyzing the characteristics of the different livestock enterprises.
3. Choosing livestock enterprises that fit the resources of the farm.
4. Deciding whether to raise purebred livestock.

Analyzing the Farm and the Operator

Perhaps you have observed that the amount of emphasis placed on different livestock enterprises varies greatly among farms in the same community. There are even greater differences among different areas of the country. Why do these differences exist? Why is a certain combination of livestock enterprises the most profitable for one farmer but not the most profitable for another? The answer, of course, is that there are wide differences among farms and farmers.

No one livestock enterprise or combination of enterprises is the most profitable for all farmers over a period of years. If it were, more farmers would shift into the favored enterprise, production from it would increase and selling prices therefore decline, until the advantages that it enjoyed over other enterprises no longer existed. But one enterprise or combination of enterprises may well be the most profitable for an individual farmer. As we shall see, livestock enterprises differ in the resources they require. Likewise different farmers have different amounts of resources to put into livestock production. The job of the farm manager in organizing the livestock program is to select enterprises that best fit his resources and his abilities. What factors should be considered in fitting livestock enterprises to the farm?

Size of farm and labor supply

On small farms there often is a high proportion of labor relative to the number of acres of land. Unless the operators of these farms buy feed, they are also likely to have a relatively small feed supply. For this reason they will be interested in intensive livestock enterprises, those that make profitable use of a large amount of labor and produce a large amount of income per unit of feed fed. Farms also differ widely in the amount of family labor available. If you have a large supply of labor, you will want to look for enterprises that will make profitable use of it.

Topography and type of soil

As we have seen from Chapters 6 and 7, there are wide differences among farms in the ratio of grain to forage crops that should be grown to maintain grain production at a high level. If you are operating a hilly farm where erosion is a hazard, you should emphasize those enterprises that use a high proportion of forage relative to grain. In addition, some farms have land that must remain in permanent pasture. Attention should be given to the profitable use of this land in planning the livestock program.

Capital position and risk preference

These two factors are closely related. If you are just beginning and are short on capital, you will want to choose enterprises in which you are unlikely to encounter large losses. In addition, some livestock enterprises require more capital than others. When capital is limited, the enterprises that use a large amount of feed and labor in proportion to capital have an advantage.

Interests and skills of the operator

Most farmers do not succeed well with enterprises in which they have little interest. The difference between success and failure in an enterprise often depends on giving careful attention to details at critical periods. For example, producing high-quality market milk requires close attention to sanitation measures. Hog production demands extra effort at farrowing time. Success in cattle feeding requires that the feeder follow market trends closely. If an operator is not interested in an enterprise, he is less likely to give proper attention to these details.

The special skills required in most enterprises can be acquired. But farmers have an advantage in those enterprises in which they already have the necessary skill. Hence, if you were raised on a successful dairy farm and played an active part in managing the dairy enterprise, you have a background that would be a valuable asset in dairy farming. Or, if you have carried on successful projects in swine production in FFA or 4-H club work, you should take into consideration the skills you have already developed when you are planning a livestock program.

Buildings and equipment already on the farm

You should take into account the buildings already on the farm in selecting enterprises. A well-equipped dairy barn on the farm gives the dairy enterprise an advantage. However, it is not always desirable to fit livestock to the buildings already on the farm. In some situations, livestock enterprises that are suitable for the buildings may not be adapted to the labor supply or the capital position of the operator. Sometimes it is better to remodel buildings to fit the enterprises that are best adapted to the other resources on the farm.

Available markets

With some types of enterprises, the availability of markets is not a problem. Hogs and beef cattle can always be shipped long distances to terminal markets. But, in dairying, a dependable outlet

Figure 52. One of the factors that must be considered in selecting livestock enterprises is the type of market outlet available for each product. (Courtesy *Farm Journal*)

for the product is of great importance. A good market milk outlet is much more advantageous than a cream market. Some farmers are situated near large population centers where they can work out arrangements for selling eggs and dressed poultry directly to consumers. In these situations, poultry has an advantage over the other types of livestock.

Analyzing the Characteristics of the Different Livestock Enterprises

In the previous section we noted that there are differences among farmers in the resources they have to put into livestock production. Now let us examine the characteristics of the major livestock enter-

Figure 53. In planning the place of dairying in the livestock program, you should consider the type of market available. Selling fluid milk usually results in a higher return than selling cream. (Courtesy Union Pacific Railroad)

prises. This will help us to determine where each of the enterprises fits the best.

Returns per $100 feed fed

Over a long period of years, dairy cattle and poultry have given the highest and beef cattle and sheep the lowest return per $100 of feed fed. Returns realized from the different enterprises by farmers in the Illinois Farm Business Associations from 1933 through 1953 are shown in Table 26. The average return for dairying was $172. This meant that, for every $100 worth of feed fed to dairy cows, farmers realized a gross return of $172. Out of the $72 return above the cost of the feed, the dairyman had to pay the other expenses before he had any return for his labor and the capital he had invested.

Although dairy cows and poultry give the highest feed returns,

Table 26. Returns per $100 Feed Fed to Different Classes of Livestock*

Year	Beef Cow Herds	Dairy Cow Herds	Dual-Purpose Herds	Feeder Cattle Bought	Native Sheep Raised	Feeder Sheep Bought	Hogs	Poultry
1933	$ 90	$152	$112	$ 97	$ —	$ —	$128	$217
1934	84	145	118	125	—	—	127	198
1935	110	143	141	152	93	163	174	211
1936	85	150	109	96	109	101	155	180
1937	99	159	116	106	123	50	122	157
1938	119	193	151	142	98	153	184	208
1939	146	204	162	131	136	136	144	195
1940	134	198	173	136	142	149	118	177
1941	136	212	162	124	160	122	193	202
1942	127	176	151	136	131	147	201	187
1943	108	160	118	105	93	108	136	169
1944	94	166	120	107	88	136	125	140
1945	110	174	128	119	117	120	138	159
1946	130	183	148	135	138	194	154	141
1947	130	162	147	138	130	131	150	117
1948	143	183	152	137	138	79	131	137
1949	132	175	137	136	142	104	144	161
1950	169	173	173	170	177	182	152	122
1951	170	187	163	142	171	111	127	137
1952	99	175	120	86	67	44	116	116
1953	64	147	71	81	84	113	178	148
21-year average	118	172	137	124	123	123	147	166

* *Illinois Farm Bur. Farm Management Serv. Ann. Rept.* 1952. The long-term average for sheep raising and feeding covers a 19- instead of a 21-year period.

they are not necessarily the most profitable enterprises. As we shall see later, these two enterprises make heavy demands on other resources, particularly labor. Thus, it takes a higher feed return to make an equivalent amount of profit in dairy and poultry production than in pork and beef production. However, where a farm operator has a limited feed supply and an ample supply of labor, he can get more out of his feed by processing it through poultry or dairy cattle than through any other class of livestock.

The return per $100 feed fed is calculated by putting a market price on the feed. Hence, even though the return per $100 feed fed in beef production over a long period of years has been low, keeping beef cattle may have provided some farmers with a profitable outlet for roughage that might otherwise have been difficult to market and that had little or no actual market value.

You should notice also that the relationship among the enterprises has changed over time. In the postwar years, feed returns for poultry were below the long-time average and returns for beef, with the exception of 1952 and 1953 were above average. This may represent a change in the long-run position of poultry because of the striking improvements in methods of feeding and managing the laying flock that have taken place. Because of these improvements,

Figure 54. Egg production requires a large amount of labor per $1,000 output. Raising the young flock is an important part of the egg production process.

farmers apparently are willing to continue producing large supplies of eggs, even though egg prices remain low relative to other farm prices. Feed returns for beef cattle have declined from their postwar high, owing to the increase in the total number of cattle and in the number being marketed.

Make-up of the feed supply

Livestock enterprises differ greatly in the relative amounts of forage and grain that they utilize. These differences are shown in Figure 55. This diagram shows the acres of hay and pasture and grain crops needed to produce feed crops in the proportions used by the different types of livestock. The proportions in which forage and grain can be fed to livestock are not entirely rigid. For example, hogs can be raised in drylot or on pasture; dairy cows can be fed different combinations of grain and forage. The proportion of grain to forage for feeder cattle shown in Figure 55 is an average of several different feeding programs. The relative amount of forage to grain utilized in cattle feeding depends somewhat on the type of program you choose. Hogs use the lowest and beef cow herds and farm flocks of sheep the highest proportion of forage to grain.

There are also differences in the quality of forage needed for the different classes of livestock. Beef cow herds and native sheep can

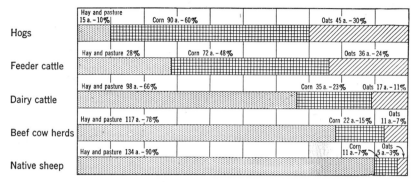

Figure 55. Relative acres of hay and pasture and grain produced when all of a 160-acre farm is devoted to feed crops in the proportions used by the livestock.

(The data are based on the approximate yields of crops and on the actual rations used on 1,035 Illinois farms enrolled in the Farm Bureau–Farm Management Service in 1943. From "Getting Money Income From Legumes and Grasses," by M. L. Mosher, *Illinois Farm Economics,* Jan. and Feb. 1945)

make good use of poor-quality roughages. On the other hand, dairy cows and feeder calves should have high-quality forage.

Feed requirements

Let us now examine the amounts of feed needed to raise different classes of livestock. An estimate of the quantities of feed needed for the major types of livestock and poultry are given in Tables 27 through 33.

There is considerable variation among farmers in the efficiency with which they feed livestock. Hence, it is impossible to present one estimate that will apply to all farmers. The requirements shown in the tables were brought together from farm records and from experimental studies by workers at the South Dakota Agricultural Experiment Station. These estimates apply to farms on which good livestock management practices are followed. Even though you may not get exactly the same results, information of this kind can be of great help in fitting your livestock program to your feed supply. We will discuss this problem at greater length in Chapter 14.

Figure 56. Beef cows make use of feed such as cornstalks that would otherwise go to waste on many farms. (Courtesy J. I. Case Co.)

Table 27. Feed Requirements in Hog Production*

	Corn,† bu	Protein Supplement, lb
Sow and 1 litter of 7 pigs to 220 lb	115	400
Sow and 2 litters with 13 pigs to 220 lb	225	1,000
Feeder pigs (100 lb gain)	7	50

* Adapted from *Farm Management Facts and Figures*, agricultural economics department, Michigan State College.

† Wheat and rye may be substituted for corn on a bushel-for-bushel basis; oats may be substituted at the rate of 2 bushels of oats for 1 bushel of corn. Feed requirements in the table assume that hogs are provided with legume pasture.

Table 28. Estimated Feed Requirements for Raising 100 Pullets* or Cockerels

	Total Feed Requirements, lb†			
	Light Breeds		Heavy Breeds	
Weight, lb	Male	Female	Male	Female
2.0	600	700	500	600
2.5	800	800	600	700
3.0	1,000	1,200	900	1,000
3.5	1,400	1,700	1,200	1,400
4.0	...	2,100	...	1,800
4.5	...	...	...	2,400

* Adapted from *S. Dakota Agr. Expt. Sta. Agr. Econ. Pamphlet* 39.
† Requirements are for a 20% protein ration.

Table 29. Estimated Feed Requirements for Beef Breeding Herd *

Annual Feed Requirement per Head

	Grain, bu	Hay, lb	Pasture, days
Cows	..	3,000	200
Bulls	20	3,000	200

* Adapted from *S. Dakota Agr. Expt. Sta. Agr. Econ. Pamphlet* 39.

Table 30. Estimated Feed Requirement for the Replacement Herd and Dairy Bull *

	Milk, lb	Skim Milk, lb	Corn, bu	Oats, bu	Alfalfa Hay, tons	Iodized Salt, lb	Pasture, days
Veal calves (fed to 180 lb)	1,300	...	...	...	...	...	...
Calves (birth to 12 months)	300	2,000	3	5	0.3	5	150
Yearlings (12 to 24 months)	...	...	3	5	1.5	10	150
Bull	...	...	15	30	3.0	20	...

* Adapted from *S. Dakota Agr. Expt. Sta. Agr. Econ. Pamphlet* 39.

Table 31. Estimated Feed Requirements for 100 Laying Hens*

	Annual Egg Production, dozens	Annual Feed Requirement†		
Ration		Corn, bu	Oats, bu	Mash, lb
Light Breeds (4 to 4½ pounds)				
25% corn, 25% oats, and 50% commercial mash	1,420–1,500	39	69	4,400
40% corn, 26% oats, and 34% commercial mash	1,380–1,440	62	71	3,000
Heavy Breeds (5 to 5½ pounds)				
25% corn, 25% oats, and 50% commercial mash	1,320–1,400	44	77	4,900
40% corn, 26% oats, and 34% commercial mash	1,280–1,360	70	80	3,300

* Adapted from *S. Dakota Agr. Expt. Sta. Agr. Econ. Pamphlet* 39.
† 300 lb of oyster shells and 100 lb of grit required annually per 100 hens.

Table 32. Estimated Feed Requirements for Fattening Beef Cattle*

Kind of Feeders	Initial Weight, lb	Final Weight, lb	No. of Days in Feed Lot, days	Daily Gain, lb	Slaughter Grade†	Feed Required per Head ‡		
						Corn, bu	Protein Supplement, lb	Alfalfa Brome Hay, lb
Full Fed in Drylot								
Calves good to choice	400	950	975	2	Choice–prime	58	175	1,700
Yearling good to choice	750	1,200	205	2.2	Choice–prime	55	150	1,500
Fattening Beef Cattle on Pasture								
(Winter phase; limited grain feeding)								
Good to choice	400	650	195	1.3	.....	10	...	2,900
(Plan 1—grain full fed during entire grazing period)								
Good to choice	650	950	136	2.2	Choice	36	80	....
(Plan 2—grain full fed only during second half of grazing period)								
Good to choice	650	950	158	1.9	Good to choice	26	105	....
Fattening Beef Cattle Carried on Roughage Followed by Full Feed in Drylot								
(Winter phase; roughage only)								
Good to choice	400	537	195	0.7	.....	...	...	2,900
(Grazing phase; no grain)								
Good to choice	537	750	165	1.2	.....	...	...	....
(Full fed in drylot)								
Good to choice	750	1,200	205	2.2	Choice–prime	55	150	1,500

* Adapted from S. Dakota Agr. Expt. Sta. Agr. Econ. Pamphlet 39.
† 1951 grades.
‡ Approximately 5 lb of salt required in addition.

172

Table 33. Estimated Feed Requirements for Feeding Dairy Cows on Good Alfalfa-Brome Pasture*

Annual Feed Requirements†

Production		Corn, bu	Oats, bu	Protein Supplement, lb	Silage, tons	Hay, tons	Pasture, days
Butterfat, lb	Milk, lb						
Cows of Low-Producing Capacity‡							
175	5,000	...	...	...	2.5	2.8	150
200	5,714	6	10	75	2.5	2.6	150
225	6,428	9	15	112	2.5	2.4	150
235	6,714	12	22	161	2.5	2.3	150
245	7,000	18	33	245	2.5	2.0	150
255	7,285	28	49	368	2.5	1.5	150
Cows of Medium-Producing Capacity							
250	7,143	...	...	...	3	2.7	150
275	7,857	4	6	48	3	2.6	150
300	8,571	11	19	143	3	2.3	150
325	9,268	21	37	277	3	2.2	150
330	9,429	24	42	313	3	1.8	150
340	9,714	32	55	415	3	1.3	150
Cows of High-Producing Capacity							
350	10,000	12	21	157	3.3	1.9	150
400	11,429	23	41	307	3.3	1.6	150
450	12,859	37	65	485	3.3	1.5	150
470	13,429	44	77	577	3.3	1.3	150
475	13,571	48	84	627	3.3	1.1	150

* Adapted from *S. Dakota Agr. Expt. Sta. Agr. Econ. Pamphlet* 39, May 1952.

† In addition, 50 lb of steamed bonemeal and 35 lb of iodized salt are required per head annually.

‡ Low-producing cows are cows capable of producing 6,500 to 7,000 lb of 3.5% milk annually when fed 1 lb of grain for 4 lb of milk; cows of medium-producing capacity are those capable of producing 9,000 to 9,500 lb of milk annually; and high-producing cows are capable of producing 10,500 to 11,500 lb when fed at the 1–4 grain-milk ratio.

You should observe that feed requirements are given for cows of different milk production capacities (Table 33). In addition, the table indicates the feed needed at several different levels of grain feeding. We will discuss the problem of determining the most profitable level of feeding grain to dairy cows in Chapter 11.

There are a wide variety of cattle feeding programs. The feeds needed in several of the most common programs are shown in the tables. If you are interested in feed requirements for a program that is not included in the tables, you may be able to find it in bulletins or budgeting data published by your state college.

The listing of certain feed combinations does not mean that the feeds must be fed in the exact combinations shown in the tables. Often one type of feed can be substituted, at least partially, for another. If silage is not available for feeding dairy cattle, hay may be substituted for it at the rate of 1 pound of hay for $2\frac{1}{2}$ pounds of silage. On the other hand, if corn silage is available for feeding beef cattle, it may be substituted for alfalfa-brome hay and corn as follows: 100 pounds of silage plus 2 pounds of protein supplement will replace 30 pounds of hay and 15 pounds of corn. In feeding hogs, skim milk may be substituted for tankage at the rate of 7 pounds of skim milk for 1 pound of tankage. Similarly, oats may be substituted for corn in hog production on the basis of 2 bushels of oats for one bushel of corn until oats make up a fourth of the grain ration. If more oats than this are fed, it takes about 1.33 pounds of oats to replace 1 pound of corn. The desirability of substituting feed grains for each other depends to a high degree on their relative prices. For example, if 2 bushels of oats are cheaper than 1 bushel of corn, oats should be substituted for corn until one fourth of the hog ration consists of oats. Beyond this, oats must be considerably cheaper to justify their use in place of corn.

Pasture requirements

Estimating the amount of pasture required for livestock is complicated by the fact that pasture yields vary greatly from one year to another and from month to month during the year. In our study of the pasture program in Chapter 6, we observed that one of the best ways of making efficient use of forage was to make hay or silage from part of the acres during June and then pasture the land later in the summer. For this reason, it is more realistic to consider hay and pasture together in estimating the total number of acres that will be needed to supply forage for the livestock program.

You can estimate the number of acres of hay and pasture needed by using Table 34. You must first estimate the yield that you would get from the land if it were harvested for hay. Then you can determine from Table 34 the number of acres per head that will be needed to supply both hay and pasture for each class of livestock.

Estimating the carrying capacity of permanent pastures is made difficult by the fact that there are no hay yields to serve as a guide to

their productivity. You should use the 1.5-ton column in estimating
the number of acres that will be required for high-quality permanent
pastures. For poorer pastures, you should increase the number of
acres given in this column from 20 to 100 per cent, depending on their
quality.

Suppose you had a 30-cow beef breeding herd and planned to raise
20 litters of pigs on pasture. You have 10 acres of improved permanent pasture. How many additional acres of rotation forage
would be needed? We could count on the 10 acres of permanent
pasture taking care of the equivalent of the hay and pasture needs
of two cows (10 divided by 4.9). We estimate that the rotation
forage would yield 3 tons of hay if used for hay. Thus, it would
take 2.4 × 28 or 67 acres of hay and pasture for the remaining beef
cows. The 20 litters of pigs would require 0.39 × 20 or 7.8 acres.
Thus 67 plus 7.8 or a total of approximately 75 acres of rotation hay
and pasture would be needed in addition to the 10 acres of permanent
pasture.

Of course, not all the hay and pasture requirements can be supplied from permanent pastures. There must be enough acres from

**Table 34. Number of Acres of Hay and Pasture Required for Different
Classes of Livestock Based on Estimated Yield per Acre***

When Estimated Hay Yield per acre is

Class of Livestock	1.5 tons	2 tons	2.5 tons	3 tons	3.5 tons	4 tons
For each cow in beef breeding herd †	4.9	3.7	2.9	2.4	2.1	1.8
For each cow in dairy herd ‡	5.6	4.2	3.3	2.9	2.4	2.1
For each sow and litter §	0.79	0.59	0.47	0.39	0.34	0.30
For each feeder steer ‖	1.9	1.4	1.1	0.9	0.8	0.7

* From *Mich. Agr. Expt. Sta. Bull.* 391.

† Based on an 80% calf crop with 20% of heifer calves saved annually to
replace the cows as two-year-olds.

‡ Requirements are for large cows. 15 to 20% less acreage required for
small breeds. Includes hay and pasture needed to carry about 6 head of
young stock for every 10 cows in herd. Assume cows are fed no corn silage.

§ Requirements may be used for either one- or two-litter system and are
based on 7 pigs per litter on one-litter system and 6½ pigs per litter on two-
litter system.

‖ Requirements are based on choice feeder steers purchased in October
weighing 400 to 500 lb, wintered on roughage, and put on pasture about
May 15. During the first 4 weeks on pasture, steers were brought up to a
full feed of grain and kept on full feed until sold in October at 900 to 1,000 lb.

which hay can be harvested to meet the minimum hay needs. If you want to estimate only the hay acreage that will be required by a livestock program, you can use the hay requirements given in Tables 27 through 33 to get the total tons needed. Then you can estimate the number of acres that will be needed to supply this many tons.

Labor requirements

Next to feed, labor is perhaps the most important input in livestock production. Estimates of the labor required for the major livestock enterprises are shown in Tables 35 and 36. Labor require-

Figure 57. Beef cattle produced under range conditions usually require less labor than those raised in smaller herds on general farms. The greater economy in the use of labor results from the much larger herds and more efficient methods of wintering the breeding herd. (Courtesy American Hereford Assoc.)

ments per unit of livestock production differ greatly from one farm to another, depending on the size of the enterprise, the type of facilities provided, and how the work is organized. You should observe in the tables that the labor needed per animal decreases as the size of the herd or flock increases. For example, where less than 5 litters of pigs are raised labor needs are 60 hours per litter where no self-feeders or hog waterers are used. On farms where 10 to 14 litters are farrowed, 38 hours are required per litter. Where 20 to 30 litters are produced, the hours of labor needed per litter drops to 35. The labor estimates shown in Table 35 also indicate that considerably

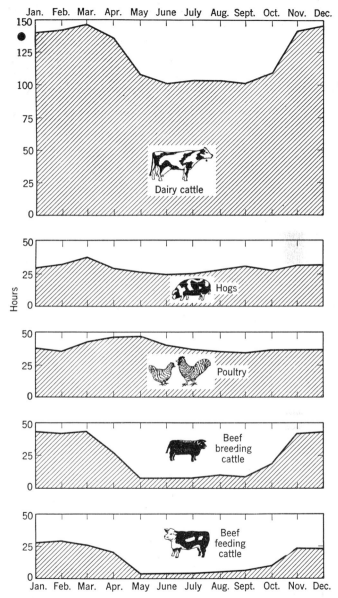

Figure 58. Average seasonal distribution of labor on various livestock enterprises in Southeastern Indiana, 1948. (From *Purdue Agr. Expt. Sta. Bull.* 550)

less time is required where self-feeders and automatic waterers are used.

Many studies have been made of the labor required in livestock production. The procedure typically followed in these studies is to observe the amount of labor actually used on a group of farms. Since labor efficiency varies among farms, no two studies based on different groups of farms report quite the same labor requirements.

Table 35. Estimated Annual Labor Requirements for Dairy Cows, Poultry, and Hogs*

Hours per Cow

No. of Cows in Herd	When Product is Marketed as Cream		When Product is Marketed as Fluid Milk	
	Without Milking Machine	With Milking Machine	With Milking Machine Only	With Labor-Saving Equipment†
Less than 5	165	...	...	...
5–9	145	125	140	105
10–14	135	115	130	93
15–19		108	124	85
20–29		104	121	80
30–39		...	118	76

No. of Hens in Flock	Hours per 100 Hens
Less than 100	300
100–199	260
200–299	225
300–500	200

Hours per Litter

No. of Litters	With No Self-Feeders or Automatic Waterers	With Self-Feeders and Automatic Waterers
Less than 5	60	45
5–9	46	32
10–14	38	25
15–19	36	21
20–30	35	20

* Information in this table and in Table 36 was adapted from "Labor Inputs for Livestock Enterprises," *S. Dakota Agr. Expt. Sta. Agr. Econ. Pamphlet* 40. The estimates presented were based on studies conducted in South Dakota and from reports of similar studies conducted in other states.

† For farms with pen-type housing or stanchion barn equipped with watering bowls, mechanical barn cleaner, silage unloader, and feed and silage carts.

Studies may have been made in your state that apply more closely to your conditions than the estimates we have reported. If this is so, you should use information from these reports instead of from Tables 35 and 36 for calculating labor requirements for a livestock program.

In addition to the total amount of labor required, you will also be interested in the way labor needs are distributed through the year. One of the problems in planning a livestock program is to avoid excessively high labor peaks. The distribution of the time spent on livestock enterprises on 136 farms in southeastern Indiana are shown in Figure 58. Here again the distribution would vary some-

Table 36. Labor Requirements for Beef Production

No. of Cattle	Labor Required per Head, hours
Beef Breeding Herd Including Replacements and Calves	
Less than 10	42
10–19	29
20–29	22
30–39	19
40–49	18
Beef Feeding	
Less than 10	6.0
10–19	4.0
20–29	3.0
30–39	2.4
40–49	2.0
50–59	1.8
60–69	1.6

what from one farm to another, depending on how farrowing, calving, and the purchase and sale of feeder cattle were timed. Dairy cattle and beef breeding herds require more labor in the winter. Labor demands for poultry and hogs produced under a two-litter system are fairly stable during the year. The peak requirements for hogs come at farrowing time, and for poultry at the time the baby chicks are started.

Labor required per $1,000 gross output

Which livestock enterprises require the most labor? We cannot answer this question from the information given in Tables 35 and 36. In comparing labor requirements, we must find some meaningful basis on which to make the comparison. For example, comparing the amount of labor required per dairy cow with the amount needed to raise one hog would not be helpful.

We can overcome this difficulty if we make the comparison on the basis of the amount of labor needed to produce $1,000 gross output from each enterprise. The labor needs shown in Tables 35 and 36 were used in making these comparisons. The value of output was computed from prices farmers received for these products in 1952. To produce $1,000 gross output with these prices requires the following numbers of livestock:

> 3½ litters of pigs (7 pigs per litter; 25 litters in herd).
> 3 dairy cows (producing at the rate of 7,000 lb of milk per cow per year, 20 cows in herd).
> 130 laying hens (producing 17 doz eggs per hen per year, 200 hens in the flock).
> 5½ head of feeder calves (fed for 9 months and producing 550 lb of beef per head, 30 head in the feed lot).
> 10½ beef cows (each cow raising one calf per year, 25 cows in herd).

The amount of labor required to produce the $1,000 gross output under these conditions is as follows:

Hogs	70 hr
Dairy cows	372 hr
Laying hens	292 hr
Beef breeding herd	221 hr
Feeder cattle	104 hr

Figure 59. Dairy production yields a high return per $100 feed fed but requires a large amount of labor. (Courtesy Union Pacific Railroad)

Dairying takes the most and hogs the least labor. The labor requirements on the beef breeding enterprise were computed on the basis of raising the calves to 400 pounds. You may be surprised to find the labor requirements for beef cattle raising so high. Taking care of beef cows requires less labor than keeping an equal number of dairy cows, but it takes more than three times as many beef as dairy cows to realize $1,000 gross income. The labor spent on the beef breeding herd on the general farm is typically much greater than under range conditions where herds are larger and labor-saving methods are used.

Capital requirements

The amount of capital required by a livestock enterprise consists of the initial investment needed for livestock plus that needed for buildings and equipment. Let us consider first the initial investment in the livestock itself. In the section on labor requirements we estimated the number of different types of livestock needed to produce $1,000 gross income. The total investment this number of livestock would represent under 1952 prices is as follows:

3½ brood sows	$ 175
3 dairy cows	700
130 laying hens	162
5½ feeder calves	520
10½ beef cows	1,840

The greatest initial investment is needed for beef raising and dairying and the least for hog and poultry production. These relationships were computed on the basis of 1952 prices. You may wish to bring the calculations up to date to see if the relative amount of capital required by the different enterprises has changed.

We can also look at capital requirements in another way. How much gross output could be realized from each $1,000 invested in different types of livestock if the necessary feed, labor, buildings, and equipment were available? Under these conditions the gross output possible from a $1,000 investment in each class of livestock would be as follows:

Hogs	$5,714	(20 litters; 7 pigs per litter)
Dairy cows	1,427	(7,000-lb cows)
Laying hens	6,152	(800 hens producing 17 doz eggs per hen per year)
Feeder calves	1,727	(9½ calves, 550-lb gain per calf)
Beef cows	570	(6 cows, each cow raising one calf)

Dairy and beef cows would bring in the smallest and hogs and laying hens the greatest gross output per dollar invested.

Estimating the cost of the buildings and equipment needed is more difficult. One can observe in any community that some farmers have much more invested in buildings and equipment to keep the same class of livestock than others. However, in estimating how much it will cost to get established in an enterprise, you should be guided by what is needed rather than by what others have invested. The latter often is not a good guide to the wise use of money in buildings and equipment.

Both dairying and poultry require a large investment in buildings and equipment. The money invested in hog equipment can be kept at a minimum by using portable housing. The amount of housing provided for beef cows and feeder cattle enterprises need not be great. Some farmers get along with only windbreaks or strawsheds. Paved lots increase the equipment investment for feeder cattle. Although they are not a necessity, they are becoming increasingly popular among cattle feeders.

Rate of turnover

Farmers, especially those with limited capital, are interested in the length of time they have to wait before an enterprise begins returning income. This is sometimes called the rate of capital turnover. Dairying and egg production, if you start by buying a herd or a laying flock, begin returning income almost immediately. You do the work and provide the feed today and in a week or two at the longest you begin to be repaid. With hogs you usually must wait 6 months or longer. With beef cattle the waiting period may be a year or more.

Risks involved

Differences among several of the major livestock enterprises in the probabilities of not meeting costs are illustrated in Table 37. This table shows the number of years out of the 32-year period from 1917 to 1948 that different levels of return per $100 all costs would have been realized under typical farm conditions. To break even, it is necessary to realize $100 or more return per $100 of all costs. Therefore, when returns drop below $100, a loss is involved. All inputs going into production, including the operator's labor and interest on his investment, have been included in the cost figures in Table 37.

Table 37.   Distribution of Returns per $100 All Costs for Various
Livestock Enterprises, 1917–1948 *

Returns per $100 All Costs	No. of Years in Which Returns Were in Each Range			
	Dairy Cows	Feeder Calves	Yearling Steers	Hogs
$ 0–$ 19				
20– 39		1	1	
40– 59		2		1
60– 79		4	6	2
80– 99	7	3	6	4
100– 119	10	12	7	10
120– 139	15	6	5	7
140– 159		4	3	5
160– 179			3	
180– 199				2
200– 219			1	1

* Adapted from *Iowa Agr. Expt. Sta. Bull.* 390.

Chances of incurring a severe loss were least with dairying and
greatest with feeding yearling cattle. Raising hogs and feeding beef
calves ranked between dairying and feeding yearling cattle. On the
other hand, the chances of large returns per $100 all costs were least
for dairying. This tended to offset the advantage of dairying in not

Figure 60. Turkey production requires a high degree of management skill
and is a high risk enterprise. (Courtesy Union Pacific Railroad)

involving heavy losses. Feeding heavy cattle, producing turkeys, and feeding lambs are also risky ventures.

Most of the risks in livestock production arise out of price fluctuations. Occasionally disease with its resulting unthriftiness and death loss causes heavy financial losses. Disease and parasites are particularly troublesome with hogs and sheep. Many inexperienced lamb feeders have found that death loss can cut into profits heavily. Severe death losses with beef and dairy cattle are infrequent. When they occur, they often are the result of bloat or lightning.

Summary

Before we turn to some examples of planning livestock programs, let us summarize the characteristics of the major livestock enterprises:

1. Dairy and poultry production give the highest return per dollar of feed, and beef and sheep raising and feeding the lowest.

2. Dairying and beef raising enterprises can make efficient use of a high proportion of forage to grain in the ration. Hogs and poultry require a high proportion of grain.

3. Dairy cows and beef calves need high-quality forage. Beef cows and farm flocks of sheep can utilize low-quality forage efficiently.

4. Dairy cows and poultry require a large amount of labor per unit of output. Beef breeding herds also have a high labor requirement per $1,000 income produced on general farms where herds are small. Under range conditions where herds are larger, much less labor is used. Beef feeding requires the least labor of all the major enterprises.

5. Beef raising and dairying require the heaviest investment in livestock. Dairying and egg production typically require the heaviest outlay for housing and equipment.

6. Cattle and lamb feeding involve the most risk of the major livestock enterprises. Feeding heavy cattle is more risky than feeding calves. Dairying gives the most dependable and stable income.

Choosing Livestock Enterprises That Fit the Resources of the Farm

The following rules should be followed in fitting livestock enterprises to the resources of the farm:

1. Enterprises with a high capacity to make productive use of the resources of which you have the most will tend to have an advantage

on your farm. For example, if you have plenty of labor relative to feed, dairy and poultry will tend to have an advantage. If you have plenty of feed relative to labor, feeder cattle will be in a favored position.

2. Enterprises that save on inputs that are in limited supply relative to other inputs will also tend to have an advantage. Thus, if you are short on capital relative to labor and feed, hogs tend to have an advantage. If you are short on labor relative to feed and capital, beef cattle feeding is in a favored position.

These two rules serve as guides to the enterprises that are likely to be most suitable for you. In addition, other factors such as risk, special markets, and the skills and interests of the operator must be considered in making a final choice.

How can these rules and the study we have made of the characteristics of livestock enterprises be used in planning a livestock program? We will examine three different farm situations to determine which livestock enterprises seem to be best adapted to them. Later in Chapter 14 we shall study ways of checking our judgment by the use of budgeting.

Farm A

This 120-acre farm which is all tillable is owned and operated by a farmer, his wife, and their five children. All of the children already have reached or soon will reach the age when they can do some work on the farm. The farm is well improved and has ample buildings for a heavy livestock program. The livestock and machinery on the farm are free of debt, but there is a fairly heavy mortgage against the farm. The operator prefers not to assume the risk involved in buying feed grains in quantity. The farm is located within the milkshed of a small city. The market for milk is considerably better than the cream market, but not so favorable as is usually found in the milksheds of larger cities. Although the operator is following a corn–corn–oats–meadow rotation, the land could also be cropped successfully under a corn–soybeans–corn–oats–meadow rotation or a corn–corn–oats–meadow–meadow rotation.

The farm operator himself has several serious limitations as a manager. He is overcautious. He does not keep in touch with current or prospective changes in farm prices, and he is slow to anticipate and correct difficulties that arise on the farm. However, this weakness is overcome in part by the active and intelligent role the housewife plays in the management of the farm.

Dairying and poultry production immediately suggest themselves as likely enterprise for this farm. The available feed supply and capital are the limiting factors. Dairy cows and laying hens will give the highest returns for the feed. Both these enterprises require large amounts of labor. But, since the family has an ample supply of labor, this presents no difficulty. Although these two enterprises require a considerable investment in buildings and equipment, buildings that can be used for dairy and poultry housing are already available on the farm. However, some additional work would have to be done on the barn in order to sell market milk.

The principal problem in planning the livestock program for this farm is to determine the number of hogs, if any, that should be raised and the proper balance among dairy, poultry, and hog production. The final decision should be reached through the use of a budget.

A group of advanced college students who analyzed this farm concluded that the operator should continue on a corn–corn–oats–meadow rotation and adapt the size of the dairy herd to the amount of hay and pasture that would be available, after a small acreage had been used to provide pasture for hogs. They recommended that as large a poultry flock should be kept as present housing facilities would accommodate. This meant a flock of 400 to 500 laying hens. The hog enterprise would be adapted to utilize the remaining grain supply.

There are a number of other possibilities. The rotation could be changed from CCOM to CCOMM. Such a shift would increase the amount of forage produced, and hence the number of dairy cows that could be kept. However, it would mean reducing the acreage of corn and a decrease in total grain production. On the basis of a careful budget, the students who analyzed the farm concluded that income would be greater if the CCOM rotation were continued and the size of the dairy enterprise fitted to it.

Farm B

This is a 260-acre farm with 60 acres of nontillable permanent pasture. At the time the organization of the farm was studied, the operator was in his early sixties. The farm was debt-free, and the operator had accumulated a sizable quantity of other assets. He had no intention of retiring from the farm, but he wanted to reduce his activity. His past record with hired help was one of constant difficulty, and he anticipated that keeping a dependable supply of labor would continue to be a problem.

The shortage of labor ruled out poultry and dairying as major enterprises. On the other hand, the large acreage of permanent pasture plus the ready availability of capital suggested a beef cow herd. The students working with this farm recommended a beef cow herd with some calves to be purchased each fall and fed out along with the calves raised on the farm. The cow herd would make good use of the permanent pasture and other cheap roughages on the farm with a minimum of labor. The beef program would be supplemented by a one-litter hog program with sows farrowed in June. This program would permit a large volume of hog production with a minimum amount of work.

Farm C

This is a 160-acre Iowa farm that is all tillable. The operator had just purchased the farm and taken it over at the time it was studied. The buildings other than the house were small and in poor condition. Although there was a moderate mortgage on the land, the operator could and was willing to obtain working capital by borrowing. He was much more willing to take risks than most farmers. This could be explained partly by the fact that his wife expected to inherit a farm in the near future. The family apparently felt they could fall back on this if the present venture went badly.

This farm operator had demonstrated an unusual ability to follow and analyze market trends. He was a shrewd buyer and seller and a skillful manager of hired labor. He was in his late thirties and was willing to work hard himself.

The high proportion of grain to forage that could be successfully grown in the rotation, the indifference to risk, the managerial talent, and the lack of buildings pointed to a hog–beef feeding program for this farm. Since this operator was willing to buy feed, the students analyzing this farm recommended that the hog program be expanded beyond the home-raised feed supply.

Deciding Whether to Raise Purebred Livestock

Many farm youth develop an interest in purebred livestock production as a result of FFA or 4-H club projects. Often they look forward to developing a purebred livestock herd on their own farms. Farmers may keep purebred livestock because (1) they want high-quality livestock to produce beef, pork, or dairy products for the commercial market or (2) they want to sell purebred breeding stock, especially bulls and boars, to other farmers and breeders. Purebred livestock producers serve a useful purpose in supplying good breeding stock to commercial producers.

Purebred livestock breeding involves different problems and requires different skills from commercial livestock production. Labor and capital requirements are also greater. What factors should you consider in deciding whether to go into purebred livestock?

Characteristics of purebred enterprises

Raising purebred livestock requires more capital than producing for the market. It is possible to invest a large amount of money in even a single animal. This is particularly true of beef and dairy stock. The initial investment necessary to establish a herd can be

Figure 61. Purebred beef cattle that are fitted for the showing must be fed to a higher finish than is economical for a commercial beef cow herd. (Courtesy Union Pacific Railroad)

lessened by buying a few foundation animals and building a herd gradually by saving the best young stock for breeding purposes. However, building a dairy or beef herd in this way is a long-drawn-out process.

Labor requirements are also greater in purebred production. The added labor arises principally from the way in which purebred livestock is marketed. A large herd is necessary to justify the expense involved in holding an auction sale each year. Some breeders overcome this difficulty to some extent by holding cooperative sales. Breed associations often cooperate in organizing and promoting these auctions. But most breeders sell their stock in private bargaining. In doing so, they must show their herd to many prospective buyers. Most customers are interested in buying only one or perhaps two or three animals. Unless the breeder has his stock priced below going prices, he cannot count on every prospect becoming a buyer. After an animal is sold, it must be loaded and transported individually. Thus, purebred breeders usually spend much more time selling their product than do commercial livestock producers.

In addition, extra labor may be needed to fit animals for sale. This is especially true if the breeder decides to exhibit his stock at fairs and breed shows. Even if he does not enter the show ring, he still must keep the herd and particularly those animals that are for sale in condition to show to prospective customers.

Figure 62. Purebred livestock production requires special skill in judging and marketing livestock. In addition to making money, many farmers enter the purebred business because they enjoy working with fine animals. (Courtesy American Hereford Assoc.)

Success in the purebred livestock business depends importantly on the individual's ability to judge livestock. This skill is important in selecting the breeding stock for his own herd. If he does not recognize the characteristics that are desirable in his type and breed of livestock, he will be handicapped in developing an outstanding herd.

The ability to judge livestock is also important in marketing. If the breeder cannot judge the quality of individual animals accurately, he is likely to price some animals too high and some too low. If he makes this mistake, he will find that his customers tend to buy the animals priced too low and to leave those priced too high. Eventually he will have to lower the price on the overpriced, lower-quality individuals to sell them. The net result is that he may, on the average, sell his animals at too low a price.

In addition to being a good livestock judge, skill as a salesman is also highly desirable. The purebred breeder must be able to impress the prospective buyer with the strong points of his product. He must sense the needs of his customers and convince them that they can best meet their needs by buying from him. In addition, the successful breeder must know how to attract prospective customers by advertising and other publicity.

Advantages of purebred livestock production

Purebred livestock breeding has a number of attractions. Good-quality purebred animals usually sell well above the market price. This premium compensates the producer for the extra cost involved. However, the beginner should not be misled concerning the size of these premiums. Typically the purebred producer gets a large pre-

Figure 63. The show ring adds interest to the purebred business. Showing animals helps to advertise the herd. However, getting animals in condition for the show ring and showing them requires considerable labor and is costly. (Courtesy Holstein-Friesan Assoc.)

mium over market livestock for only a few outstanding individuals. Often he must sell some of the poorer animals at market price.

But perhaps the chief attraction for most farmers in the purebred business is the personal satisfaction they get from working with fine livestock. Pedigrees, the show ring, purebred sales, and the development of young animals into outstanding individuals add interest to the business. Purebred livestock breeding presents a constant challenge to the farmer to develop a better herd. It offers the individual an almost unlimited opportunity to develop and use highly skilled management.

In deciding whether to go into purebred livestock production, you should bear in mind that the business is highly competitive. You should convince yourself that you have the skill and the interest essential to success in the business before going into it. Finally, unless you have sufficient capital to make heavy outlays for breeding stock at the outset, you must be willing to wait several years for your efforts to pay for themselves.

Fluctuations in purebred livestock prices

If we can judge from past experience, the prices of purebred livestock tend to fluctuate more widely through the years than commercial livestock prices. Purebred prices seem to be characterized

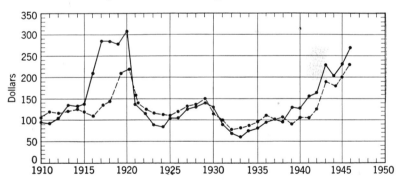

Figure 64. Prices received for purebred beef and dairy cattle, 1910–46.
(1935–39 = 100)

by "boom and bust" swings. When things are going well and breeders are receiving good prices for their livestock, they are likely to become overoptimistic about the future. As a result, they set out to expand and improve their herd by buying more and better breeding stock. Newcomers enter the business and increase the demand for stock. As a result of this expansion, prices rise. Then the attitude changes, and prices drop sharply. The pattern just described is illustrated by the trend in purebred beef and dairy cattle prices shown in Figure 64. Notice that the ups and downs are more pronounced for beef cattle. The prices shown in the graph stop with the late '40's. However, if we were to extend the price trends further we would find that prices rose sharply, reached a peak in the early 1950's, and then dropped sharply.

How should the purebred breeder adjust to these price swings? Usually it is not good business to attempt to buy a herd and "get in on the gravy" when the price of breeding stock has been undergoing a rapid rise. It is better to either begin on a small scale and grow into the business or wait until prices have stabilized. Similarly the established breeder must be careful not to put all of his profits back into inflated breeding stock to improve and expand his herd when prices are high.

Problems

1. In our discussion on organizing a livestock program, six factors that should be considered in analyzing the farm and the operator were pointed out. Make a brief analysis of your home farm on the basis of each one of these points. Do you think you have the right enterprises?

2. From Tables 27 through 33, estimate the total amount of feed that would be needed for each class of livestock you had on your home farm during the last year. Do you think that this checks fairly well with the feed that was actually used?

3. Estimate the total number of hours spent on livestock enterprises on your home farm during the last year. Use information from recent studies in your own state if these are available. If not, use the information presented in Tables 35 and 36 to make the estimate. Do you think more time is spent on the livestock program than on the cropping system?

4. Make a list of successful livestock farmers in your community whom you know. Select from among them farms with different livestock programs. Then study the farms and the operators to see if you can explain why the livestock programs differ.

5. What characteristics should a farm operator have to make a good purebred livestock breeder? What resources beside the skill of the operator are necessary? After analyzing your home farm, do you think it offers the right type of situation into which purebred livestock fits?

References

Case, H. C. M., and Paul E. Johnston, *Principles of Farm Management*, Chapter 8, J. B. Lippincott Co., Chicago, Philadelphia, New York, 1953.

Denis, Elmer C., and Ronald H. Bauman, "Livestock Costs and Returns in Southeastern Indiana," *Purdue Agr. Expt. Sta. Bull.* 550, May 1950.

Efferson, J. Norman, *Principles of Farm Management*, Chapter 8, McGraw-Hill Book Co., New York, 1953.

Forster, G. W., *Farm Organization and Management*, 3d Ed., Chapter 6, Prentice-Hall, New York, 1953.

Heady, Earl O., and Russell O. Olson, "Substitution Relationships, Resource Requirements and Income Variability in the Utilization of Forage Crops," *Iowa Agr. Expt. Sta. Res. Bull.* 390, 1952.

Hecht, Reuben W., "Labor and Power Used for Farm Enterprises, Indiana, 1950," *USDA Bur. Agr. Econ., F.M.* 100, Dec. 1952.

Hecht, Reuben W., "Balanced Farming in Missouri," *Missouri Agr. Ext. Serv. Circ.* 537, Nov. 1946.

Hecht, Reuben W., and A. Martin Morgan, "Labor and Power Used for Farm Enterprises, Pennsylvania, 1950," *USDA Bur. Agr. Econ., F.M.* 102, Feb. 1953.

Hopkins, John A., and William G. Murray, *Elements of Farm Management*, 4th Ed., Chapter 15, Prentice-Hall, New York, 1953.

Robertson, Lynn S., and Ralph H. Woods, *Farm Business Management*, Chapter 9, J. B. Lippincott Co., Chicago, Philadelphia, New York, 1950.

Stangland, Sigurd, "Estimates of Feed Requirement for Livestock and Poultry," *S. Dakota Agr. Expt. Sta. Agr. Econ. Pamphlet* 39, May 1952.

Wilcox, R. H., and R. A. Hinton, *Detailed Cost Report for Central Illinois*, Ill. Agr. Exp. Sta., Dept. Agr. Econ., published annually.

CHAPTER

9

Managing the Hog Enterprise

Pork production is an important enterprise on most cornbelt farms. If you farm in this area, you will probably raise hogs. You must first determine how important a role hogs should play in the live-stock program. Once you have done this, you must make many decisions concerning the enterprise itself.

Management Problems

1. Selecting swine production practices.
2. Choosing between a one- versus a two- or three-litter system.
3. Timing the farrowing program.
4. Choosing the most profitable marketing weight.
5. Choosing the best combination of feeds.
6. Planning a housing system.

The first four of these decisions are closely related. However, we shall discuss them one at a time, pointing out how one decision depends on another.

Selecting Swine Production Practices

Hog production demands careful attention to many small details. The control of disease and parasites is particularly critical to the success of the enterprise. Although following a well-planned sanitation program will not guarantee freedom from these troubles, it greatly reduces the hazard. All hog producers have more or less trouble with disease. The good manager does his best to keep these troubles at a minimum, but he does not abandon the hog business when they occur. He realizes that some loss through disease is part of the normal cost of raising hogs.

The cost of disease is not measured altogether in terms of death loss. The lack of thriftiness and the resulting increase in the cost of gains on the whole are probably much more serious than death loss. Studies have shown repeatedly that there are wide differences

194

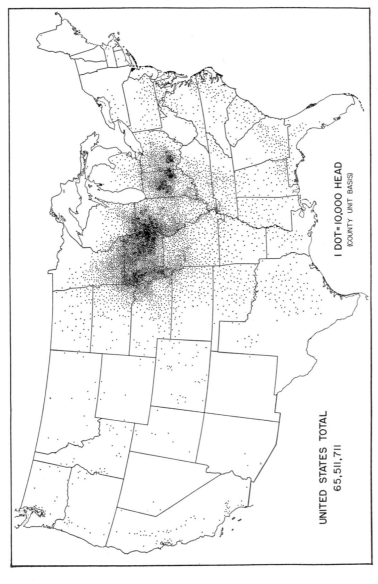

UNITED STATES TOTAL
65,511,711

I DOT=10,000 HEAD
(COUNTY UNIT BASIS)

Figure 65. The production of hogs is concentrated in the cornbelt. The states of Iowa, Illinois, Ohio, and Indiana had 47.2 per cent of the United States sales of hogs in 1949. (Courtesy Bureau of the Census)

Figure 66. Sanitation is important in hog production. Most successful hog programs make use of legume pastures. (Courtesy Union Pacific Railroad)

among hog raisers in the amount of feed needed to produce 100 pounds of gain. For example, Table 38 shows that the top 18 per cent of hog producers in the Illinois Farm Business Associations in 1952 used 382 pounds of concentrates to produce 100 pounds of pork, whereas the bottom 18 per cent used 529 pounds. Trouble with

Figure 67. Many hog producers are reluctant to raise pigs on clean ground because of the work and inconvenience involved. Proper equipment helps to overcome this disadvantage. (Courtesy *Successful Farming*)

Table 38.   Variations among Hog Producers in Amount of Feed Required to Produce 100 Lb of Pork, Illinois Farm Business Association Members, 1952 *

Items	612 Farms	110 High Farms	113 Low Farms
Lb of pork produced	50,152	61,839	40,454
Total returns from hogs	$8,457	$10,795	$6,546
Total value of feed fed	7,308	7,888	7,103
Returns per $100 feed fed	116	137	92
Returns above feed per litter	$36	$76	$−20
No. of litters farrowed	32	38	28
Pigs farrowed per litter	8.0	8.2	7.5
Pigs weaned per litter	6.5	6.8	6.1
No. of pigs weaned	209	259	172
No. that died after weaning	11	9	16
Weight of death loss, lb	993	884	1,324
% of weight produced	2.0	1.4	3.3
Average weight per hog sold, lb	243	241	241
Average price received	$17.48	$17.65	$17.44
Feed cost per 100 lb produced	14.57	12.76	17.53
Lb of feed per 100 lb produced			
Grain	392	341	475
Protein and mineral feeds	45	41	54
Total concentrates	437	382	529
Hay	3.4	3.6	3.6
Pasture (pasture-days)	2.1	2.1	2.3

* The high 110 farms were those that had returns per $100 feed fed of $130 to $149, and the low group were farms that had returns per $100 feed fed of $80 to $99.

disease and parasites accounts for a great deal of the variation in feeding efficiency so commonly observed among hog producers.

Providing pasture

On farms where hogs are a major enterprise, providing legume pastures is important. If the pastures are rotated, hogs can be raised on clean ground each year. In addition, a rigid sanitation program should be followed which includes clean farrowing quarters, washing the sows' udders, and preventing small pigs from coming in contact with contaminated lots or pastures. Halfway sanitation programs usually are not effective.

Reducing labor needs on pasture

Many farmers consider that the greatest drawback of a sanitation program is the added labor needed to raise hogs on pasture. How can the hog producer meet this problem? The best way is by providing proper equipment. This equipment need not be expensive. For example, hose or pipe laid on top of the ground can eliminate much of the labor of watering hogs. Self-feeders with sufficient capacity to supply feed for at least a week also reduce labor requirements. Capital used in this way will usually save a large amount of labor per dollar invested. Hog equipment should be given high priority in allocating capital among competing uses on farms where hogs are a major enterprise.

Choosing between a One- versus a Two- or Three-Litter System

Pigs may be farrowed once, twice, or even three times during the year. The system of farrowing pigs at only one period during the year is called the one-litter system. Similarly, when pigs are farrowed at two or three periods of the year, the arrangement is called a two- or three-litter system.

Where does the one-litter program fit in the best? What advantages does the two-litter program have?

The one-litter program

Although pigs can be farrowed at any time, they usually come during May and June on farms where the one-litter program is followed. At this time they can be farrowed on legume pasture requiring a minimum of labor and equipment. Pigs that have been farrowed this late may be used to pick up corn left in the field. They usually are fed to heavier weights than earlier pigs and marketed in late January or February after hog prices have recovered from their winter low.

Because the one-litter system managed in this way requires less labor and equipment, the over-all cost of production is lower. Farmers who want to process a large volume of feed through hogs with a minimum of labor prefer the one-litter program. The costs of producing pork under the one- and the two-litter systems are compared in Table 39. This information was collected in a study of hog production on 70 Indiana farms.

The two-litter program

One of the chief advantages of the two-litter program is that the labor needed for the hog enterprise is more evenly distributed during the year. The distribution of labor under the one- and two-litter systems on the farms in the Indiana study is shown in Table 40.

Housing and equipment are more fully used since two litters can utilize it each year instead of one. Some farmers also like to market hogs at two different periods of the year. This diversification gives them a hedge against selling all their hogs at a time when prices are particularly unfavorable. On farms where two litters are farrowed per year, more of the pork is marketed as butcher hogs instead of

Table 39. Comparison of What Was Used to Produce 100 Lb of Pork with the One- and Two-Litter Systems, 70 Selected Indiana Farms, 1947–48 *

Item	Avg. for 40 One-Litter Farms		Avg. for 30 Two-Litter Farms	
	Quantity	Value	Quantity	Value
Shelled corn or its equivalent, lb	427	$10.24	416	$10.65
40% protein supplement or equivalent, lb	38	1.88	36	1.79
Mineral, salt, lb	2	0.07	2	0.06
Pasture used, animal unit months	0.1	0.35	0.1	0.34
Man labor, minutes	93	0.93	112	1.12
Tractor and truck use, minutes	21	0.43	26	0.53
Use of buildings, feeders, equipment		0.64		0.43
Bedding used, lb	19	0.12	23	0.13
Vaccination cost		0.26		0.27
Interest on capital at 5%		0.53		0.45
Personal property taxes		0.10		0.16
Miscellaneous: medicine, disinfectant, etc.		0.06		0.13
Death loss, lb	0.86	0.15	0.85	0.16
Overhead		1.58		1.62
Total cost		$17.34		$17.84

* From *Purdue Agr. Expt. Sta. Bull.* 565.

as lower-priced sows. This comparison was made in the Indiana study referred to above and is shown graphically in Figure 68.

The two-litter system has the disadvantage of providing less flexibility in the timing of farrowing. Sows usually farrow a second litter. If they are to be rebred in time to farrow September pigs, they must farrow the first time fairly early in the spring. This handicap can be overcome by saving gilts out of the fall litters and having them farrow their first litters the next fall. Sows can then be rebred to farrow as early or as late the next spring as desired. One disadvantage of this system is that you cannot have more sows farrow in the spring than in the fall, as many hog producers prefer.

Table 40. Approximate Monthly Operations and Approximate Percentage Distribution of Labor by Months for the Two Systems*

		Operations			Hog Labor Load % Distribution	
		Two Litters				
Month	One Litter	Spring	Fall	Entire Farm	One Litter	Two Litters
Jan.	Breed gilts Market hogs	Gestation	Feed		12.2	7.6
Feb.	Gestation	Gestation	Feed		5.7	7.6
Mar.	Gestation	Farrow	Market		5.7	19.7
Apr.	Gestation	Suckle	Market	Oat sowing	5.7	9.5
May	Farrow	Suckle and wean	Breed sows	Soybean and corn planting	27.0	6.1
June	Suckle	Feed	Gestation	Hay harvest and cultivation	3.8	5.6
July	Suckle and wean	Feed	Gestation	Small grain and harvest	3.8	5.6
Aug.	Feed	Feed	Gestation	Small grain and hay harvest	8.3	5.6
Sept.	Feed	Market	Farrow	Wheat sowing	8.3	10.3
Oct.	Feed	Market	Suckle	Soybean harvest	6.5	8.1
Nov.	Feed	Breed sows	Suckle and wean	Corn harvest	6.5	6.7
Dec.	Feed	Gestation	Feed	Corn harvest	6.5	7.6

*From *Purdue Agr. Expt. Sta. Bull.* 565.

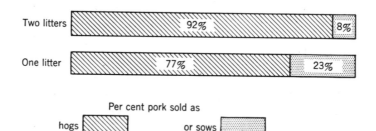

Figure 68. Percentage of pork sold as butcher hogs and sows under the one- and two-litter systems. (From *Purdue Agr. Expt. Sta. Bull.* 565)

The three-litter system

Hog producers following the three-litter system typically have the pigs come in the spring, summer, and fall. In this way, equipment, housing, and boars may be used three times instead of once or twice each year. Generally gilts from the summer farrowing are bred to farrow the next summer. They are kept for only one litter. The sows farrowing the spring and fall litters are usually kept for at least two litters.

Timing the Farrowing Program

Seasonal price changes

Seasonal changes in the prices of hogs follow a fairly regular pattern from year to year. Prices usually start a gradual upward movement in January and early February. However, as the fall crop of pigs starts coming to market, prices begin a decline that usually lasts until April or May. Then prices begin to go up during the summer as hog marketing dwindles. A price peak is reached in August. In late September or early October a sharp seasonal drop in prices

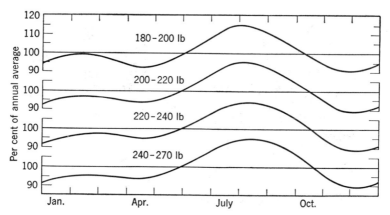

Figure 69. Seasonality in barrow and gilt prices, by weight groups. Chicago prices, normal for postwar years (1947–53). (Courtesy Agr. Research Serv.)

begins, with a low being reached in late November or December (Figure 69).

The seasonal pattern is fairly stable from one year to another. There has been some evidence that the price break is now occurring earlier in the fall than in previous years. The reason for this is that more and more farmers are competing for the higher prices available on the early fall market.

Balancing returns from early farrowing against the added costs

How should you time your hog production and marketing to fit seasonal price changes? Should you attempt always to hit the seasonal peaks? Sizable premiums can be obtained by marketing at the seasonal peaks. For example, a 230-pound hog marketed the second week in September in 1953 would have grossed $10.75 more than one marketed during the second week in November. In 1954, the advantage would have been $3.05. However, this does not mean that everyone should strive to sell hogs at their peak price. The cost side of the picture must also be considered. You must ask yourself the now familiar question: Do the added returns from marketing at the peak exceed the added costs? Selling on the September market means that pigs must be farrowed in early March, if they can be brought to market weight in 6 months. The additional cost of early farrowing occurs mainly in the form of more and better housing and equipment, lamps and brooders to supply artificial heat, and

Figure 70. Early farrowed pigs require better equipment and more labor than those farrowed later. However, these added costs should be weighed against the higher price typically received for hogs that are marketed early. (Courtesy Wallaces' *Farmer and Iowa Homestead*)

increased labor. If you already have the equipment needed plus adequate labor and skill, it will likely be to your advantage to farrow early in the spring. Although early spring litters take more labor, the peak labor demand during farrowing comes before spring work. On the other hand, early fall farrowing does not involve greater costs; instead, gains are often cheaper than for pigs farrowed later in the fall.

Importance of the length of the production period

Advantages of early farrowing largely hinge on getting hogs to market before the severe seasonal price decline begins in the fall.

Many hog producers consistently take more than 6 or 7 months to bring hogs to marketing weight. Sometimes this may result from deliberately following a limited grain feeding program. But it is more likely to result from the producer's inability to find the combination of practices needed for rapid gains.

How should hog producers in this class time their farrowing and marketing program? Producers who require 7½ to 9 months to bring hogs to market weight most likely would be better off to follow the one-litter system with May or June farrowing. Production costs are lower with this system, and hogs can be marketed after prices have begun to recover from their winter low. By farrowing early, the producers who cannot market hogs at 200 to 230 pounds in 6½ to 7 months must stand the higher costs of early farrowing without the advantage of the higher late summer and early fall prices to offset them.

Choosing the Most Profitable Marketing Weight

Once the hog producer has decided when he will have his sows farrow, he has a general idea of the weight and time at which his hog crop will be marketed. But how should he go about making the short-run decision of the exact week or day on which to sell hogs? Should he count on selling them when they reach a certain weight without considering market trends? Or should he study expected price relationships and attempt to maximize profits by selling at the best time?

Guideposts from past years

We can suggest the following guideposts in choosing a marketing weight on the basis of past relationships:

1. If hogs reach 180 pounds by September 1, the fall drop in prices usually limits the most profitable marketing weight to 220 pounds or less. The same commonly holds true for later hogs, those reaching 180 pounds by October 1, though there are some exceptions.

2. The seasonal price pattern becomes less important for hogs reaching 180 pounds in November and December. Ordinarily, by this time the seasonal price decline has spent itself, and prices begin to move upward. As a result, hogs often can be fed profitably to much heavier weights. However, the added cost of putting on more weight eventually builds up to the point where it is greater than the added value.

Figure 71.　The most profitable weight at which to market hogs depends largely on expected price changes in the near future as well as on the relationship between the cost of feed and the price of pork.　(Courtesy *Successful Farming*)

Balancing added costs and added returns

The relationships that have prevailed in the past give us a starting point in determining the best time to sell hogs.　But there have been many times when profits could be boosted by selling hogs at lighter or heavier weights than the typical most profitable marketing weight for a given time of year.　The principle involved in deciding on the most profitable marketing weight is the familiar one of balancing added costs against added returns.　Thus, in deciding how heavy to feed hogs, you should continue adding weight as long as the increase in value exceeds the cost of putting on the extra weight.

Effect of price changes

A change in hog prices affects not only the value of additional pounds of pork that are put on but also of all the pounds that have been put on earlier. Thus, a relatively small change in price can make a great difference in the profitability of bringing hogs to heavier weights. For this reason, it is highly important to understand the seasonal price trend that can normally be expected for the time of year when you are planning to market your hogs.

Other factors to consider

In addition to prospective changes in the price level, the following factors must be considered in choosing the most profitable marketing weight:

1. Rate at Which You Convert Feed into Pork. The amount of feed required to put on each additional pound increases as hogs are fed to heavier weights. For example, it takes 17 per cent more feed to put 25 pounds on hogs in the 275-to-300-pound range than on hogs in the 200-to-225-pound range. In addition, some hog producers can produce pork with less feed than others. Farmers who get a relatively large amount of gain for the feed they use can feed to heavier weights more profitably than less efficient producers.

2. Relationship between Feed Costs and Pork Prices. The higher the price of pork in relation to feed costs, the heavier will be the most profitable marketing weight. Added costs do not "catch up" with the added value so soon when feed costs are low relative to pork prices.

3. Price Differentials among Weight Ranges. Packers commonly pay different prices for hogs in different weight ranges. These differentials change from season to season and from year to year. In the past, butcher hogs below 220 pounds have sold for less than hogs weighing 220 to 240 pounds during the late summer and early fall but for slightly more during the winter. As hogs get past the 220-to-240-pound range, their price is usually lower. The discount normally increases as hogs get heavier.

Necessary selling price

Table 41 has been designed to help you in making the short-run decision of how long to carry hogs. It can give you a good idea what future pork prices must be in order to make feeding hogs to heavier weights profitable.

Table 41. Selling Prices Needed to Break Even in Carrying Hogs One Additional Month*

If Corn is Valued at	With Current Price of Hogs at					
	$16	$18	$20	$22	$24	$26
For Hogs Weighing 200 lb Now						
$1.25	15.18	16.79	18.39	20.00	21.61	23.21
1.50	15.54	17.14	18.75	20.36	21.96	23.57
1.75	15.97	17.58	19.18	20.79	22.39	24.00
2.00	16.41	18.01	19.62	21.23	22.83	24.44
For Hogs Weighing 225 lb Now						
1.25	15.33	16.97	18.61	20.26	21.90	23.54
1.50	15.66	17.31	18.95	20.59	22.23	23.87
1.75	16.08	17.72	19.36	21.00	22.64	24.29
2.00	16.49	18.13	19.77	21.41	23.05	24.70
For Hogs Weighing 250 lb Now						
1.25	15.55	17.23	18.90	20.58	22.26	23.94
1.50	15.87	17.55	19.23	20.91	22.59	24.26
1.75	16.28	17.95	19.63	21.31	22.99	24.66
2.00	16.68	18.36	20.03	21.71	23.39	25.07
For Hogs Weighing 275 lb Now						
1.25	15.58	17.28	18.99	20.70	22.41	24.12
1.50	15.87	17.58	19.28	20.99	22.70	24.41
1.75	16.23	17.94	19.65	21.35	23.06	24.77
2.00	16.59	18.30	20.01	21.72	23.42	25.13

* Calculations in this table based on feeding performance of medium-efficient hog producers in the Iowa Farm Business Associations. Costs include corn and other feed inputs; labor expenses were not estimated. Thus, if a return is to be made on added labor for an extended feeding period, prices must be somewhat higher than those indicated in the table.

Choosing the Optimum Combination of Feeds in the Ration

What is the best combination of feeds in the ration? How do changes in feed prices affect the most profitable combination of feeds? Unfortunately, this combination cannot be determined solely on the basis of a physical balance of nutrients. The relative prices of feed inputs must also be taken into account. In this section, we shall study the principles involved in selecting the optimum combination of soybean oil meal and corn to use in pork production. Although we shall limit our discussion to this one combination of feed inputs in pork production, the principle involved applies to all feeds and types of livestock. In addition, the principle applies to choosing the

Table 42. Combinations of Corn and Soybean Oil Meal That Can Be Used to Produce 100 Lb of Pork with Pigs of Different Weights*

	Pigs Weighing 35 to 75 lb				Pigs Weighing 75 to 150 lb				Pigs Weighing 150 to 200 lb		
% Protein in Ration	Lb of Feed per 100 lb Gain		Lb Gained per day	% Protein in Ration	Lb of Feed per 100 lb Gain		Lb Gained per day	% Protein in Ration	Lb of Feed per 100 lb Gain		Lb Gained per day
	Soybean Oil Meal	Corn			Soybean Oil Meal	Corn			Soybean Oil Meal	Corn	
12.7	31.2	224	1.21	10.0	15.5	335	1.42	9.3	10.4	386	1.60
13.2	34.0	213	1.21	10.1	17.3	328	1.42	9.4	11.7	381	1.60
13.9	37.5	202	1.24	10.4	19.7	320	1.42	9.5	13.5	375	1.60
14.8	42.2	189	1.32	10.8	23.0	311	1.63	9.8	15.9	368	1.63
16.0	48.7	175	1.37	11.3	27.8	300	1.63	10.1	19.4	360	1.63
17.9	58.5	158	1.46	12.2	35.4	297	1.70	10.7	25.2	351	1.88
21.0	75.9	136	1.46	13.9	49.9	269	1.79	11.8	36.3	337	1.97

* Adapted from "Getting Greater Hog Profits," by Earl O. Heady, Damon Catron, Dean McKee, and Gordon Ashton, *Iowa Farm Science*, Apr. 1954.

best combination of other types of inputs used in farm production.

Pork could be produced by feeding all corn or all soybean oil meal, but, under nearly all conditions, the prices of both corn and soybean oil meal would be too high for this to be profitable. But pork can also be produced by feeding many different combinations of corn and soybean oil meal. The pounds of soybean oil meal and corn that can be used to produce 100 pounds of pork with hogs of different weights are shown in Table 42. In addition to soybean oil meal and corn, the ration should include proper amounts of vitamins, minerals, and antibiotics. The pigs in the experiment on which the results are based were raised in drylot. Within each of the three weight ranges shown, increasing the amount of protein supplement fed decreases the amount of corn that is needed. For example, as the amount of soybean oil meal fed to pigs weighing 35 to 75 pounds increases from 31.2 to 76.9 pounds, the number of pounds of corn needed decreases from 224 to 136 pounds for each 100 pounds of pork produced.

An important characteristic of the decreased amount of corn needed as the amount of soybean oil meal fed is increased is shown in Table 43. As the percentage of protein in the ration is increased from 12.7 to 13.2, each pound of soybean oil meal saves 3.9 pounds of corn. As the percentage of protein increases from 13.2 to 13.8, the amount of corn saved by each pound of soybean oil meal drops to 3.1 pounds. Beyond that, the amount of corn saved by each pound of soybean oil meal continues to decrease as the percentage of protein in the ration increases.

Principle of substitution

Which of the combinations of oil meal and corn will result in the cheapest gains? Or, stated in another way, how much corn can we profitably replace with soybean oil meal? Let us state the principle that should guide us in making this decision: When an input A can be substituted for an input B in production, costs will be lowered by replacing B with A as long as the value of B saved by an additional input of A is greater than the cost of A.

The value of corn saved per additional pound of soybean oil meal fed in the hog feeding example is shown in Table 43. If the price of soybean oil meal were four cents and corn was three cents per pound, it would be profitable to substitute soybean oil meal for corn up to the 17.9 per cent level. Up to this point, the value of the corn saved by each additional pound of soybean oil meal is greater than the cost of the soybean oil meal. Beyond this point, the value of

Table 43. Rate at Which Soybean Oil Meal Substitutes for Corn for Pigs Weighing 35 to 75 Lb

% Protein in Ration	Lb of Corn Saved by Each Lb of Soybean Oil Meal	Value of Corn Saved by Each Lb of Soybean Oil Meal	
		Corn Worth 3 cents per lb	Corn Worth 2 cents per lb
12.7			
13.2	3.9	11.7	7.8
13.9	3.1	9.3	6.2
14.8	2.8	8.4	5.6
16.0	2.2	6.6	4.4
17.9	1.7	5.1	3.4
21.0	1.3	3.9	2.6

the added corn saved is less than the cost of an added pound of soybean oil meal. We can check the conclusion that we have reached (that the 17.9 per cent ration is the lowest-cost combination of soybean meal and corn) by observing Table 44. The costs of the feed necessary to produce 100 pounds of pork with the different combinations are shown when soybean oil meal is priced at 4 cents per pound and corn at 3 cents per pound.

What happens to the best combination of two inputs (that can be substituted for each other) as their relative prices change? Let us now expand the principle just stated: As the price of input A increases, relative to the price of input B, less of input A and more of input B should be used. In the previous example, the price of soybean oil meal was 4 cents per pound and corn 3 cents. Now let us see

Table 44. Least-Cost Combination of Corn and Soybean Oil Meal That Can Be Used to Produce 100 Lb of Pork on Pigs in the 35- to 75-Lb Weight Range

% Protein in Ration	Lb Needed		Cost with Soybean Oil Meal at 4¢ and Corn at 3¢			Cost with Soybean Oil Meal at 4¢ and Corn at 2¢		
	Soybean Oil Meal	Corn	Cost of Soybean Oil Meal	Cost of Corn	Total Cost	Cost of Soybean Oil Meal	Cost of Corn	Total Cost
12.7	31.2	224	$1.25	$6.72	$7.97	$1.25	$4.48	$5.73
13.2	34.0	213	1.36	6.39	7.75	1.34	4.26	5.60
13.9	37.5	202	1.50	6.06	7.56	1.50	4.04	5.54
14.8	42.2	189	1.69	5.67	7.36	1.69	3.78	5.47
16.0	48.7	175	1.95	5.25	7.20	1.95	3.50	5.45
17.9	58.5	158	2.34	4.74	7.08	2.34	3.16	5.50
21.0	75.9	136	3.04	4.08	7.12	3.04	2.72	5.76

what happens as the price of corn decreases from 3 cents to 2 cents per pound while the price of soybeans remains at 4 cents per pound. Again it will be profitable to continue adding soybean oil meal to the ration as long as the value of corn saved by each additional pound of soybean oil meal is just greater than the cost of an added pound of soybean oil meal. This point is reached at the 15 per cent ration. Again the accuracy of this conclusion can be checked by reference to Table 44. The substitution can also work in the other direction. If the price of A (soybean oil meal) were to decline relative to the price of B (corn), it would pay to use more of A.

In Table 44, we have shown you the least-cost combination of soybean oil meal and corn for only two price ratios and one weight range. The graph in Figure 72 will help you find the least-cost combination for hogs weighing 75 to 200 pounds for any ratio of soybean oil meal and corn prices that is likely to occur. Let us again estimate the least cost combination when soybean oil meal is 4 cents and corn 3 cents per pound as we did before. Only this time we will use the graph in Figure 72. You will recall that we were concerned with hogs in the 35-to-75-pound weight range. First find the price of soybean oil meal, in this case $4 per 100 pounds, on bottom of the graph. Then move upward until you meet a line drawn horizontally from a price of $1.68 per bushel for corn. This is the price of corn per bushel when it is worth 3 cents per pound. The point where these two lines intersect is marked by an x in the graph. Notice that this point falls within the area labeled B. The B row in the table gives the number of pounds of soybean oil meal that should be fed with each 100 pounds of corn for hogs of different weights. Note that 37.1 pounds of soybean oil meal should be fed to hogs in the 35-to-75-pound range with each 100 pounds of corn for the price ratio we are using. This ration would contain 17.9 per cent protein. You will remember that we came to the same conclusion previously by studying Table 44. The graph can be used in the same way to compute the best combination of soybean oil meal and corn for a wide range of prices.

The graph, like Table 44, refers only to hogs fed on drylot. Where hogs are raised on good legume pasture, somewhat less soybean oil meal is needed. Although we have used soybean oil meal in our example, the graph can also be used with any balanced protein supplement that contains approximately the same percentage of protein as soybean oil meal.

Several complications arise in applying the principle of substitu-

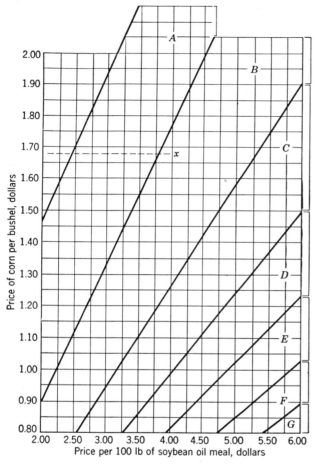

Figure 72. Chart for estimating the amount of balanced soybean oil meal that should be fed with each 100 pounds of corn with soybean oil meal and corn prices at different levels. (Adapted from "Getting Greater Hog Profits," by Earl O. Heady, Damon Catron, Dean McKee, and Gordon Ashton, *Iowa Farm Science*, Apr. 1954)

	Hogs Weighing 35 to 75 lb		Hogs Weighing 75 to 150 lb		Hogs Weighing 150 to 200 lb	
Row	Lb of Soybean Oil Meal for Every 100 lb of Corn Fed	Average Daily Gain	Lb of Soybean Oil Meal for Every 100 lb of Corn Fed	Average Daily Gain	Lb of Soybean Oil Meal for Every 100 lb of Corn Fed	Average Daily Gain
A	55.7	1.46	18.5	1.79	10.8	1.97
B	37.1	1.46	11.9	1.70	7.2	1.88
C	27.9	1.37	9.3	1.63	5.4	1.63
D	22.3	1.32	7.4	1.63	4.3	1.63
E	18.6	1.24	6.2	1.42	3.6	1.60
F	15.9	1.21	5.3	1.42	3.1	1.60
G	13.9	1.21	4.6	1.42	2.7	1.60

tion to hog feeding. The rate of gain is decreased somewhat by decreasing the proportion of protein in the ration. If this difference were sizable, the cost of production might be increased, since the cost of other inputs such as labor and equipment may increase as the feeding period is lengthened. Lengthening the production period may also mean selling the hogs at lower prices because of a seasonal decline in prices. However, postponing the marketing date can also result in higher prices if the seasonal trend is upward. Information on rates of gain is given in Table 42 and in Figure 72. The rates are not greatly different within the range where soybean oil meal and corn are likely to be substituted one for the other. In addition, in order to control the combination of grain and protein supplement consumed by hogs, it is often necessary to grind and mix the feed.

Figure 73. The best combination of grain and protein supplement in the swine ration depends on the price of supplement relative to corn.

This involves an added cost. The best plan is to observe the combination of protein and grain that the hogs consume when they have free choice in feeding. If the combination they take differs greatly from the least-cost combination, then the feeds should be mixed in order to control the amount of protein fed.

What are some decisions other than the best combination of corn and protein to which the principle of substitution applies? It applies to nearly all feeding problems. The combination of oats and corn that should be fed to hogs and the right proportion of forage and concentrates to feed dairy cows are two examples.

The major drawback to applying the principle of substitution to feeding problems is lack of the necessary physical information. Workers in the various agricultural experiment stations are attempting to gather this type of information. But, even if you do not have all of the information you would like to have, you are much more likely to do an economical job of feeding if you understand and attempt to apply this principle than if you do not.

The substitution principle also applies to broader farm management decisions. For example, the best combination of labor and machinery to use in farming operations is a substitution problem. Where labor is relatively cheap and the opportunity cost of the capital tied up in machinery is high, it is not economical to go so far in substituting machinery and mechanical power for labor as where labor is high priced and capital is not severely limited.

Planning a Housing System

It is necessary to follow proper sanitation measures to be a successful hog producer. This complicates the problem of providing housing for hogs. Since growing pigs must be kept away from contaminated lots, fitting a central farrowing house into the sanitation program is difficult. Portable houses that can be moved to clean pasture each year are best from the standpoint of sanitation, but they increase the difficulty of feeding, watering, and caring for pigs.

Some farmers still attempt to raise pigs from birth to market age with only central housing facilities. Occasionally you will find a farm where the operator apparently is managing fairly well by following this system. But, even on these farms, lack of thriftiness due especially to parasites can retard gains without the operator being aware of it. Few hog programs using only central housing are successful over a long period of years.

Some hog producers have dealt successfully with the sanitation problem by confining their hogs to a central house and a concrete feeding floor during the entire production period. One drawback to this system is that no pasture can be used in the swine ration. In addition, floors must be cleaned daily and close attention given to every detail of the sanitation program. Few farmers have the time or patience needed to give sufficient attention to these details.

What types of housing systems have proved most successful? What factors should you consider in choosing a housing system? Following are three farrowing programs that are widely used:

1. Farrowing in portable houses located on rotated pastures.
2. Farrowing in portable houses located at the farmstead, and moving the pigs to rotated pasture several weeks later.

3. Farrowing in central housing, and moving pigs to pasture when they are 10 days to 2 weeks old.

Let us summarize the advantages and disadvantages of each of these three systems:

System 1. Farrowing in Portable Houses in Rotated Fields.*

Advantages:

1. The total investment in housing is low.
2. The sanitation program is simplified by houses being moved to clean fields each year.
3. Pigs and houses do not have to be moved during the season once they have been located.
4. Control of anemia is aided by the ready access that pigs have to the soil.

Disadvantages:

1. Pigs and sows are sometimes neglected because they are located a considerable distance from the farmstead.
2. Providing artificial heat is difficult and expensive.
3. Labor requirements at farrowing time are higher.

System 2. Farrowing in Portable Houses near Farmstead.

Advantages:

1. Wiring for electric brooders may be provided more conveniently at the farmstead.
2. Labor requirements during the farrowing season are low.
3. The total investment in housing is low.
4. Control of anemia is aided by the ready access that pigs have to the soil.

Disadvantages:

1. Houses, pigs, and sows must be moved to the rotated pasture after the pigs have been farrowed and started.
2. Precautions must be taken to provide the pigs with sanitary surroundings during the farrowing period. This means either providing a concrete floor that can be cleaned daily or rotating lots from year to year.

System 3. Farrowing in Central House and Moving to Pasture in Portable Houses within 10 Days or 2 Weeks.

Advantages:

1. Artificial heat may be provided easily.

* Adapted from *Purdue Agr. Expt. Sta. Bull.* 506.

2. Labor requirements during farrowing are low.

3. Cleaning farrowing pens is less difficult.

Disadvantages:

1. Providing proper sanitation is difficult.

2. Housing costs are higher, as both central and portable housing are required.

3. Houses, pigs, and sows must be moved to pasture during the season.

Which of the three systems should be followed? Most farmers who already have a good central farrowing house attempt to work out a system that makes use of it. The time of the year at which pigs are farrowed is an important factor in the type of system that works best; it is difficult to farrow pigs in portable houses in fields away from the farmstead during February and early March.

Problems

1. Farmer Smith operates a 120-acre farm. He has both a central farrowing house and facilities for raising hogs on pasture. He does his own work and finds that typically he is not pressed to do his work well. Do you think a one-litter system or a two-litter system would fit the best on his farm?

2. Suppose you had hogs on hand September 15 weighing 225 pounds each. The price of corn is $1.25 a bushel and the price of hogs $20 per cent. How high would hog prices have to be on October 15 to justify carrying the hogs one additional month? Use Table 41. Are prices likely to increase or decrease at this season of the year?

3. Plot the seasonal price pattern for hogs at a near-by market during the last 2 years. Assume you had some 180-pound hogs in the feed lot on September 1 of each year and that they would gain 1.8 pounds per day on a good ration. Determine what would have been the most profitable marketing weight during each of these years.

4. When were pigs farrowed on your home farm during the last two years? When were they marketed? What changes if any would you recommend in the time of farrowing? How would your proposed changes affect the distribution of labor requirements on the farm and the amount of equipment and housing you would need?

5. The least-cost combination of corn and soybean oil meal for pigs in the 35-to-75-pound range is given in Table 44. Figure out the least-cost combination for hogs in the 75-to-150-pound range and the 150-to-200-pound range. The different combinations of corn and soybean oil meal that can be fed are shown in Table 42. Use the prices now prevailing for corn and soybean oil meal in your community. Check the results you obtain in this way against the answer you would obtain by using Figure 72.

6. Which of the three systems of housing for the hog enterprise described in this chapter do you think best fits your home farm? Why?

References

Annual Report of the Illinois Farm Bureau Farm Management Service, Ill. Agr. Ext. Serv., Dept. Agr. Econ., published annually, 1952.

Case, H. C. M., and Paul E. Johnston, *Principles of Farm Management*, Chapter 8, J. B. Lippincott Co., Chicago, Philadelphia, New York, 1953.

Efferson, J. Norman, *Principles of Farm Management*, Chapter 8, McGraw-Hill Book Co., New York, 1953.

Hardin, Lowell S., R. N. Weigle, and H. S. Wann, "Hogs—One- and Two-Litter Systems Compared," *Purdue Agr. Expt. Sta. Bull.* 565, Nov. 1951.

Hopkins, John A., and William G. Murray, *Elements of Farm Management*, 4th Ed., Chapter 16, Prentice-Hall, New York, 1953.

Robertson, Lynn S., and Ralph H. Woods, *Farm Business Management*, Chapter 9, J. B. Lippincott Co., Chicago, Philadelphia, New York, 1950.

CHAPTER

10

Managing the Beef
and Sheep Enterprises

BEEF PRODUCTION

Beef production involves two steps: (1) raising the calves and (2) feeding them out. To a large extent, beef producers specialize in one process or the other. Although beef cattle are raised in all parts of the United States, the range areas of the West and Southwest tend to specialize in beef raising. Farmers in the cornbelt are more likely to buy cattle from the range and feed them out. In this section we will focus our attention on the problems of the beef feeder and the small beef raiser.

Management Problems

1. Analyzing the sources of profit in cattle feeding.
2. Adapting the cattle feeding program to the feed supply.
3. Timing the program to fit seasonal price trends.
4. Achieving economy in wintering and housing the beef cow herd.

Analyzing the Sources of Profit in Cattle Feeding

Where should the cattle feeder look for profits? Where do the dollar and cents returns come from? Direct returns from feeding cattle must come from one of two sources: (1) price margin on the original weight, and (2) value of gain over feed cost. Following through an example will help clarify these two sources. The results of a typical steer feeding program during the 1946–50 period is shown in Table 45. Note in this example that the purchase price of the cattle was $22.60 per hundredweight, and the selling price $26.00 at the farm. Therefore the price margin was $3.40 per hundredweight, or $21.76 per head.

In addition to improving the quality of the original pounds of beef put into the feed lot, the feeder also added 400 pounds to the weight of each steer. This 400 pounds was sold for $26 per hundred-weight or a total of $104 per head. After death loss was taken into account (at the rate of one steer per 100 fed), the value of the gain added to the entire 50 head was $5,073. The cost of the feed was

Table 45. Resu'ts from a Typical 50-Steer Feeding Program*

Purchase and Sale Results

50	1,040-lb steers sold for $26.00 at farm†	$13,385
50	640-lb yearlings cost $22.60 at farm	7,232
	Increase in value while on farm	$ 6,153

Two Sources of Increase in Value

Price margin of $3.40 on purchase weight	$ 1,080
Value of gain from feeding	5,073
Increase in value (same as above)	$ 6,153

Feed Needed Was

Corn, 2,600 bu at	$ 1.35	$3,510
Protein, 100 sacks	4.50	450
Hay, 50 tons	17.00	850
Total value of feed fed		$4,810

Summary

Income from price margin	$1,080
Feeding gain over feed cost	263
From feeding operation	$1,343

* From *Iowa Agr. Ext. Serv. Pamphlet* 127.

† An allowance has been made for death loss of one steer out of 100 head or one-half steer from a 50-head lot.

$4,810; therefore the value of the gain from feeding exceeded feed costs by $263 for the 50 head. In this type of feeding program, a yearling program, much more of the return came from the price margin on the purchased weight than from the value of the gain over feed cost ($1,080 as compared to $263).

Differences among cattle feeding programs

How does the type of cattle feeding program being followed influence the returns that can be expected from price margin and from the value of the gain over feed cost? The first general rule is this: As the weight of the cattle we feed increases (say, from calves to two-year-olds), we must depend for returns more on price margin and less on the value of the gain over feed costs. We are assuming, in this statement, that the same quality of cattle are being fed in each weight range.

Why is this rule true? Studying Table 46 will help you find the answer. As cattle are fed to heavier weights, the amount of feed needed to put on 100 pounds of gain increases sharply. The table shows the number of feed units needed to put on each added 100 pounds of gain on calves, yearlings, and two-year-olds. The feed unit, as it is used in the table, is the equivalent in feeding value of a bushel of corn. A calf requires only 8.7 feed units to make the 100-pound gain between 400 and 500 pounds. But it takes 21.9, or nearly 2½ times as many feed units, to add the 100 pounds that will increase the weight of the animal from 1,000 to 1,100 pounds.

Table 46. Feed Needed to Put 100 Lb of Gain on Steers at Various Weights*

Feed Units Needed for†

Kind of Feeder	1st 100 lb Gain	2d 100 lb Gain	3d 100 lb Gain	4th 100 lb Gain	5th 100 lb Gain	6th 100 lb Gain	7th 100 lb Gain
400-lb calf	8.7	9.7	10.9	12.4	15.6	17.4	21.9
640-lb yearling	10.5	12.3	14.3	17.5	22.4		
840-lb 2-year-old	10.7	13.1	16.8	23.4			

* From *Iowa Agr. Ext. Serv. Pamphlet* 127 and *USDA Bull.* 900.
† A feed unit as here used is the amount of digestible nutrients equal to that in a bushel of shelled corn (44.8 TDN). These data are based on research with good choice drylot fed steers.

Because of the efficiency with which calves gain, making money with a negative price margin (selling the cattle for less per hundredweight than the original purchase price) is sometimes possible. This is true because the value of the gain in weight may often exceed the feed cost by a considerable amount.

On the other hand, it rarely is possible to make money feeding two-year-olds without getting some return from price margin. Added gains in this weight range are too costly for you to expect any return from the value of the gain over the feed cost.

A second general rule that we can make is this: As the quality of the cattle that are being feed decreases, within a given weight range, more of the return must be expected from price margin and less from the value of gain over the feed cost. An example will help to show why this is true. Suppose we bought one lot of 600-pound yearling cattle for 15 cents per pound and a second lot for 20 cents per pound. We fed the two lots to 1,000 pounds and sold each lot for exactly the same price per hundredweight as we paid for it. Hence, there would

Figure 74. Price margin is more important for a profitable cattle feeding operation when heavy cattle are fed than when calves are fed. Heavy cattle require more feed per pound of gain than calves. (Courtesy Union Pacific Railroad)

be no price margin in either lot. If the cost of adding the 400 pounds were $60 per steer, there would be no profit from the 15-cent cattle since the value of the gain in weight would be only $60 for each steer. But the outcome would be more favorable with the 20-cent cattle. With these the value of the gain would be $80 for each steer, and so each steer would return $20 over the $60 cost of putting on the 400 pounds of gain.

The important point is this: where low-quality cattle are fed, the added gain that is put on is worth less. In order to provide any return for the labor, capital, and the other resources used, the feeder of the 15-cent cattle needed some price margin. But the feeder of

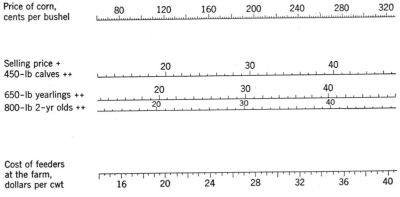

Figure 75. Choice steers. (From *Iowa Agr. Ext. Serv. Pamphlet* 127)

Method. Lay a ruler across Figure 75 or 76. Place the edge on the cost of feeders and on the cost of corn. The point where the ruler crosses the center line shows the selling price needed to pay feed costs, interest on cost of feeders, and normal death risk for the kind of cattle you are feeding.

Source of Data. Based on records of several thousand cattle fed by members of Iowa farm business associations.

Other Costs. The selling price allows for normal shrink in marketing but no selling costs. No credit is allowed for feed saved by hogs or for manure. No costs other than feed, interest, and death risk are covered.

Other Feeds. In the chart, protein, hay and pasture costs have been figured at their normal relation to corn prices.

+ Needed to pay feed, interest, and death risk.
++ Weight and kind of feeder steer put in the feedlot. The weights shown are those at place of purchase. The calves were fed to gain about 550 lb, the yearlings 400 lb, and the 2-year-olds 350 lb. The selling weight is the weight of the feeder plus the amount of gain and is the weight to which the selling price applies. Selling price is that of the steer when marketed. (Copyright ISC Research Foundation)

higher-quality cattle could make money without a price margin because the pounds of beef he added were worth more.

Relationship between feed and beef prices

When beef prices are high relative to the cost of feed, the cattle feeder can count on more return from the value of gain over feed costs. Hence, under these conditions, he can make money with a lower price margin than when the price spread between beef and feed is narrow.

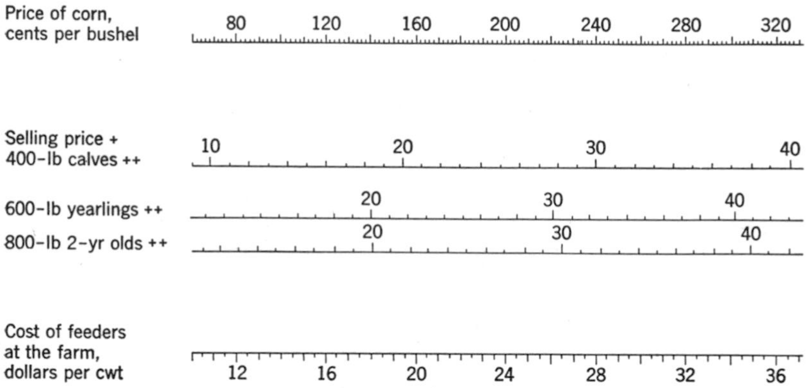

Price of corn,
cents per bushel

| 80 | 120 | 160 | 200 | 240 | 280 | 320 |

Selling price +
400-lb calves ++

| 10 | 20 | 30 | 40 |

600-lb yearlings ++

| 20 | 30 | 40 |

800-lb 2-yr olds ++

| 20 | 30 | 40 |

Cost of feeders
at the farm,
dollars per cwt

| 12 | 16 | 20 | 24 | 28 | 32 | 36 |

Figure 76. Medium steers. (From *Iowa Agr. Ext. Serv. Pamphlet* 127)

+ Needed to pay feed, interest, and death risk.
++ Weight and kind of feeder steer put in the feedlot. The weights shown are those at place of purchase. The calves were fed to gain about 470 lb, the yearlings 300 lb, and the 2-year-olds 250 lb. The selling weight is the weight of the feeder plus the amount of gain and is the weight to which the selling price applies. Selling price is that of the steer when marketed.
(Copyright ISC Research Foundation)

Figures 75 and 76 show the selling price necessary to break even. You can test the rules that we have just set forth through use of these scales.

Indirect returns

If we return to Table 45, it is apparent that the $1,303 realized from the feeding operation shown is a modest return. This is even more apparent when we consider that the $1,303 was not clear profit but included returns for 8 months of work and on an investment of over $7,200. The returns per $100 feed fed from beef feeding on farms in the Illinois farm business associations (Table 26, Chapter

8) support the view that, year in and year out, cattle feeding profits are not great.

Table 47. Amount of Pasture and Hay Required in Proportion to Corn by Different Cattle Feeding Programs*

	Acres for 10 Head		Hay and Pasture Used for Each 10 acres of Corn	
Kind of Program	Corn	Hay and Pasture	Corn	Hay and Pasture
Strong on Corn (mostly drylot)				
Good–choice long-fed yearlings	10.7	6.7	10	6.3
Good–choice steer calves	10.5	6.3	10	6.0
Good–choice short-fed yearlings	8.3	5.3	10	6.4
Good–choice 2-year-olds	8.2	4.9	10	6.0
Good–choice heifer calves	7.3	4.2	10	5.8
Intermediate on Corn				
Common–medium yearlings	6.2	6.4	10	10.3
Common–medium 2-year-olds	5.5	4.3	10	7.8
More Hay and Pasture				
Good–choice steer calves	8.7	14.5	10	16.7
Good–choice yearling steers	8.3	11.4	10	13.7
Medium–good steer calves	6.8	9.5	10	14.0
Medium–good yearling steers	5.3	9.8	10	18.5

* From *Iowa Agr. Ext. Serv. Pamphlet* 127.

Why do farmers continue to feed cattle in view of these modest profits? The answer, in part at least, seems to be that there are important indirect returns to cattle feeding. Most farmers have hogs follow cattle in the feed lot. The pork produced in this way represents an indirect return to cattle feeding. Cattle feeders often remark in a joking way, when their cattle feeding operations turn out badly, that they did not lose any money feeding cattle but they have some high-priced manure. This attitude is a recognition of the indirect return in the form of higher crop yields that result from returning manure to the land. In addition, cattle feeding provides a market for forage. This is important since there often is no dependable cash market for hay and pasture.

Adapting the Cattle Feeding Program to the Feed Supply

What type of cattle feeding program should you follow? Should you feed calves, yearlings, or two-year-olds? What quality of cattle

Figure 77. Although direct profits from cattle feeding are not great over a period of years, indirect returns are important. One of these indirect advantages is the fertility that is returned to the land in the form of manure. Feed for hogs following the cattle is another. (Courtesy Deere & Co.)

should you feed? One of the important factors in making these decisions is the type of feed supply you have to give the cattle. The ratio in which different programs use hay and pasture is shown in Table 47. The column showing the acreage of hay and pasture needed for every 10 acres of corn is based on a 60-bushel corn yield and a 2-ton hay yield. Calves and yearlings are well suited to long feeding programs. If the animals are roughed through the winter and fed on pasture during the next summer, these programs use large amounts of forage in relation to grain. Drylot short-run feeding programs tend to use less forage in relation to grain. If you have low-grade roughage and a relatively small amount of grain, common-to-medium-grade yearlings or two-year-olds probably will fit best into your plan.

Timing the Cattle-Feeding Program

Cattle prices follow a fairly regular seasonal pattern, but the prices of different grades of cattle follow different patterns through the year. Feeder cattle prices are typically highest in the spring and lowest in the fall. Prices of medium and common grades of slaughter steers follow much the same pattern. However, good and choice cattle tend to be lowest in the spring and highest during the summer and fall. The seasonal trend of prices on slaughter steers

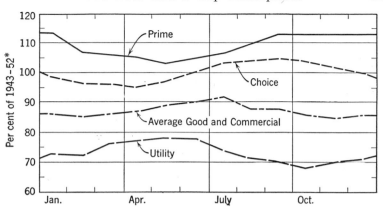

Figure 78. Seasonality in steer prices. Cornbelt slaughter steers at Chicago. (Agr. Marketing Serv., USDA)

of different grades is shown in Figure 78. Seasonal prices on feeder steers are shown in Figure 79.

How do these price trends affect the cattle feeder? Suppose you have more pasture than you can use and decide to buy cattle in the spring to put on pasture with the expectation of selling them in the fall. You would be buying the cattle at the time of the year at which their price is the highest. If you sold them off pasture in the fall, they would have only a grass finish and would have to compete with many other grass-fat cattle coming on the market. With this type of program, you would be buying on a seasonally high and selling on a seasonally low market.

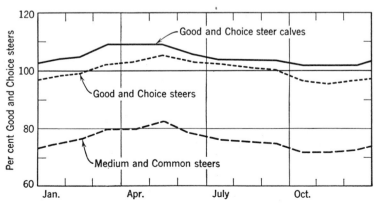

Figure 79. Seasonality in stocker and feeder prices at Kansas City. (Agr. Marketing Serv., USDA)

It is usually best to plan to buy feeder cattle when prices are at or near their seasonal low. It is impossible to predict the exact time at which the seasonal low will come, but you can be reasonably sure that it will be in September, October, or November. On the other hand, it is usually best to sell at a time of year when the price for the quality you are feeding is at or near its seasonal peak. Thus lower grades of cattle should be sold in the spring and choice and prime cattle during the late summer and fall.

Achieving Economy in Beef Raising

Farmers who keep a beef cow herd as part of a general farming program are in competition with beef raisers in the range areas. If they are to be justified in using their feed, labor, and capital to raise calves, they must learn how to maintain the beef cow herd at a low cost.

Table 44. Budget of Cost and Return from a 30-Cow Beef Breeding Herd

Costs

		Price	Total Cost
30 cows and 1 bull			
Hay	46½ tons	$20	$ 930
Pasture	68 acres	10 per acre	680
Labor	589 hr	1 per hr	589
Housing			95
Miscellaneous (taxes, insurance, veterinary fees, equipment, bedding)			205
			$2,499

Returns

27 calves, marketed at 400 lb, or 10,800 lb at
24¢ per lb $2,582

An estimate of the return over costs that a farm operator might expect from a commercial beef cow herd of 30 cows where hay and pasture are valued at market price is shown in Table 44. The labor used on the enterprise has been charged at $1 per hour, and housing costs have been figured on the basis of sheds typically provided in the cornbelt. The example assumes that a 90 per cent calf crop would be marketed at 400 pounds. Notice that the return over cost from the 30 cow herd totals only $83, an exceedingly low return for the operator's capital and management.

In view of these modest returns, how can a beef breeding herd be justified on a cornbelt farm? The answer is that it cannot if the feed, labor, and housing going into the enterprise must be charged at the prices we have used in the budget, either because they could be marketed at these prices or because they would yield an equal or greater return in some other enterprise. To be profitable the commercial beef cow herd on the cornbelt farm must be built on cheap pasture and roughage such as permanent pasture, cornstalks, and aftermath grazing. The labor used must be low in cost in terms of its alternative uses on the farm; housing costs must be kept at a minimum.

Keeping feed costs low

What can farmers do to keep feed costs on the beef breeding herd low? Usually a good place to start is on the wintering phase of the feeding program. Although many farmers apparently like to see their beef cows come through the winter in good condition, this extra finish is not reflected in higher returns. Beef cows should be wintered so that they produce vigorous, healthy calves. To do this, certain nutritional requirements must be met. But any finish beyond this means that the cows have been fed too liberally. If cows are given a small amount of good-quality legume hay, the bulk of the wintering ration can consist of low-quality roughage such as cornstalks, straw, and poor-quality hay. Wintering costs can also be kept down by extending the pasture season over as long a period as possible. Purdue studies show that the cost of the wintering ration per day was more than 2½ times greater than the cost of pasture per day.

Economy in housing

Beef cows do not need elaborate housing. Many cows are wintered successfully with little or no housing. Gullies or ravines that break the wind or strawstacks or strawsheds are usually sufficient. If the farm already has shed space or barn room that is not in use, cows should be housed. But ordinarily beef raisers are not justified in spending money for costly housing for the beef cow herd.

Reducing labor requirements

We pointed out in Chapter 8 that much more labor per cow is needed on the general farm than under range conditions. This is due to the smaller herd size on the general farm and to a failure to provide labor-saving facilities for feeding and caring for the herd. How important it is to economize in the use of labor in wintering the beef cow herd depends on how much labor you have available and what alternative uses you have for it. If you must hire the labor or if it must be taken away from some other enterprise, it may be highly important to cut labor requirements.

One basic rule that should be followed is to have the cows come to the feed supply instead of moving the feed to them. If cows are wintered in sheds or barns, they should be arranged so that bedding can be hauled in and manure taken out with a loader in the spring or summer.

Sheep Production

Mutton producers, like beef producers, tend to specialize in either raising or feeding lambs. Lambs are raised on the range and shipped

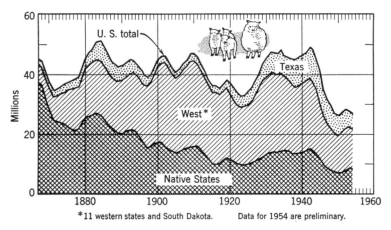

*11 western states and South Dakota.   Data for 1954 are preliminary.

Figure 80. The number of sheep in the United States has fluctuated widely in the past. There has been a sharp decrease in numbers since prewar years. Both western sheep and native sheep raised in small farm flocks have decreased sharply. (Agr. Marketing Serv., USDA)

into the cornbelt to be fed. However, the specialization is not so pronounced as with beef cattle. Many farmers keep a small flock of ewes, raise the lambs, and feed them out. In this section we will discuss some of the problems of the lamb feeder and the producer who keeps a small farm flock.

Management Problems

1. Analyzing the source of returns in lamb production and feeding.
2. Timing lamb production.
3. Keeping sheep healthy.

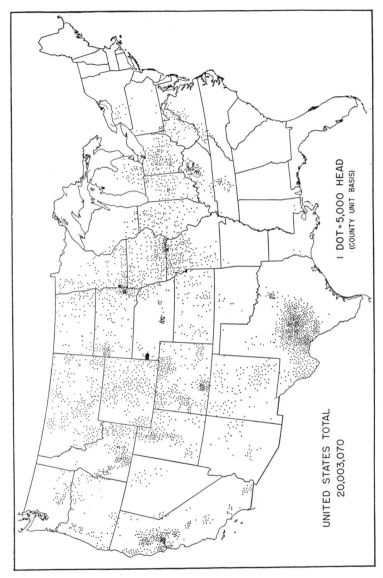

Figure 81. Many of the lambs sold from the western states and from Texas are shipped to feedlots in the irrigated areas of the West and to the cornbelt for further growth and fattening. (Bureau of the Census)

UNITED STATES TOTAL
20,003,070

I DOT=5,000 HEAD
(COUNTY UNIT BASIS)

Recognizing the Sources of Returns

Lamb feeding is like cattle feeding in several respects. Returns come from improving the quality of the purchased weight as well as adding more weight. Some price margin on the original weight is ordinarily necessary to make money from lamb feeding. This is true because the cost of putting on weight is usually as great as the selling price of the added weight.

In most lamb programs at least 2 pounds of lamb will be purchased for every pound added through feeding. For this reason, buying ability is an important element in the success of the enterprise. The high ratio of purchased weight to gain also makes returns from lamb feeding highly dependent on price changes.

Returns from the farm flock come from the sale of wool as well as from the sale of lambs. Receipts from wool usually make up about 25 per cent of total returns.

Timing the Sheep Enterprise

Lamb prices like the prices of other livestock products follow a fairly consistent pattern from season to season. They are highest in the early spring and summer and then begin a gradual decline, reaching their low point in October or early November (Figure 82).

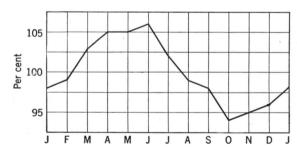

Figure 82. Index numbers of seasonal variation of prices received by farmers for choice and prime slaughter lambs at Chicago. (Agr. Marketing Serv., USDA)

Lambs marketed early bring more than lambs sold later in the fall. In order to get lambs on the market early, they should be dropped in February or early March. Whether this will be the most profitable timing depends on what labor and housing are available and how the sheep fit in with the other enterprises. Early lambing requires more labor and better housing than April or early May lambing. On some farms early lambing conflicts with early farrowing. In addition, early lambs will get less of their feed from pasture.

Lamb feeding operations are carried on almost altogether in the fall and winter because feeder lambs move to maket in the fall. Feeders often like to buy their lambs early and let them clean up cornfields and pasture oat stubble and new seedings. Some feeders handle two lots each fall, thus making fuller use of their equipment

Figure 83. Farm flocks of sheep frequently make use of roughage for which there is no alternative use on the farm. (Courtesy Soil Conservation Serv.)

and labor. Timing the lamb feeding program is largely a short-run decision. The feeder can best decide when to buy or sell on the basis of the supply and demand factors prevailing at the time.

Keeping Sheep Healthy

One of the most difficult problems of the lamb producer or feeder is keeping the flock healthy. Sheep are beset by many ills. They do not have so great a capacity to withstand disease and parasites as other types of livestock. The amount of death loss is often a critical factor in determining the outcome of the lamb feeding venture.

The lamb feeder must constantly be on the lookout for trouble. Worms, disease, and scours often cause death or unthriftiness. Keeping lambs healthy and getting good gains from them calls for a high degree of skill. It is not unusual for the beginning lamb

Figure 84. Lamb feeding is a good example of an enterprise requiring a high degree of skill. Buying and selling and keeping lambs healthy are major problems. Beginning lamb feeders can reduce the risk arising out of lack of experience by starting on a small scale. (Courtesy Allis-Chalmers Mfg. Co.)

feeder to be disappointed at the amount of gain he has been able to get. Occasionally, if he has done a poor job in selecting the lambs in the first place and has had a heavy death loss, he may sell fewer pounds than he purchased.

Problems

1. If you purchased choice yearling steers at 650 pounds for 20 cents per pound, fed them to 1,050 pounds on $1.40 corn, what selling price would be necessary for you to break even. (Use Figure 75.) Would the break-even price be higher or lower than for calves purchased for the same price at 450 pounds and fed to 1,000 pounds?

2. Explain why bankers and other credit agencies are usually willing to finance a larger proportion of the purchase price of calves than of two-year-old steers.

3. Outline the factors you would consider in deciding whether to feed calves, yearlings, or two-year-olds.

4. Plot on graph paper the seasonal price pattern for feeder cattle during the last 2 years. How do the patterns in the last 2 years compare with the long-time averages shown in Figure 79?

5. Plot the seasonal price pattern for choice slaughter steers at a near-by market during the last year. Do the same for common steers. Compare your graph with the seasonal price pattern for choice and common steers shown in Figure 80. Explain any differences you see.

6. Determine the cost of 400-pound feeder calves and 750-pound yearlings during the second week of last October. How much would it cost to feed the calves to a weight of 950 pounds and the yearlings to 1,200 pounds? Use the feed requirements given in Table 32 for feeding steers on drylot. Use current prices for feed. Which puts on 100 pounds of gain the cheaper, the calves or the yearlings? At what price per hundredweight must each of the steers be sold at the end of the feeding period in order to cover the cost of the feed?

7. Compare the price of feeder lambs in late September with the price of slaughter lambs in December during each of the last 5 years. How much price margin, if any, could the lamb feeder have counted on during each year?

References

Anderson, W. T., and Henry Mayo, "Producing Beef Calves in Indiana," *Purdue Agr. Ext. Serv. Bull.* 371.

"Annual Report of Feeder Cattle," *Illinois Agr. Expt. Sta. Mimeo. Rept.*, published annually, 1952.

Annual Report of the Illinois Farm Bureau Farm Management Service, Ill. Agr. Ext. Serv., Dept. Agr. Econ., published annually, 1952.

Burge, Charles A., and James A. Christian, "Beef Cattle in Pennsylvania," *Penn. Agr. Ext. Serv. Circ.* 402, Apr. 1952.

Case, H. C. M., and Paul E. Johnston, *Principles of Farm Management*, Chapter 8, J. B. Lippincott Co., Chicago, Philadelphia, New York, 1953.

Connell, W. B., and W. L. Henning, "Sheep Management," *Penn. Agr. Ext. Serv. Circ.* 416, Apr. 1953.

Hauser, E. R., and J. J. Lacey, "Beef Cattle in Wisconsin," *Wisconsin Ext. Circ.* 413.

Hopkins, John A., and William G. Murray, *Elements of Farm Management*, 4th Ed., Chapter 16, Prentice-Hall, New York, 1953.

Malone, Carl C., "Guides to Profit for Cattle Feeders," *Iowa Agr. Ext. Serv. Pamphlet* 127 (revised), Sept. 1950.

McDonald, C. W., "Quality Lamb Production," *Iowa Agr. Expt. Sta. and Ext. Serv. Bull.* P. 4, Dec. 1941.

Miller, J. I., and C. B. Morrison, "Use of Pasture for Fattening Steers," *Cornell Agr. Expt. Sta. Bull.* 890, Mar. 1953.

Nodland, T. R., and G. A. Pond, "Managing Sheep for Greater Returns," *Minn. Agr. Expt. Sta. Bull.* 382, Feb. 1945.

Robertson, Lynn S., and Ralph H. Woods, *Farm Business Management*, Chapter 9, J. B. Lippincott Co., Chicago, Philadelphia, New York, 1950.

11

Managing the Dairy Enterprise

In Chapter 8 we noted that dairying yields a high return per dollar of feed fed and produces a stable income. However, success in the dairy enterprise requires skillful management. Should you sell cream or whole milk? How much grain should you feed? How high should you attempt to push milk production per cow? When should you have the cows freshen? These are some of the economic decisions that the dairyman must make.

Management Problems

1. Analyzing market outlets for dairy products.
2. Choosing the most profitable rate of feeding dairy cows.
3. Determining the most profitable output per cow.
4. Fitting production to seasonal price changes.
5. Planning a housing system.

Analyzing Market Outlets for Dairy Products

The prices that dairy farmers get for their product may vary considerably from one community to another. One locality may have a market milk outlet. Market milk is milk sold for consumption as whole milk. The market milk outlet may be a grade-A market. Grade-A milk is milk produced under strict sanitation regulations. Another community may have a manufacturing milk outlet where butter and dried skim milk or cheese are made from whole milk. Still another community may have only a cream market. These differences in markets arise principally out of the difficulties involved in transporting milk for long distances. Heavy concentrations of market milk producers are usually found in areas close to large population centers. However, improved methods of transporting milk are beginning to make market milk outlets available to producers in areas long distances away from the cities where the milk is consumed.

In the past, the only market available to dairy producers in many areas remote from population centers has been a cream market. The skim milk has been fed largely to hogs and chickens. There is a growing tendency to make greater use of the nutrients in skim milk for human consumption by processing milk into cheese, ice cream, and dried skim milk. Cheese production in the United States increased from an average yearly output of 669 million pounds in 1935 to 1939 to 1,135 million pounds in 1952. Nonfat dry milk production increased from 243 million pounds to 785 million pounds during the same period. This has made a manufacturing milk outlet available to many farmers who formerly sold cream.

Importance of market outlets in management

How great are the differences in price among these outlets? The dairyman who sells his product as whole milk usually receives more for it than the farmer who sells cream. Market milk sells for more

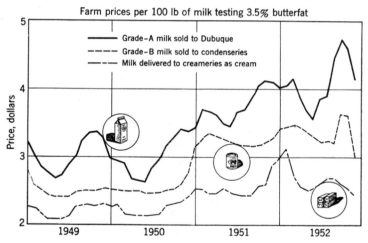

Farm prices per 100 lb of milk testing 3.5% butterfat

— Grade-A milk sold to Dubuque
--- Grade-B milk sold to condenseries
-- Milk delivered to creameries as cream

Figure 85. Prices received by farmers in the Dubuque, Iowa, area for market milk, manufacturing milk, and for cream. (Source Iowa Agr. Expt. Sta.)

than manufacturing milk. You can get an indication of the differences in prices farmers receive for these products from Figure 85. This graph shows the prices that farmers in the Dubuque, Iowa, area received for market milk, manufacturing milk, and cream during the 4-year period from 1949 through 1952.

The price for cream is given in terms of the return that farmers would realize from the butterfat in 100 pounds of milk containing 3.5 per cent butterfat. The prices shown pertain to only one area. Differences in prices may be even greater in other areas. You should also observe that the relative prices received for the products varied from year to year and even from month to month during a given year.

Choosing a market

Producers in areas where both market and manufacturing milk outlets are available in addition to a cream market should consider the following factors in choosing a market:

1. The relative prices received for the different products.
2. The dependability of the market.
3. The relative costs of producing the different products.
4. The value of skim milk as a hog or poultry feed.

In comparing prices, you should compare the average prices you can expect to receive throughout the entire year for milk and butter-

Figure 86. Many milk marketing organizations are changing to the bulk system of collecting milk from farms. This system requires an additional capital outlay for milk producers, but it increases the efficiency of the marketing process. (Courtesy *Farm Journal*)

fat rather than their prices during any one month. During the spring and early summer months, market milk producers often supply more milk than their distributor can sell as fluid milk. A part of this output must be used for other purposes such as butter, cheese, or dried milk. As a result, producers are paid a lower price for that part of their milk diverted to these uses.

Occasionally milk distributors adjust to the seasonal surplus by cutting off some of their producers from the market. Often these are producers marketing through a distributor who is located some distance from the central market. A market milk outlet is usually more dependable if it is associated directly with a large market.

Before going to the expense of equipping yourself for market milk production, you should investigate the dependability of your market. You should find out how well the price has held up in the past, during periods of falling demand or seasonal increases in supply. You should also attempt to find out what policy the distributor has followed in cutting off producers from the market during these periods.

Producing market milk is usually somewhat more costly than producing manufacturing milk or cream. These added costs arise from the stricter sanitation measures required of market milk producers. To qualify for market milk and especially for grade-A milk production, you must have a mechanical milk cooler. You must have better equipment, and usually a water heater for cleaning your milk utensils and your milkhouse. As a result, a considerable outlay of capital is usually required to change from cream to grade-A milk production.

The size of the dairy enterprise plays an important role in determining how much more it will cost to produce grade-A milk than grade-B milk or cream. A study of the cost of changing from grade-B to grade-A production, on 140 farms in the Omaha–Council Bluffs milk marketing area, showed that the average outlay on farms with 10 cows was $112 per cow. With herds of 20 cows, the cost was $64 per cow. The reason for this difference is that many of the changes required, such as barn and milkhouse alterations, addition of mechanical milk coolers and other utensils, do not cost proportionally more for 20 cows than for 10 cows.

In addition to providing more expensive facilities and equipment, the grade-A milk producer must give more attention to the cleanliness of his cows, his barn, and milkhouse. These added costs must be weighed against the added returns expected from selling grade-A milk.

In choosing between a whole-milk and a cream outlet, the dairyman should estimate the value of skim milk as a poultry or hog feed. He can then compare this value with what he gets for skim milk when he sells whole milk. The value of the skim milk as feed for hogs or chickens plus what the butterfat in the milk would return when sold as butterfat may be greater than the whole-milk price. The value of skim milk as a feed depends on the price of

Figure 87. In comparing the returns from selling cream with those from selling whole milk farmers should consider the value of skim milk fed on the farm. (Courtesy DeLaval Separator Co.)

the grain and protein supplement that it replaces and on the proportion of skim milk to other feeds in the ration.

An Iowa study showed that, with the price of corn at $1.25 per bushel and tankage at $92 per ton, 100 pounds of skim milk was worth 86 cents for hogs when they were fed 2 to 4 pounds of milk daily.* Its value dropped to 42 cents when hogs were fed 10 to 32

* From "What Is Skim Milk Worth as Hog Feed?" *Iowa Farm Science,* Aug. 1946.

pounds daily. Thus skim milk substituted for other feeds at a diminishing rate as more and more of it was fed. We observed this same tendency in the previous chapter when soybean oil meal replaced grain in the ration for hogs.

Choosing the Most Profitable Rate of Feeding Dairy Cows

Feed costs constitute about 50 per cent of the cost of producing milk. What economic problems are involved in the feeding program? What principles can the dairyman apply in solving them? The following factors must be considered in determining the most profitable amount and combination of feeds for dairy cows:

1. Individual cows vary greatly in their capacity to convert feed into milk.

2. The amount of milk resulting from each additional pound of feed declines as cows are fed at higher rates.

3. Feeding more grain reduces the amount of hay that cows will consume.

4. It is profitable to give dairy cows more feed when the price of milk is high relative to the price of feed.

5. Feeding high-quality roughage reduces the amount of grain required to produce a given output of milk.

Differences among cows

How do differences in the way cows respond to feed affect the most profitable level of grain feeding? Differences among cows in their response to increased grain feeding are illustrated in Figure 88. For example, increasing the amount of grain feed yearly to an average cow from 1,000 to 2,000 pounds increases her annual milk output from 6,580 to 7,120 pounds, or 540 pounds. But increasing the amount of grain fed to a very good cow from 1,000 to 2,000 pounds increases her milk output from 10,690 to 11,870 pounds, or 1,180 pounds. It is evident that you should feed the very good cow more than the average cow.

In order to maximize returns from feed, it is necessary to feed each cow according to her production. The rate of feeding is commonly expressed in terms of a pound of grain for so many pounds of milk. For example, a common level of feeding is 1 pound of grain for every 3 pounds of milk the cow produces. If feed is allocated on this basis, a high-producing cow gets more feed than a low-

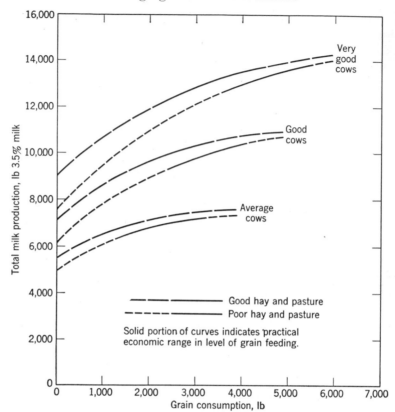

Figure 88. Response in milk production to increased grain feeding when Holstein cows are fed good and poor quality hay and pasture freely. (From *Mich. Agr. Expt. Sta. Spec. Bull.* 376)

producing cow. Should the ratio of grain to milk remain the same in spite of changes in feed and milk prices? These are the questions that we will try to answer next.

Declining output of milk from each additional input of feed

Feeding additional pounds of grain to a dairy cow has two effects: (1) It decreases the amount of hay that the cow will eat (for every additional 100 pounds of grain fed, 60 to 75 pounds less hay is consumed); and (2) it increases the amount of milk the cow produces. Both these factors must be considered in determining the most profitable rate at which to feed grain.

The amount of added milk resulting from each additional pound of feed declines as cows are fed more and more grain. Eventually a point is reached where the cost of the added feed is greater than the value of the added milk. Even though we could get more milk per cow by feeding beyond this point, it would not be profitable to do so. The diminishing returns from added grain fed to dairy cows is parallel to the decline in additional yield that results from adding more and more fertilizer to crops. The principle of balancing

Figure 89. Increasing output per cow usually results in lowering the cost of labor and housing per 100 pounds of milk produced. Production per cow can be increased through better breeding and feeding. Cows should not be fed beyond the point where the cost of an added pound of grain is equal to the value of the increased milk that results from feeding it. (Courtesy DeLaval Separator Co.)

added costs with added returns applies in finding the optimum level of feeding, just as it did in finding the optimum rate of fertilizer application.

How can you find the most profitable level of feeding grain? How can you tell how much more milk you are getting for each added input of grain? You will find it impossible to arrive at exact answers to these questions. However, the relationship between added rates of grain feeding and added pounds of milk for cows fed at different levels has been estimated from experiments. These estimates are given below:*

Level of Feeding Grain	Lb of Milk from Each 100 lb of Grain Added to That Already Being Fed
1 lb of grain to 6 lb of milk	97
1 lb of grain to 4 lb of milk	77
1 lb of grain to 3 lb of milk	59
1 lb of grain to 2½ lb of milk	45
1 lb of grain to 2 lb of milk	31

Note that the first column gives the rate of grain feeding. It is expressed in terms of 1 pound of grain for so many pounds of milk produced. Cows that are fed 1 pound of grain for every 6 pounds of milk they produce are fed less grain than cows fed 1 pound of grain for every 4 pounds of milk.

For example, suppose two dairy herds produced an average of 10,000 pounds of milk per cow annually. The herd fed at the 1-to-4 rate would get 2,500 lb of grain per cow during the year while the herd fed at the 1-to-6 rate would consume only 1,666 pounds per cow. The second column gives the added milk from each added 100 pounds of grain fed to cows already being fed at the rate shown in the first column. Feeding 100 pounds more grain to cows already fed at the 1-to-6 rate would add 97 pounds of milk. More grain fed to cows at the 1-to-4 rate yields milk at the rate of 77 pounds of milk per 100 pounds of feed. And, if cows are fed at the 1-to-2 rate, the return from added grain would be only 31 pounds of milk per 100 pounds of grain.

Balancing added costs and added returns

How can we determine the most profitable rate of grain feeding from the grain-to-milk relationships shown above? This rate will vary with the price of milk and the cost of feed. Let us start with an example. Assume that you have a herd of medium-size cows giving milk testing 4 per cent butterfat. Assume, in addition, that the price of milk is $4.25 per 100 pounds and that the grain mixture is worth 3 cents per pound and hay $25 per ton.

We will determine first if it would be profitable to feed at as high a rate as the 1-to-3 ratio. The first step is to find the number of

* From "More Grain for Your Dairy Cows," by Ralph D. Jennings and John W. Klein, *Agricultural Situation*, Feb. 1949.

pounds of milk produced from the 100 pounds of added feed at the 1-to-3 rate of feeding. The information given above indicates that this would be 59 pounds of milk. You should proceed as follows:

Value of 59 lb of milk ($4.25 per 100 lb)	$2.51
Value of hay saved (68 lb at 1¼ cents per lb)	0.83
Total returns from adding 100 lb of grain	$3.34
Cost of additional 100 lb of grain	3.00

The returns from 100 pounds of added grain was greater than the cost of the grain. This indicates that feeding at an even heavier rate than the 1-to-3 ratio would be profitable.

Let us follow through the same calculations for the 1-to-2 ratio to see if feeding this much grain would pay. At this ratio an added 100 pounds of grain would result in an increase of 31 pounds of milk. Hence, your calculations should be as follows:

Value of 31 additional lb of milk (4.25 per 100 lb)	$1.32
Value of 68 lb of hay saved by 100 lb of grain	0.83
Total return from 100 lb of additional feed	$2.15
Cost of additional 100 lb of grain	3.00

In this case, the cost of the added 100 pounds of feed is much greater than the return from feeding it. Because of this spread between cost and returns, we can be quite sure that feeding at as heavy a rate as the 1-to-2 ratio would not be profitable. The most profitable ratio, with the prices of milk and feed used here, is somewhere between the 1-to-2 and the 1-to-3 ratio.

How can you determine exactly the most profitable rate? You can find it through a trial-and-error process of budgeting as we have done above, using rates between the 1-to-2 and the 1-to-3 ratio. Later, we will present some additional information that will make it easier for you to estimate the best rate of feeding. But, before we do this, we will consider how the most profitable rate of feeding is affected by the relationship between the price of feed and the price of milk.

Effect of milk and feed prices on most profitable rate of feeding

Our calculations in the examples shown above were based on a price of $4.25 per 100 pounds for milk and 3 cents per pound for feed. Suppose that, instead of selling milk for $4.25, you had only a cream market, and, as a result, milk, including the value of skim milk, was worth only $3 per 100 pounds on your farm. How would this affect the most profitable level of grain feeding? Let us calculate the returns we could expect from feeding at the 1-to-3 ratio under these circumstances. We will use the same prices for grain and hay as before. Therefore our calculations would be as follows:

Value of 59 lb additional milk ($3 per 100 lb of milk)	$1.77
Value of hay saved (68 lb at $25 per ton)	$0.83
Total return from feeding 100 lb of additional grain	$2.60
Cost of additional 100 lb of grain fed	3.00

With these prices, feeding at as heavy a rate as the 1-to-3 ratio would not be profitable. You will recall that it was profitable to feed at this heavy a rate in the previous example where the price of milk was $4.25 per 100 pounds.

We can summarize the effect of changes in the price of milk in relation to feed prices on the most profitable rate of feeding as follows: As the price of milk increases relative to the price of feed, the most profitable level of grain feeding increases. As the price of milk decreases relative to the price of feed, the most profitable level of grain feeding decreases. A change in the ratio of milk to grain prices can also arise out of a change in feed prices. Thus, as feed prices decrease (the price of milk staying the same), the most profitable rate of grain feeding increases, or, as the price of feed increases (the price of milk staying the same), the most profitable rate of grain feeding decreases.

Selecting the best grain-milk ratio

Let us now improve on the method of trial and error that we used before for determining the most profitable rate of grain feeding. The information given in Table 49 will help to do this. The first step in using the table is to determine the number of pounds of milk that are equal in value to 100 pounds of grain. We can do this by dividing the price of grain per 100 pounds by the price of milk per 100 pounds and multiplying by 100. Thus in our first example, where the price of milk was $4.25 per 100 pounds and feed $3.00 per 100 pounds, the pounds of milk equal in value to 100 pounds of grain would be 70, since $\frac{3.00}{4.25} \times 100 = 70.5$.

The next step is to move down the first column in the table until you come to the number 70. Then move across the table until you find the column that most nearly fits your situation. If you have medium-sized cows that produce milk testing 4 per cent you value hay at $25 per ton, you should feed 1 pound of grain for every 2.7 pounds of milk produced. You will notice that the table makes provisions for different rates of feeding for cows producing milk of different tests. Our previous calculations were based on 4 per cent milk. Cows producing high-test milk should be fed at heavier rates. When hay prices are low relative to grain prices, it pays to feed

Table 49.   Most Profitable Rate of Grain Feeding*

Feed 1 lb of Grain to no. of lb of Milk Given Below

Lb of Milk Equal in Value to 100 lb of Grain or Mixed Feed	Hay Price per ton 3 to 4 times Milk Price per 100 lb			Hay Price per ton 5 to 7 times Milk Price per 100 lb		
	Large Cows Testing 3½% Fat	Medium Cows Testing 4% Fat	Small Cows Testing 5% Fat	Large Cows Testing 3½% Fat	Medium Cows Testing 4% Fat	Small Cows Testing 5% Fat
120	7.7	8.2	8.5	6.3	6.5	6.6
110	6.1	6.2	6.3	5.2	5.2	5.2
100	5.0	5.0	5.0	4.4	4.3	4 2
90	4.2	4.1	4.1	3.7	3.6	3.4
80	3.7	3.5	3.4	3.3	3.1	2.8
70	3.2	3.1	2.8	2.8	2.7	2.4
60	2.8	2.6	2.4	2.4	2.3	2.1
50	2.4	2.3	2.1	2.1	2.0	...

* From Ralph D. Jennings and John W. Klein, "More Grain for Your Dairy Cows?," *Agricultural Situation*, USDA, Feb. 1949.

less grain. This is true because the value of hay saved by each 100 pounds of grain is not so great when hay prices are low. The information given in the table provides for these adjustments.

Feeding high-quality forage

How does high-quality forage affect milk production? How much added cost can you afford in order to produce higher-quality forage? Dairy cows make good use of high-quality forage. Cows fed good legume hay or silage usually produce more milk than those fed low-quality roughage. In addition some saving in grain and protein supplement is possible through feeding higher-quality forages. These savings are illustrated by the Michigan study reported in

Table 50. The herds fed hay and grass silage classified as excellent in quality required more hay but less corn silage, grain and protein. They produced slightly more milk per cow than the herds fed medium- or poor-quality hay. The total cost of producing milk was also lower under the conditions prevailing on these farms. However, you should not conclude from this study that feeding

Figure 90. Feeding high-quality forage to dairy cows increases output and reduces the amount of protein supplement needed in the ration. However, farmers must weigh the added cost of producing high-cost forage against these added returns. (Courtesy Soil Conservation Serv.)

high-quality hay always results in lower production costs and higher farm income. Each farmer must balance the value of any increase in milk production plus the saving in grain and protein supplement against the added cost of producing high-quality forage on his own farm.

There are several methods available for improving the quality of hay. Some of these, such as better timing of the hay harvest, involve little if any added cost. Experimental data indicate that

Figure 91. Harvesting forage in the form of grass silage usually results in a high-quality feed. The benefits from feeding high-quality forage must be weighed against the added cost of harvesting forages in this way. (Courtesy Soil Conservation Serv.)

grasses and legumes harvested at an early bloom stage are higher in protein and also contain other factors that stimulate milk production. Other methods such as mow-finishing hay, crushing, or making grass silage involve higher costs and greater inputs of

Table 50. Milk Production, Feed Fed, and Costs of Producing Milk during Barn Season on Farms Producing Excellent Medium- and Poor-Quality Hay and Grass Silage*

	Quality of Hay and Grass Silage		
	Excellent	Medium	Poor
Days barn fed	196	202	201
Lb milk produced per cow	6,531	6,454	6,289
Lb feed per cow			
Hay	4,272	4,087	4,056
Grass silage	2,055	2,083	1,317
Corn silage	3,085	4,085	4,347
Grain	1,587	1,825	2,205
Protein	141	323	372
Lb milk produced per lb grain			
mixture fed	3.8	3.0	2.5
Feed cost per cwt. of milk	$1.62	$1.88	$2.08

* From *Mich. Agr. Expt. Sta. Bull.* 390.

capital. Estimates of the cost of mow-finishing hay are shown in Table 51. Notice that the cost per ton is lower, the larger the tonnage of hay that is dried. This relationship is typical of the cost of forage harvesting methods that result in a higher-quality product. This is true because these methods involve a sizable investment in machinery and equipment and a high fixed cost unless the operation is custom-hired. Producing high-quality forage also requires considerable labor at a busy time of the year.

Table 51. Annual Cost per Farm and per ton of Hay-Finishing Systems*

Type of Unit	Estimated Tons of Hay Cured	Total Fixed Cost	Total Cost of Electricity	Total Cost Per Farm	Total Cost Per ton
Propeller, 36 in.	57	$112	$ 92	$204	$3.58
Propeller, 42 in.	84	144	60	204	2.43
Drum	60	111	108	219	3.65
Average	70	123	86	209	2.99

* From *Vermont Agr. Expt. Sta. Pamphlet* 20.

Determining the Most Profitable Output per Cow

Studies show that the amount of milk produced per cow is one of the most important factors affecting the cost of producing milk. A study of the cost of producing milk in Pennsylvania in 1948 showed that the cost per hundredweight for herds producing less than 6,500 pounds per cow was $5.41 but dropped to $4.34 for herds averaging 9,500 or more pounds per cow (Table 52).

How do these decreases in costs come about? Some elements of cost remain partially fixed as the output per cow is increased. High-producing cows tend to save on the amount of labor, housing, and equipment needed to produce 100 pounds of milk. For example, it would take longer to care for and milk a cow producing 10,000 pounds of milk every year than one producing only 5,000 pounds. But it would not take twice as long. The amount of barn space required to house a 10,000-pound cow would be no greater than that needed for a 5,000-pound cow. Owing to the maintenance requirements of the cow, the feed used per hundredweight of milk would also be less with high-producing cows unless the cows are overfed.

Increasing output through selection and breeding

Because of these economies associated with high-producing cows, one of the important management problems of the dairyman is to find ways of increasing output per cow if it is low or of maintaining output if it is high. But how far can the dairyman profitably go in attempting to increase output?

One way of increasing output is through a constant process of culling out low producers and replacing them with heifers that hold promise of being good producers. In order to do this, you must have some way of identifying the cows that are the high producers. You can get some idea of how well a cow is producing by observing how much milk she gives. But, since the butterfat content of the milk varies greatly among cows, an accurate check of the production per cow requires that milk be tested periodically. Many dairymen belong to an organization known as a Dairy Herd Improvement Association. This organization hires a man on a cooperative basis to weigh and test the milk produced by each cow in the herd once a month. This provides dairymen with a good basis for deciding which cows to keep and which to discard. It also helps them to feed each cow according to her production.

Table 52. Relation of Milk Produced per Cow per Year to Net Costs of Production and Marketing Milk on 273 Pennsylvania Farms*

Lb 4% Fat-Corrected Milk Produced per Cow	Number of Farms	Cost per Hundredweight
Less than 6,500	48	$5.41
6,500–7,499	75	5.00
7,500–8,499	70	4.55
8,500–9,499	37	4.63
9,500 and more	43	4.34

* From *Penn. Agr. Expt. Sta. Bull.* 549.

If the herd is to be improved by discarding poor cows, the culls must be replaced with better individuals. On most farms this can be accomplished best through raising the heifers on the farm. Using bulls that have proved their ability to sire high-producing offspring is the key to raising high-quality heifers for replacements. The rapid development of artificial insemination has made the use of outstanding sires in the breeding program economical for many commercial dairymen. What are the advantages and disadvantages of using artificial breeding?

One of the major advantages is the lower cost of using superior sires. The cost advantage is greatest for the small producer. The estimated cost of keeping a bull on Minnesota dairy farms at 1954 prices was $222.62 per year (Table 53). If 10 cows are served per year the cost per cow is $22.26; if 20 cows are served the cost drops to $11.13 per cow. Service fees for artificial breeding typically range from $6 to $8 per head. In addition, there usually is a small membership charge at the time the dairyman joins the breeding association. Thus the artificial insemination is less costly for herds of less than 20 to 25 cows. The advantage may be even greater than

Table 53.   Cost of Keeping a Bull *

Items of Cost	Amount
Feed	$ 92.18
Labor	98.00
Shelter and equipment	23.64
Interest on investment	8.80
Total	$222.62

* Adapted from *Univ. Minn. Div. Agr. Econ. Rept.* 146. Feed was valued at 1954 prices and labor at $1 per hr.

our comparisons indicate if we measure the cost of keeping the bull in terms of what the feed, labor, and investment would return if they were used instead to add one more cow to the heard. In addition to the lower cost, using artificial breeding usually enables the dairyman to breed his cows to a better bull than if he used his own bull.

It is not unusual for dairymen using artificial breeding for the first time to experience some difficulty. Often they do not observe their herd closely enough to call the inseminator when a cow is in heat. At other times associations have had difficulty with unskilled inseminators. Conception rates with artificial insemination can be as good as with natural service under proper management. However, the herd owner should not expect them to be better than with natural service.

Increasing output through feeding and care

In the section on feeding we observed that output per cow can be increased through heavier grain feeding. But we also found that, beyond a certain point, the cost of the added feed was greater than the value of the added milk it produced. Of course, increasing output per cow through feeding at this heavy a rate would not be profitable. Similarly, output can be increased by improving the quality of forage fed. But here again there is an economic limit to how far you can do so with profit. You must weigh the value of the added output from high-quality forage against the added cost of producing it.

Some farm management specialists have also observed that dairy-men who place too much emphasis on high production per cow some-times are inclined to slight other enterprises. It takes special care and skill to push production per cow to a very high level. If added output is obtained at the expense of other enterprises on the farm, such as timeliness in crop operations or care to pigs during farrow-ing, then it likely is not profitable. You must apply the principle of alternative returns in allocating your time between the dairy herd and other enterprises on the farm. You must decide if your time and effort can be more profitably used in striving for an exception-ally high herd average or in attempting to improve other phases of your business.

Fitting Production to Seasonal Price Changes

The dairyman, like the producer of other livestock products, has a timing problem. He must time the freshening period to fit seasonal price patterns and to fit in with other work on the farm. The seasonal price pattern of milk is shown in Figure 92 and that for butterfat in Figure 93. The price of milk is noticeably lower in

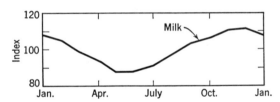

Figure 92. Seasonal pattern of milk prices. Index numbers of prices re-ceived by Indiana farmers for milk, November 1946 to October 1950. (Yearly average = 100. From *Purdue Agr. Expt. Sta. Bull.* 566)

late spring and early summer. Although there is some tendency for butterfat prices also to be lowest during this period, the trend is not nearly so pronounced. It should be pointed out that there is a difference among markets in the seasonal price pattern for milk, depending on the way in which surplus milk is handled.

A cow's production increases for the first month or two after freshening and then gradually decreases until the end of her lacta-tion period. When she freshens in the spring, the cow is at her peak production during the early summer period when prices are lowest. Studies of herds in the Iowa Dairy Herd Improvement Associations show that there is some advantage in fall and winter freshening over spring and summer freshening. Though there was

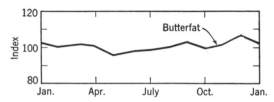

Figure 93. Seasonal pattern of butterfat prices. Index numbers of prices received by Indiana farmers for butter, November 1946 to October 1950. (Yearly average = 100. From *Purdue Agr. Expt. Sta. Bull.* 566)

little or no difference in feed costs, production per cow was somewhat higher from the cows that freshened in the fall and winter. This higher output per cow, coupled with the fact that the cows were at their production peak when prices were the highest, accounts for the higher return for fall and winter freshening. These results are summarized in Table 54. When fall-freshened cows go to pasture in the spring, the change to the pasture ration tends to stimulate milk production at a time when it is beginning to decline. The cow freshening in the fall will have her rest between lactation periods during the late summer season when conditions are the poorest for production.

There is some tendency, particularly for dairymen selling market milk, to have cows freshen uniformly throughout the year. This

Table 54.   The Relationship of the Freshening Season to Production and Income over Feed Costs*

Season of Freshening	Per cent of Cows Freshening	Average lb Milk per Cow	Average lb Fat per Cow	Average Feed Cost per Cow	Average Income over Feed Cost per Cow
Fall (Sept.–Oct.–Nov.)	33.7	9,567	381	$130	$251
Winter (Dec.–Jan.–Feb.)	29.2	9,566	380	130	250
Spring (Mar.–Apr.–May)	20.9	9,261	374	130	244
Summer (June–July–Aug.)	16.2	8,799	361	129	232

* From *Annual Summary of Iowa Dairy Herd Improvement Associations,* July 1951 to July 1952.

practice tends to even out the labor load and results in a more uniform production pattern during the year. However, it complicates raising young stock, since there will be calves of all ages on the farm. Under this system, part of the herd also freshens in the summer, and the cows are at their peak production when prices are lowest and pastures are poorest.

Planning a Housing System

Many dairymen have changed to the loose housing or pen-type system for housing the dairy herd since its development in the '30's. In the loose housing arrangement, cows are sheltered, bedded down,

Figure 94. Pen-type housing and a milking parlor reduce the labor required in dairying. Also, when new structures are being built, the investment per cow in housing and equipment is somewhat lower than when stanchion barns are built. (Courtesy DeLaval Separator Co.)

and sometimes fed roughage in an open barn or shed. They are brought into a milking room to be milked and fed grain and supplement. This arrangement is also referred to as the milking parlor system.

A loose housing system contains the following parts:

1. Milking room, sometimes called the milking parlor.
2. Milkroom.
3. Bedded area.
4. Feeding area.

5. Storage space.
6. Exercise yard.

Advantages of pen-type housing over a stall barn

1. Lower construction cost is possible with pen-type housing because many costly items such as stanchions, expensive concrete work, insulation, ventilation facilities, and individual drinking cups are eliminated.

2. Labor is used more efficiently if the routine is well organized. Cows travel to their feed and to the milking parlor.

3. Greater comfort of animals promotes better health, and less leg, teat, and udder injury is experienced.

4. The building is more flexible. It is possible to increase the number of cows or change to other livestock enterprises with little or no remodeling.

Disadvantages of pen-type housing

1. More bedding is required, because manure is usually hauled from the loafing area only once or twice a year. The area is kept clean by addition of more straw.

2. More of the dairy chores must be done in the loafing and feeding area where the temperature may be too low for comfortable working conditions in cold weather.

3. More difficulty is experienced with "bossism" among cows. Dehorning cows is usually necessary if the loose housing system is used.

Comparison of construction costs

Loose housing facilities can be provided at considerably less cost than a stanchion barn. Any type of shed or barn can be made to serve as a loafing area. Using an old barn or shed for this purpose greatly reduces the cost of establishing a loose housing system. But, even where new construction is necessary, structures suitable for pen-type housing can be built much more cheaply than a stanchion barn. The pole-frame design is probably the cheapest type of structure for the pen barn. No foundation is used in such a building, and the framing consists of creosoted posts set in the ground. In this type of structure, hay and bedding are stored on the ground instead of in a supported mow. One farmer visited in a Michigan study built such a pole-frame barn, including the milking parlor, for a 30-cow herd at a cost of about $200 per cow.* A 30-cow stanchion-type barn would have cost a minimum of $400 per cow had it been built at the same time.

Savings in labor

The loose housing system saves labor because the cows come to the milking parlor instead of the workman going to the cow. Hay can be self-fed, and the feeder filled only once a day. Cleaning out the

Table 55. Comparison of Estimated Time Required to Perform Dairy Chores in Stanchion and Pen-Type Barns, Assuming Most Efficient Methods and Arrangements of Work Area*

Minutes per Cow per day

Job	Stanchion Barns		Pen-Type Barns	
	Minutes	Per cent	Minutes	Per cent
Feeding hay	0.6	4.7	0.2	2.2
Feeding silage	0.8	6.3	0.4	4.3
Feeding grain	0.4	3.1	...	...
Cleaning mangers	0.3	2.4	...	...
Milking	6.2	48.8	6.0	65.3
Care of equipment	1.0	7.9	1.1	13.0
Clean stables	1.1	8.7	...	...
Bedding cows	.05	3.9	0.4	4.3
Getting cows in or out of barn or pasture	1.0	7.9	0.2	2.2
Miscellaneous	0.8	6.3	0.8	8.7
Total	12.7	100.0	9.2	100.0
Hours per cow per year	75		60	

* From "Pen-Type Dairy Barns" by L. H. Brown, B. F. Cargill, and B. R. Bookhout, *Mich. Agr. Expt. Sta. Spec. Bull.* 363.

barn takes much less time, since this job is done only once or twice a year instead of daily. In most cases, a manure loader can be used in the loafing area.

A comparison of the estimated time required to perform dairy chores in stanchion and pen-type barns is given in Table 55. Both these estimates are based on well-organized chore routines.

Problems

1. List the different ways of increasing output per cow. Explain under what circumstances increasing output in each of these ways would result in greater profits to the farm business.

* From *Mich. Agr. Expt. Sta. Spec. Bull.* 363.

2. Find out what market outlets are available for dairy products in your community. Determine the average price that farmers received for milk on each of the markets during the last year. If both a cream market and a whole milk market are available, determine how much you would get for skim milk by selling it in the form of whole milk. Would skim milk be worth this much for feed on your farm?

3. Determine the number of pounds of milk that would be equal in value to 100 pounds of grain mixture fed to dairy cows. Use current feed prices and the price that you can get for milk or its equivalent in cream in your own community. Using Table 49, determine the most profitable rate of grain feeding for the type of dairy cows you have in your herd.

4. Determine the number of pounds of milk or cream sold each month during the last year on your home farm. Was the most milk sold during the months of the year when the price was highest? Could you increase profits by altering the time of freshening? If so, how would these changes fit in with the work schedule and the pasture season?

5. What changes would be necessary in the dairy barn on your farm to convert it to a loose housing system, if you do not already use this system? What would be the advantages of a loose housing system on your farm? What would be the disadvantages?

6. Suppose a dairy farmer in your community has a 25-cow herd. Would you recommend natural or artificial breeding? Why?

References

Barr, W. L., K. R. Bennett, and R. D. Hess, "Survey and Cost Account Methods of Estimating Costs of Milk Production," *Penn. Agr. Expt. Sta. Bull.* 549.

Cunningham, L. C., "Commercial Dairy Farming in New York," *Cornell Agr. Expt. Sta. Spec. Bull.* 376.

Hoglund, C. R., "High-Quality Roughage Reduces Dairy Costs," *Mich. Agr. Expt. Sta. Bull.* 390, 1954.

Hoglund, C. R., and K. T. Wright, "Reducing Dairy Costs on Michigan Farms," *Mich. Agr. Expt. Sta. Spec. Bull.* 376.

Hopkins, John A., and William G. Murray, *Elements of Farm Management,* Chapter 16, Prentice-Hall, New York, 1953.

Jennings, Ralph D., and John W. Klein, "More Grain for Your Dairy Cows," *Agricultural Situation,* USDA, Feb. 1949.

Paarlberg, Don, "Seasonal Variations in Indiana Farm Prices," *Purdue Agr. Expt. Sta. Bull.* 566.

CHAPTER

12

Managing the Laying Flock

The efficiency with which eggs are produced in the typical farm flock has increased more than the efficiency of any other livestock enterprise in the last 20 years. A good indicator of this increased efficiency is the number of eggs produced per hen. A high production per hen results in low-cost production per egg because it also increases the output of eggs per square foot of housing, per hour of labor, and per dollar invested in hens and equipment. The average increase in yearly egg production per hen in the United States from 1930 through 1951 is traced in Figure 96. The rate of lay increased 46 per cent from 1939 to 1952.

How has this increase been accomplished? The answer lies not in any single improvement or practice but in the combination of a great many. Genetically the hen has been improved. She now inherits a greater capacity to lay eggs. We also have learned more about the nutritional requirements of laying hens. We have learned to take advantage of these improvements by supporting them with better management practices.

In this section we will limit our discussion primarily to the problems of the laying flock on the diversified farm. However, several of the principles that will be discussed can be applied to the commercial poultry farm as well.

Management Problems

1. Feeding the laying flock.
2. Adjusting flock size to year-to-year price changes.
3. Timing production to meet seasonal price changes.
4. Recognizing the relationship between costs and flock size.
5. Managing the poultry replacement flock.

Feeding the Laying Flock

Proper feeding is essential to a profitable poultry enterprise. Laying hens are highly sensitive to the make-up and quantity of feed

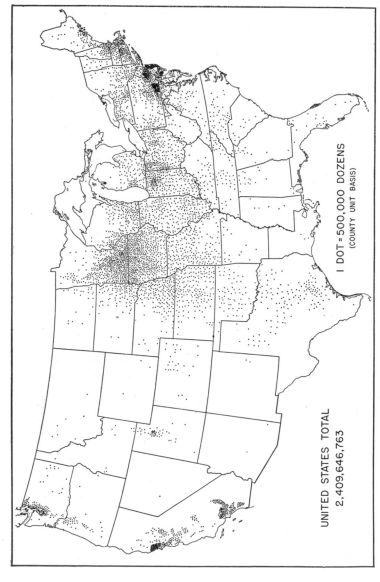

I DOT = 500,000 DOZENS
(COUNTY UNIT BASIS)

UNITED STATES TOTAL
2,409,646,763

Figure 95. Egg production is concentrated in the northern states and in sections of California and Washington. (Bureau of the Census)

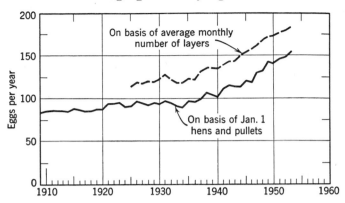

Figure 96. Egg production per bird. (Agr. Marketing Serv., USDA)

they receive. If the hen's nutritional requirements are not met, her egg production drops off sharply. To meet these nutritional requirements, a flock owner must feed a fairly definite combination of feeds.

Studies have shown that hens should be fed as much as they will eat. This is true because the added output of eggs resulting from each additional input of feed does not decline noticeably as hens are fed more and more feed. If it pays to feed a hen at all, it pays to give her all the feed she can consume. You should recall that this is a different conclusion from the one we came to in feeding dairy cows. With the dairy cows the added milk resulting from providing more and more feed declines in quantity. For this reason, added returns become less than added costs before the limit of the cow's capacity to consume feed is reached.

Adjusting Flock Size to Year-to-Year Price Changes

What adjustments in flock size should you make to meet changing prices? Should you continue your usual program, greatly reduce the size of the flock, or shift out of egg production altogether when price prospects are not favorable? To answer this question, it is necessary to understand the nature of the costs involved in producing eggs.

We can divide these costs into two categories: fixed and variable. Fixed costs involve such items as housing and equipment. They stay the same, even though you reduce the number of hens or keep no hens at all. Variable costs involve such items as feed and mortality of the hens. In order for you to be better off staying in than going out of egg production in any one year, variable costs must at least be met.

Fixed costs make up only 10 to 15 per cent of all costs when labor is considered a variable cost. Labor is a variable cost if it is hired or drawn away from some other enterprise. But, if the labor is already on the farm and has no other use, you should treat it as a fixed cost. Under these circumstances, fixed costs make up 30 to 40 per cent of the total cost of producing eggs. An egg producer in this situation, with housing and equipment already available, is rarely ahead by dropping out of production when a year of unfavorable price relationships comes along. The price situation is seldom so unfavorable that well-managed poultry flocks do not return enough to meet feed expenses and flock depreciation and mortality costs.

The number of eggs per hen each year necessary to break even with eggs and feed at different prices once you are equipped to keep a laying flock is shown in Table 56. The table shows the average number of eggs per hen needed to cover only the variable items of cost: feed, mortality, and flock depreciation. To get a return for your labor and your investment in housing and equipment, production per hen must exceed this figure.

Level of crowding the laying house

Although farmers ordinarily should not switch in and out of egg production with changing price relationships, they can make some adjustments in the number of birds they keep. The best number of hens to put into a laying house of a given size depends on the relationship between egg and feed prices. The changes in the egg-feed price ratio that have occurred since 1925 are shown in Figure 97. When the prospective egg-feed price ratio is favorable (the number of pounds of feed that can be purchased with the proceeds from the sale of a dozen eggs is high), you can afford to increase the number of pullets put into the laying house. When the egg-feed ratio is unfavorable, it pays to reduce the level of crowding.

Let us see why this is true. As more and more hens are crowded into a given amount of housing space, the added eggs from putting in one more hen declines. This relationship for laying hens of the light breeds is shown in the first three columns of Table 57. For example, the 29th hen put into each 100 square feet of floor space adds 188 eggs and the 30th hen adds 185 eggs. The number of eggs from each additional hen housed in 100 square feet of floor space

Table 56. Average Annual Production Needed per Hen to Cover Feed Costs, Mortality, and Depreciation on Flock with Eggs and Feed Prices at Different Levels*

Price per lb of Feed, cents	Egg Price per dozen, cents								
	20	25	30	35	40	45	50	55	60
	Number of Eggs Needed								
2.5	157	129	110	98	88	79	74	72	67
3.0	184	152	129	115	92	93	86	82	76
3.5	213	174	148	128	116	105	97	92	86
4.0	241	196	166	146	130	117	108	102	96
4.5	269	220	185	163	144	140	120	112	105
5.0	298	242	204	179	159	143	131	123	114

* Average annual production based on the average number of birds in the laying flock through the year. Estimates based on light breeds and assuming the hens are full fed and that a mortality loss of 25% occurs during the laying period.

continues to decline as crowding increases until the 42nd hen adds only 104 eggs.

Where is the best place to stop? Poultry specialists usually recommend stopping at about 33 birds per 100 feet of floor space (or 3 square feet per hen) for the light breeds under usual price

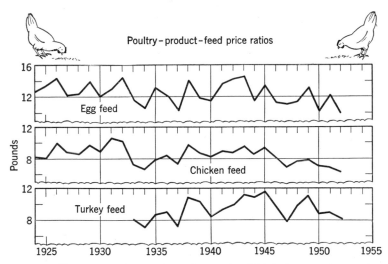

Figure 97. Changes in the number of pounds of feed that can be purchased with the money from the sale of a dozen eggs. (Bur. Agr. Econ. USDA)

relationships. But let us see how the most profitable level of crowding varies with changes in feed costs and egg prices. The principle of balancing added costs and added returns applies here as it did in determining the most profitable amount of fertilizer to use and the best level of feeding grain to dairy cows. Returning again to Table 57, we see that the cost of keeping one more hen is $4.73 (based on 1952 prices). It is profitable to continue adding hens as long as the return from one more hen is greater than the

Figure 98. The best number of laying hens to put into a laying house depends in part on the price of eggs in relation to the price of feed. When the price outlook for eggs is favorable, it is profitable to house more pullets than when the price outlook is less favorable. If carried too far, however, crowding reduces profits from the laying flock. (Courtesy Union Pacific Railroad)

cost of maintaining her. This point is reached with the 28th hen with the price of eggs at 25 cents per dozen, since added costs exceed added returns when the 29th hen is added. However, when eggs are 48 cents per dozen instead of 30 cents (feed costs remaining the same), it pays to crowd 39 hens into 100 feet of floor space instead of only 28.

The information given in Table 57 explains why poultry specialists place so much emphasis on not overcrowding laying houses. Crowding reduces egg production per hen. If it is carried to the point

Table 57. The Relationship between the Most Profitable Level of Crowding Laying Hens and Egg and Feed Prices*

Hens per 100 sq ft of Floor Space	Total Egg Production	Added Eggs from One More Hen	Value of Added Eggs with Eggs Priced at 30 cents per doz	Value of Added Eggs with Eggs Priced at 48 cents per doz	Cost of Keeping One More Hen
28	5,726	. . .			
29	5,914	188	$4.70	$7.52	$4.73
30	6,099	185	4.63	7.40	4.73
31	6,275	176	4.47	7.04	4.73
32	6,445	170	4.25	6.80	4.73
33	6,608	163	4.07	6.52	4.73
34	6,764	156	3.90	6.24	4.73
35	6,914	150	3.75	6.00	4.73
36	7,058	144	3.60	5.76	4.73
37	7,195	137	3.42	5.48	4.73
38	7,325	130	3.25	5.20	4.73
39	7,449	124	3.10	4.96	4.73
40	7,566	117	2.92	4.68	4.73
41	7,676	110	2.75	4.40	4.73
42	7,780	104	2.60	4.16	4.73

* Feed prices were calculated on the basis of 4 cents per lb. A charge for mortality was made at the rate of $1.25 for each hen that died.

where the added returns are less than the added costs, crowding decreases instead of increases total profits from the laying flock.

Using Table 58 will help you in applying the principle set forth above. The first step is to calculate the number of square feet of

Table 58. The Most Profitable Number of Hens per 100 Square Feet of Housing Space with Eggs and Feed at Various Prices

Price of Eggs, cents	Price of 1 lb of Poultry Ration							
	$0.025	$0.0275	$0.03	$0.0325	$0.035	$0.0375	$0.04	$0.0425
	Number of Hens							
25	35	33	31	29	27	25	23	21
30	39	37	36	34	32	31	29	27
35	41	40	38	37	36	34	33	31
40	43	42	41	40	38	37	36	34
45	45	44	43	42	40	39	38	37
50	46	45	44	43	42	41	40	39
55	47	46	45	45	44	43	42	41

floor space in the poultry house. Then you must estimate feed costs and prospective egg prices. When you have done this, you can determine the number of hens you should put into each 100 feet of floor space from the table. Then you can multiply this number by the square feet of floor space you have in your poultry house and divide by 100. For example, if you expect egg prices to average 40 cents per dozen and feed to cost 4 cents per pound, you should house 39 birds for every 100 feet of floor space. If you have 600 feet of floor space in the laying house you should house 234 birds since

$$\frac{600 \text{ sq ft of housing space} \times 39 \text{ (optimum no. of birds for 100 sq ft)}}{100} = 234$$

Timing of Production

Gearing production to meet seasonal price variations is another management problem the egg producer encounters. Although there has been a long-time trend toward a leveling out of seasonal price variations, they are still sufficiently wide to be of importance to the flock owner.

The seasonal price pattern for eggs is fairly stable during the first half of the year. However, in late summer, prices begin to move upward and reach a peak in late September and October. After this, they decline fairly sharply during late fall (Figure 99).

Like egg prices, egg output from a laying flock follows a fairly definite pattern through the year, starting with the time pullets are housed. A typical production pattern for an all-pullet flock, well housed and managed is shown in Figure 100. Production during the first month after the pullets are housed is low, but it picks up rapidly in the second month. It reaches a peak in the third and fourth months. From then on production gradually drops off through the rest of the year because of mortality and additional culling.

To get the greatest gross return, the production pattern shown in Figure 100 must be fitted to the price pattern, so that the months of highest production correspond to the months of highest prices. This would be accomplished most often if pullets are housed August 1, or at least by September 1.

However, this relationship does not mean that you should always try to house pullets by August 1. The cost side of the picture must also be considered. Having pullets mature enough to house by

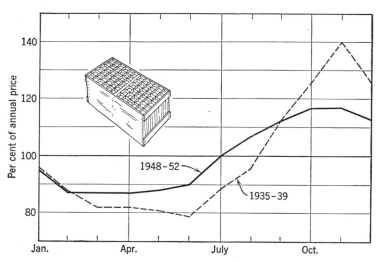

Figure 99. Seasonal changes in egg prices received by farmers. (Bur. Agr. Econ., USDA)

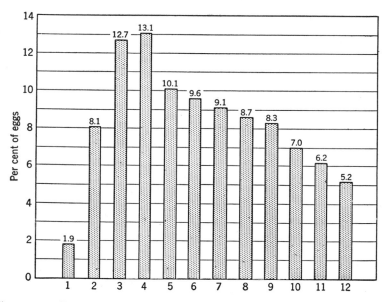

Figure 100. Percentage of total eggs produced each month after housing of pullets.

August 1 results in higher cost and some inconvenience because chicks must be started in late winter. When the costs are considered along with the returns, housing pullets on September 1 is probably the best plan for most flock owners. But, here again, other enterprises on the farm must be considered before a decision is reached. In starting baby chicks, it may be necessary to avoid conflicts with peak labor loads in other enterprises, such as the farrowing season.

Recognizing the Relationship between Costs and Size of Flock

The relationship between the size of the enterprise and the cost of producing eggs should be considered in planning the long-run role of the laying flock in the farming program. The amount of labor required per 100 hens decreases as the size of the flock is increased. The South Dakota study of labor requirements referred to in Chapter 8 (Table 35) indicated that flocks of 100 to 200 birds required 260 hours per hen per year. But flocks of 300 to 500 hens required only 200 hours. It is not difficult to explain why large flocks use labor more efficiently than small flocks. Filling a large feed hopper may take only a little more time than filling a small one. The same is true of the labor needed to water the flock. The amount of labor required to clean the laying house does not increase in proportion to the size of the house. These economies in labor use are most important where the labor involved is an out-of-pocket cost or where the poultry enterprise competes with other farm enterprises for labor. They are of less importance on farms where the poultry enterprise uses family labor for which there is no alternative use.

Investment in housing and equipment per bird declines somewhat as the size of the flock increases. Referring again to the Iowa study, investment per hen averaged $4.62 for flocks of 200 hens, although there was a great deal of variation in this figure among farms. This decreased 45 cents for every 100-bird increase in flock size. For 600 birds, which was the upper limit of the study, the average investment fell to $2.82 per hen.

Managing the Replacement Flock

Poultry specialists usually recommend starting each laying period with an all pullet flock. Pullets lay more eggs than old hens. In addition, disease is usually less of a problem when all the hens are sold each year and replaced with pullets. Under this system the replacement flock becomes a highly important part of the poultry enterprise.

Because the first cost of the chicks makes up a relatively small part of the total cost of raising pullets to maturity, it is best to buy only high-quality chicks. The young flock should be provided with clean range and kept away from the laying flock.

Usually the cost of producing a pullet is greater than her market value at the time she is housed. The Iowa study previously referred to indicated that one would have lost money by raising pullets and selling them on the market in 18 out of the 20 years from 1930 to 1950. For this reason, there is a temptation to raise only the number of pullets that one plans to house in the fall. Egg production per bird can be increased considerably if the pullets are culled rigorously at the time they are housed. Only well-developed, healthy birds should be housed. For this reason egg profits will usually be increased by raising more birds than you plan to keep for the laying flock. For example, if you planned to house 300 pullets, you could raise 400 pullets and cull out 25 per cent or 100 birds at the time they are housed.

The cost of providing the additional number of birds to choose from depends on the cost of feed and the price you can get for the culled pullets on the market. Since World War II the loss on the culls when sold has averaged about $10 per 100 birds housed when they are culled at a 25 per cent rate at housing time. However, an increase in average egg production per bird of 3 or 4 eggs for the year will cover this cost. The increase in egg production that will result from rigorous culling depends on the management given the replacement flock and the quality of pullets raised. But most flock owners should plan to provide for a 25 per cent cull.

Problems

1. Estimate the number of eggs per hen required to meet the variable cost of egg production from Table 56. Use current prices for eggs and feed in your home community.

2. Suppose a farm operator planned to house 300 pullets in the fall. How many pullets do you think he should plan to raise? Why?

3. Analyze the poultry enterprise on your home farm to determine the extent to which it competes with other enterprises for labor. To what extent has the laying flock made use of labor for which there is other use on the farm?

4. Measure the laying house or houses on your home farm. Assume that

current feed and egg prices will prevail during the next year. Under these conditions how many pullets do you think should be housed next fall?

5. If possible, determine the number of eggs that were sold during each month of the last year on your home farm. If you have total egg receipts for each month, you can make a fairly accurate estimate by dividing monthly receipts by the average price received during each month. Disregard the eggs used in your own household. How well do the months of highest egg production correspond to the months in which egg prices were highest? How, if at all, could the timing of egg production be improved? Would altering the timing interfere with other work on the farm? Would more and better equipment be required to care for the young flock?

6. How much more labor do you think would be required to increase the size of your laying flock by 100 birds? How much longer would it take to feed and water the flock? By how much would the time needed to gather and care for the eggs be increased? Would such an expansion require more housing, and more equipment for both the young flock and the laying flock?

References

Beneke, Raymond R., W. R. Whitfield, and Herbert Allen, "Your Egg Business—In or Out," *Iowa Farm Science*, Apr. 1953.

Carpenter, Kendall S., "Estimated Cost of Producing Eggs, New York State 1926–1952," *Cornell Agr. Expt. Sta. Bull.*, Aug. 1953.

Embleton, H., "Profit Calculator for Eggs," *Arizona Agr. Expt. Sta. Bull.* 219.

Hady, F. T., and T. Nodland, "Our Changing Poultry Enterprise and Its Relation to Dairy Cattle and Hogs," *Minn. Agr. Expt. Sta. Bull.* 409, 1951.

Hopkins, John A., and William G. Murray, *Elements of Farm Management*, Chapter 16, Prentice-Hall, New York, 1953.

Hoecker, R. W., "The Economics of the Poultry Enterprise on Kansas Farms," *Kansas Agr. Expt. Sta. Bull.* 308.

Johnson, H. A., S. L. Robertson, and J. W. Sicer, "Profitable Poultry Management on Central Indiana Farms," *Purdue Agr. Expt. Sta. Bull.* 531.

Johnson, H. A., S. L. Robertson, and J. W. Sicer, "Small Poultry Flocks in Central Indiana," *Purdue Agr. Expt. Sta. Bull.* 532.

Kearl, C. D., "Commercial Poultry Farm Management in New York State, 1946–47," *Cornell Agr. Expt. Sta. Bull.* 864.

Kearl, C. D., "Seasonal Cost and Returns in Producing Eggs, New York, 1946–47," *Cornell Agri. Expt. Sta. Bull.* 865.

Peckler, M. J., "Costs of Raising Pullets on New York Farms, 1947," *Cornell Agr. Expt. Sta. Bull.* 859.

Wright, K. T., "Profitable Poultry Management," *Mich. Agri. Expt. Sta. Spec. Bull.* 294.

———— 13 ————

Using Farm Power
and Machinery Efficiently

The widespread use of mechanical power and machinery to replace human labor is one of the principal reasons for the high output per worker on farms in the United States. This has helped to make the income of the American farmer many times greater than that

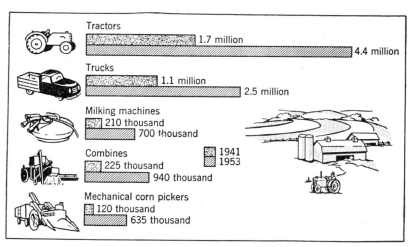

Figure 101. Mechanization has proceeded at a rapid rate since World War II. Increased farm wages and the scarcity of farm labor have made it profitable for many farmers to substitute labor-saving machinery for hired labor. Farmers also had more money to invest in machinery than before the war due to higher incomes. (Bur. Agr. Econ., USDA)

of farmers in other countries of the world where operations are not mechanized. But the use of many costly machines adds to the farmer's management problems. He must constantly be searching for ways in which he can have the benefits of these machines at the lowest possible cost. A Minnesota study of machinery costs on 32 farms showed that crop machinery costs during 1951 varied from a low of $2.09 per acre on one farm to a high of $14.09 per acre on another. This large difference suggests that there are opportunities on many farms to reduce costs and, as a result, increase income through better management of the machinery program.*

Having a complete line of the latest and best machines usually is not a good goal for the typical farm operator. Many farmers have made the mistake of investing too much money in machinery and as a result making themselves "machinery-poor." By being machinery poor, we mean that a farmer's net income is reduced as a result of high machinery expense and that he does not have money for other profitable investments because of the large amount of money invested in machinery.

Management Problems

1. Analyzing the make-up of power and machinery costs.
2. Lowering power and machine costs through increasing annual use.
3. Choosing between custom hiring and owning.
4. Deciding on the size or capacity of machine to buy.
5. Choosing between new and used machinery.
6. Choosing how many and what size tractors to buy.
7. Planning the machinery setup on farms with limited capital.

Analyzing the Make-up of Power and Machinery Costs

What items make up power and machinery costs? What are fixed and variable costs? How is the cost per unit of machine service affected by the amount of annual use? These are the questions that we will seek to answer in this section.

Types of cost in machine operation

The cost involved in doing any field operation with farm machinery can be broken down into a number of parts. For example, the items of cost that enter into using a mechanical picker to harvest corn are as follows:

1. Tractor fuel.
2. Labor.
3. Lubrication.
4. Interest on investment.

* From "Machinery—Servant or Master," S. A. Engene and Niels Rorholm, *Minnesota Farm and Home Science*, Feb. 1953.

Figure 102. The change from hand to machine picking of corn reduced labor requirements of corn production. Mechanization of farming operations is an important factor in the high productivity per worker found on farms in the commercial corn-producing areas. (Courtesy Union Pacific Railroad)

5. Housing.
6. Insurance.
7. Taxes.
8. Depreciation.
9. Repairs.

The only two items on this list with which students are sometimes not familiar are depreciation and interest. Depreciation results from the machine gradually wearing out or becoming out of date. Because most machines do not wear out in a single year, the original cost of the machine is charged off over a period of years. We will study methods of calculating depreciation in Chapter 20.

A charge for interest on investment is not the same as the charge for depreciation. The interest charge is necessary in order to arrive at a cost estimate that will aid the farm manager in making decisions concerning the most economical machinery arrangement. If he must borrow funds for the purchase of machinery, the interest rate paid on the borrowed money is the correct charge to use in computing machine costs. If the farmer has surplus funds above those used in the farm business, then he should charge the rate that would be earned on an off-the-farm loan or investment. The farmer who does not have much money should figure the cost of tying up capital in machinery on the basis of what the same money would yield in other investments on the farm. This problem is discussed more

Figure 103. Harvesting machines such as cornpickers, combines, and hay balers have high fixed costs. As these machines are used on more and more acres each year, their fixed cost per acre decreases. (Courtesy Allis-Chalmers Mfg. Co.)

fully in a later section. In all estimates of machine costs given later in this chapter, the interest rate commonly charged for borrowed funds is used.

Fixed and operating costs

The first three cost items in the preceding list are alike in that their total increases as the amount the machine is used each year increases. Furthermore, the total amount of these items increases in direct proportion to the number of acres on which the machine is used each year. For example, it takes about four times

Figure 104. The fixed cost of owning a plow is low, and most farmers plow a relatively large number of acres each year. For this reason it is economical for most farmers to own a plow with which to do their own work. (Courtesy Allis-Chalmers Mfg. Co.)

as much fuel or labor to pick 100 acres of corn as it does to pick 25 acres of corn. These costs that arise directly from using the machine are known as variable or operating costs. Although the total of these items increases with annual use, operating costs per acre remain the same, regardless of the annual use made of the machine.

The next four items on the list, interest, housing, insurance, and taxes, are different from the first three on the list. Their total remains fixed for the year, regardless of the number of acres of corn harvested with the machine during the year. Indeed, these costs would continue even if the machine were allowed to stand idle during the year. For this reason they are called fixed costs. Estimates of the fixed costs of owning a number of machines are shown in Table 59.

Although the total amount of these fixed items does not change as annual use increases, fixed cost per acre goes down as the machine is used on more acres each year. For example, if the total fixed cost of owning a two-row corn picker was $200 per year, the fixed cost per acre where only 10 acres was picked would be $20. But the fixed cost per acre would drop to $2 if the number of acres picked

Table 59. Prices and Annual Fixed-Ownership Costs for Equipment, 1949 *

Item	Size	Type	Price at Local Dealer	Annual Ownership Cost
Plow, 2-way	1 bottom, 16-inch	Tractor mount	$ 200	$ 33
Plow, 1-way	2 bottom, 14-inch	Tractor mount	160	26
Plow, 1-way	2 bottom, 16-inch	Sulky	200	35
Fertilizer spreader	8 foot	Sulky	150	23
Manure spreader	7 bushel	2-wheel trailer	375	54
Disk harrow	7 foot	18-inch disk	200	32
Grass seeder	8 foot	Broadcast	175	22
Grain drill	8 foot, 16–6	Single disk	420	65
Corn planter	2 row	Fertilizer attachment	225	35
Corn cultivator	2 row	Tractor mount	225	29
Weed sprayer	18 foot	Tractor mount	275	43
Mower	7 foot	Tractor mount	250	39
Side delivery rake	7 foot	Heavy duty	300	36
Baler, 1 man pickup	Medium	Auxiliary engine	2,400	382
Field forage harvester	Large	Auxiliary engine	2,400	334
Blower	10 inch	Auger feed	275	30
Truck	1¼ ton	Platform body	2,000	282

* Adapted from *N. Hampshire Ext. Circ.* 302. In calculating fixed-ownership costs, repairs have been included as a fixed cost.

each year increased to 100. In effect, the fixed costs are spread over more acres.

Depreciation and repairs

Depreciation and repairs are troublesome items in that they do not fit well into either the operating or the fixed-cost category. Part of the depreciation charge is an operating cost while the remainder is a fixed cost. Almost all machines depreciate some with age, regardless of the amount they are used. For example, rubber tires and the canvas conveyors on a combine deteriorate with age. In addition, machinery sometimes depreciates in value or becomes useless because it gets out of date. Much horsedrawn machinery fell into this category when the shift was made to tractor implements. These aspects of depreciation are a part of the fixed cost of using machinery. On the other hand, using most machinery causes it to wear out. A machine that is used on 50 acres per year will not last twice as long as one used on 100 acres each year. But neither will it wear out as rapidly. The part of depreciation that arises directly from using the machine is a part of operating costs.

Repair costs are similar to depreciation in that they sometimes arise out of using the machine and sometimes out of deterioration due to the passage of time. Here again repairs that become necessary as a result of using the machine are operating costs. Repairs that result from deterioration due to the passage of time are fixed costs.

Classifying costs

The nine items of cost involved in harvesting corn with a mechanical picker which were listed previously can now be classified into three groups as follows:

Operating Costs	Partly Operating and Partly Fixed Costs	Fixed Costs
Fuel	Depreciation	Interest on investment
Labor	Repairs	Insurance
Lubrication		Taxes
		Housing

In order to avoid difficulty in classifying depreciation and repair cost, it is a common practice to treat all of depreciation as a fixed cost and all of repairs as operating costs. Classifying all of depreciation as fixed cost overestimates this category of costs. But this is offset by treating all repairs as operating costs. This procedure is only an approximation. However, it enables the farm manager to make estimates that are sufficiently accurate to be useful in planning the farm machinery setup.

Relationship of machine cost to amount of annual use

How does the cost per acre of picking corn change as the number of acres picked annually increases? This relationship is shown in

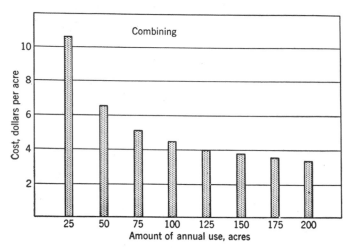

Figure 105. Relationship between the cost of combining and the number of acres combined each year.

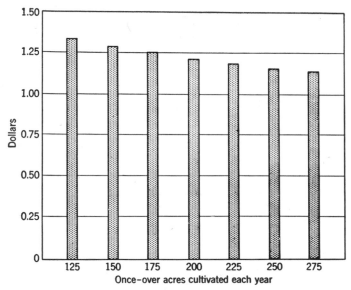

Figure 106. Relationship between the cost of cultivating with a two-row cultivator and the number of acres cultivated.

Table 60. All costs involved in using a two-row machine (not including the cost of hauling or of storing corn) are broken down into fixed and operating costs, and the total cost per acre for different amounts of annual use is given in the last column. You will notice that declining fixed costs per acre are responsible for the decrease in the cost per acre as more acres are picked.

All labor, including operator and family labor, used in the harvesting operation has been charged at $1.50 per hour. In addition, a 5 per cent interest charge has been made on the money invested in the machinery. The exact cost of picking corn per acre will not be the same on all farms as that shown in Table 60, because the cost of labor and other items will vary from farm to farm. But the general relationship between cost per acre and acres picked per year will always be the same as shown in the table.

The relationship between the cost of combining and the amount of annual use is shown in Figure 105 and between the cost of cultivating and annual use in Figure 106. These cost figures include power and labor costs. You will observe that the cost of combining drops more sharply as the amount of annual use increases than the cost of cultivating. This difference can be explained by the larger proportion of combining costs made up of fixed costs. Because

Table 60   Cost per Acre of Picking Corn with a Two-Row Picker*

Acres Picked each Year	Fixed Cost per acre	Operating Cost per acre	Total Cost per acre
40	$5.15	$2.30	$7.45
50	4.12	2.30	6.42
60	3.43	2.30	5.73
70	2.94	2.30	5.24
80	2.57	2.30	4.87
90	2.28	2.30	4.58
100	2.06	2.30	4.36
110	1.87	2.30	4.17
120	1.72	2.30	4.02
130	1.58	2.30	3.88
140	1.47	2.30	3.77
150	1.37	2.30	3.67
160	1.29	2.30	3.59
170	1.21	2.30	3.51
180	1.14	2.30	3.44
190	1.08	2.30	3.38
200	1.03	2.30	3.33

* Does not include cost of hauling or storage.   Labor is charged at $1.50 per hour.

most of the costs of cultivating are operating costs, there is no great advantage in increasing the amount of annual use made of the cultivator. The same is true for all implements with a low fixed cost.

Lowering Power and Machine Costs through Increasing Annual Use

Types of high-cost machine service

Certain types of machinery present no serious management problem. For example, few farmers debate whether or not they should own a plow or a cultivator. The fixed cost is low on both these implements, and the annual use is relatively high. Hence, there are few alternatives available to the farm operator for reducing costs. At the other extreme, few farmers have any other choice but to hire their corn shelled on a custom basis. The fixed cost of owning a corn sheller is high, and the annual use on the typical farm is limited. Therefore owning a power corn sheller is out of the question for most farmers.

But what about machines that fall between the two extremes just pointed out? These create a management problem on a farm that is average or smaller in size. The principal operations that present management problems are:

1. Harvesting forage.
2. Combining grain.
3. Picking corn.
4. Spraying crops.

This is true because in each of these operations the fixed cost of owning the machine is high and the amount of annual use is low.

Ways of increasing annual use

Increasing the amount of annual use is one of the easiest ways of reducing machinery costs on farms average or smaller in size. The amount of annual use can be increased by

1. Doing custom work for others.
2. Owning the machinery in partnership.
3. Making exchange arrangements.

Doing custom work for others

Many young farmers who have skill in operating and maintaining machinery have found that doing custom work for other farmers is profitable. In this way they can spread out the fixed cost of the machine over many units of annual use. As a result, they operate in a range where the fixed cost per acre is very low. This makes it possible for them to provide economical service for their customers while at the same time making a profit for themselves. Whether it will be good business for a farm operator to do custom work for others depends in part on how much his labor and management are needed at home. Most custom operations must be done at a time of the year when crops and livestock are particularly in need of attention. Therefore, there is danger that a farmer will neglect critical jobs on his own farm while doing work for others.

Owing machinery in partnership

Many farmers have successfully increased annual use and decreased costs by working out cooperative ownership arrangements. The most striking example of this is the threshing ring that was popular twenty years ago. Under this arrangement, farmers frequently owned the high-cost threshing equipment together and exchanged work. In recent years, the most common arrangement is for two or three farmers to own hay harvesting machinery, combines,

Figure 107. Before the combine became widely used, a number of farmers frequently owned a threshing machine together. Few farmers had enough acreage to justify the fixed cost of owning a machine for use only on their own farm. Thus they either owned the machine in cooperation with other farmers or hired it on a custom basis. Working together with a number of neighbors also helped in organizing an efficient work crew. (Courtesy J. I. Case Co.)

and corn pickers cooperatively. These arrangements work best when each of the farmers involved has about the same amount of work for the machine.

How large are the savings that cooperative ownership of machinery makes possible? They are sizable, especially when the machine involved is one with a high fixed cost. For example, as shown in Figure 105, it would cost $6.46 an acre for a farmer with 50 acres to own a combine alone and do his own work. But by buying it in partnership with another farmer with 50 acres to combine, he would reduce his costs to $4.39 per acre.

If these arrangements are to function smoothly, it is important that the partners agree on how repairs and other maintenance costs will be shared during the life of the machine. In addition, they should decide before the problem arises who will get to use the machine first during busy seasons.

Exchanging machinery

What advantages does increasing annual use through exchanging machinery have over owning machinery in partnership? Under the typical exchange arrangement, one farmer owns a machine such as a combine and his neighbor owns a cornpicker. The owner of the combine does his own combining plus that of his neighbor. The neighbor does the first farmer's corn in return. Each of the two farmers cooperating in this exchange agrees to do the other's work before he does work for anybody else. For this reason, getting work done on time is usually less of a problem with the exchange agreement than with custom hiring. The fact that each farmer participating in the exchange arrangement knows that the other will be doing work for him serves as an incentive for each to do good work.

In the exchange agreement, the owner of the machine has full responsibility for its upkeep. Since no jointly owned property is involved, the agreement can be terminated simply. If there is a sizable difference in the amount of work to be done on the two farms, an agreement should be worked out in advance, whereby the farmer with the greatest acreage pays prevailing custom rates to the other farmer on the difference in acreage.

Choosing between Custom Hiring and Owning

Operators of small farms can also reduce machine costs by hiring some jobs done. In most communities there are farmers and others who make a business of doing custom work. Since they use a machine to do a large amount of work each year, they have a low fixed cost per acre.

Comparing cost of custom work with owning

Advantages in hiring a custom worker may result from (1) lowering machinery investment and (2) reducing the cost of machine service. In most cases, it will be advantageous to hire only those machines that are expensive and have a high fixed cost. The advantage of custom hiring over owning is much greater where the machine is used on a small acreage. The estimates given in Figure 105 can serve as a basis for comparing the cost of owning with the cost of hiring a combine. For example, it would cost $6.46 per acre for a farmer who had only 50 acres of small grain and beans to combine to do the work with his own machine. If a custom worker is available to do the work for less than this amount, serious thought should be given to hiring the combining done instead of buying a combine.

The procedure that should be followed in determining the acres of annual use at which owning instead of hiring a machine becomes economical is illustrated in Table 61. This acreage is called the break-even point in the table. The procedure is explained on the left side of the table and an example applying the method to a forage harvester and blower is shown on the right side. The example assumes that the farmer already owns two tractors and a truck. In order to have a complete outfit, he would need a second truck. The example also assumes that the farmer, when custom hiring, supplies one tractor, one truck and one or two men. The custom operator supplies the harvester, blower, one tractor, one truck, and two men. You will notice that in the example operating costs and the value of labor furnished by the custom worker are deducted from the rate per hour charged for custom work. The value of this labor should be subtracted only (1) if it plus the farmer's labor is needed in the operation or (2) if it frees the farmer to do other productive work on the farm. Subtracting operating and labor costs from the custom rate gives the amount of fixed cost per hour the farmer can incur in owning the machine and still not have his costs run higher than for custom hiring.

If you are short of capital, hiring a custom worker may be desirable, even though the amount of annual use is somewhat greater than the break-even point calculated by the procedure shown in Table 61. This is true because custom hiring avoids the necessity of your

Table 61. Example Showing How the Break-Even Point between Owning and Hiring a Machine Can Be Estimated *

Step I

From: Price per hour for custom work

From: Price of custom field forage harvesting including harvester blower, 1 truck, 1 tractor and 2 men $13.00 per hr

Deduct:
  Direct operating costs of:
    1. Equipment in question

    2. Supplementary power

Deduct:
  Operating costs
    1. Gas and oil, auxiliary engine on harvester   0.35 per hr
    2. Gas and oil of 1 tractor   0.45 per hr
    Gas and oil of 1 truck   1.00 per hr

  and
  Value of freed labor

  and
  Labor of 2 men   2.00 per hr
  Total deduction   3.80 per hr

Result: Net cost per hour to farmer for custom work

Result: Net cost   9.20 per hr

Step II

Divide:
  Fixed annual ownership cost of the machines

Divide:
  Fixed costs of:
  Field forage harvester $334.00
  Blower   30.00
  Truck   282.00
  Total   646.00 per yr

  by
  Net cost per hour of custom work (result of Step I)

  by
  Net cost of custom hiring (result of Step I)   9.20 per hr

Result: Break-even point expressed in hours of work per year

Result: Break-even point   70.2 hr per yr

Step III

Divide:
  Break-even point expressed in number of annual hours (result of Step II)

Divide:
  Break-even point (result of Step II)   70.2 hr

  by
  Performance rate of the custom operator (hours required per acre of work)

  by
  Hours of work required to field-forage harvest one acre   1.3 hr

Result: Break-even point expressed in acres of work per year

Result: Break-even point   54.0 acres per yr

* From *N. Hampshire Ext. Circ.* 302.

making a fixed-capital commitment and allows you to use your capital in other more profitable alternatives.

Timeliness and quality of work

Some farmers have experienced difficulty in getting custom workers to do satisfactory work. Timeliness of operations also is a problem, especially in those operations in which timing is highly important. For example, the period during which you must harvest hay in order to have a high-quality product is typically short. If there is delay in getting the custom operator to bale or chop hay, a low-quality product is likely to result. The success of farmers in hiring custom operators who work in a careful and timely manner differs greatly from one community to another. These factors must be considered, in addition to the cost, in choosing between owning or hiring a machine.

Deciding on the Size or Capacity of Machine to Buy

Most farm machines can be purchased in several sizes or capacities. Therefore, another decision you are faced with is to select the size or capacity of machine that is best suited to your farm. Choosing between a one- or two-row corn picker, a two- or four-row corn planter, and a 5- or 6-foot combine are some common decisions of this type that farmers must make. The following factors should be considered in choosing the size of machine to buy:

1. The difference in cost between the large and small machine.
2. The amount of use that will be made of the machine each year.
3. The amount and cost of available labor.
4. The financial position of the operator.

Using large machines to do field work requires less labor per acre than using small machines. For example, about 2 hours are required to plow an acre with a one-bottom plow. The same job can be done in about 1¼ hours with a two-bottom plow. Using the larger machine involves a greater investment, but the added investment for the two-bottom over the one-bottom plow is small. On the other hand, the amount of labor saved by using the two-bottom plow is relatively great, because the plow is used on a comparatively large acreage each year on the typical farm. For these reasons most farmers who have a tractor with sufficient power buy the two-bottom instead of the one-bottom plow.

Similarly, picking corn with a one-row picker takes more labor than picking with a two-row machine. However, in this instance, owning the large instead of the small machine requires a much greater investment. Buying the one-row instead of the two-row picker means investing approximately $800 instead of $1,600. The cost of picking corn with the one-row and the two-row machines for different acreages is shown in Figure 108.

If you are interested, let us say, in computing the cost when the machine is used on 60 acres each year, find 60 acres at the bottom of the graph. Then look straight up to the first curve. By glancing from this point to the left side of the graph where the cost is given, you will find that the cost per acre is $5.29 for the one-row picker. To find the cost for the two-row picker, again find 60 acres on the bottom of the graph and then look up to the two-row curve. By looking across to the left side, you will see that the cost of picking

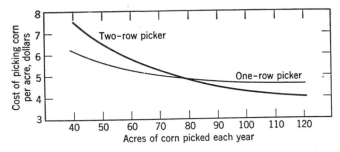

Figure 108. Comparison of the costs of picking corn with a one-row and a two-row picker.

with the two-row machine is $5.79 per acre. You can use the graph in this same way to compare the cost of the one- or two-row picker for any acreage.

Available labor and capital and machine size

If you have many competing uses for the labor available, you may be justified in owning the two-row picker even though you may have less than 70 acres of corn. Under these circumstances, the labor saved by the two-row picker may be very valuable to you, more than the $1.50 per hour we have used in our cost calculations in Figure 108. On the other hand, capital may be limited, and there may be many places on the farm where it will bring a return much greater than 5 per cent. If this is true, it is often wise to buy the smaller machine, or to get the corn picked through a partnership arrangement or through buying a used machine.

Figure 109. Using a large instead of a small machine requires a greater investment but saves labor. One-row corn pickers fit best on farms that have a limited number of acres to pick each year. Where a large acreage is picked each year, the higher machine cost associated with using the two-row picker is offset by the saving in labor. (Courtesy Deere & Co.)

Size of tractor affects machine size

The size of the tractor already on the farm influences the size of the other machines that can be used. Although you could successfully use several different sizes of machines with most tractors, overloading and underloading the tractor is not economical. For example, pulling a one-bottom plow with a two-bottom tractor results in inefficient use of fuel. As a result, power costs will be higher. Overloading a tractor will also result in higher fuel and power costs than are efficient.

High-capacity machines improve timeliness of operations

When timeliness of operations is an important factor, buying a high-capacity machine is often justified. Part of the return from the added investment in larger equipment under these circumstances comes from the higher yields resulting from doing work on time. Timeliness is especially important in choosing between the two-row and four-row corn planter and cultivator. Being able to get the corn planted and cultivated in a short time gives the farm operator a hedge against unfavorable weather. The economy of providing this added capacity depends on the number of acres of corn to be planted and cultivated and the supply of labor available. Large machinery is most easily justified where the work schedule is extremely crowded.

Choosing between New and Used Machinery

What are the advantages and disadvantages of buying used machinery? Where does it fit best? The investment in machinery can be lowered by buying second-hand implements. This does not always result in lower-cost machine service, but the money saved often can be invested more profitably in other ways. This is particularly true on farms where capital is limited.

Used machinery usually fits best on farms that do not have a large acreage on which to utilize it. Second-hand machinery is less dependable than new machinery; field operations are often slower, owing to reduced speed and to more frequent stops for repairs and adjustments. Farmers with a small acreage take less chance of not getting their work done on time if they have trouble.

Although repair costs vary according to the condition of the machinery that is purchased, they are almost always greater on second-hand than on new machinery. Not only will the cash outlay

Courtesy J. I. Case Co.

Courtesy Deere and Co.

Courtesy Deere and Co.

Figure 110. Using a hayloader to put up hay requires more labor than chopping or baling the hay. However, the investment in machinery is less. A hayloader fits best on farms that are short on capital, have a relatively small acreage of hay to harvest, and are not hard pressed for labor during the haying season.

for repairs be greater, but also more of the operator's time will be spent on maintenance and making repairs. Although repair costs are likely to be greater, depreciation costs will be less on used machinery. New machinery often depreciates a great deal during the first year or two of its life.

Because of the greater maintenance requirement involved, you should consider your own mechanical skill in choosing between used and new machinery. If you are skillful in repairing machinery, you will have an advantage over other farmers in buying second-hand machines. Starting with used machinery is often a good idea for beginning farmers because they are likely to be short of capital. They typically have fewer acres to farm, and, as a result, can use a slower machine requiring more upkeep and still get their work done on time.

One of the keys to using second-hand machinery successfully is being able to "buy it right." To do this, you must be able to judge the condition of the used machine before you buy it. If you pay too much for a second-hand machine, you defeat your purpose in buying it instead of a new machine.

Choosing How Many and What Size Tractors to Buy

Most of the farm power used on commercial farms in the United States is supplied by tractors. Electricity is used to supplement tractor power for smaller, stationary jobs. The most important decisions the farm manager must make in regard to farm power are how many and what size tractors to buy.

The make-up of tractor costs is similar to that of other machines. Part of the costs are fixed costs and part are operating costs. Cost per hour declines as the number of hours the tractor is used each year increases. The cost of operating a two-plow tractor under typical field conditions for different amounts of annual use is given in Table 62. The number of tractor-hours required to perform the most common field operations under typical operating conditions is shown in Table 63.

There is enough work on most farms to make the purchase of at least one tractor economical. The cost per hour of service does not decline greatly beyond 600 to 700 hours of use per year. Unless considerable custom work is hired, most farms in the commercial farming areas of the country require this much power.

Many farmers find it difficult to do their work with only one tractor. Should they buy a second tractor? When a second tractor

Table 62.   Hourly Cost of Operating a Two-Plow Tractor*

Annual Use, hours	Fixed Cost per hour	Operating Cost per hour	Total Cost per hour
200	$1.18	$0.54	$1.72
300	0.79	0.54	1.33
400	0.59	0.54	1.13
500	0.47	0.54	1.01
600	0.40	0.54	0.94
700	0.34	0.54	0.88
800	0.30	0.54	0.84
900	0.28	0.54	0.82
1,000	0.26	0.54	0.80
11,000	0.26	0.54	0.80
12,000	0.25	0.54	0.79

* Source: Iowa Agr. Expt. Sta.

is purchased, power costs are increased because the fixed cost on two tractors must be met. These added costs must be weighed against any added returns that will arise from more timely field work. Some farmers lessen the cost of a second tractor by keeping a used or a small one. In many cases, they keep their old tractor instead of trading it in when they buy a new one. This practice enables them to acquire a second tractor of known history at a modest annual fixed cost. When only one tractor is maintained, it is frequently attached to a cultivator, cornpicker, or some other implement. This makes it difficult to use the tractor for other work. Having a second tractor eliminates the inconvenience of either hav-

Table 63.   Tractor-Hours Required per Acre for Machine Operations under Typical Field Conditions*

Machine	Tractor-hours
Combine, 5-foot	0.83
Corn picker, 2-row	0.81
Corn planter, 2-row	0.40
Cultivator, 2-row	0.51
Disc, single, 10-foot	0.32
Disc, double, 8-foot	0.42
Grain drill, 12-foot	0.30
Mower, 7-foot	0.42
Plow, 2-tractor	1.16
Rake, dump	0.30
Rake, side-delivery	0.33
Spike-tooth harrow	0.15
Spring-tooth harrow	0.38

* Source: E. O. Heady and E. L. Barger, *Iowa Farm Science*, June 1948.

ing to remove attached implements or doing without a tractor for other work.

Planning the Machinery Setup on Farms with Limited Capital

If ample capital is available, it is profitable for you to buy a machine if the resulting addition to farm income each year exceeds the annual cost of owning and operating the machine. But farmers short of capital should apply the principle of alternative returns in making machinery decisions. This principle was first explained in Chapter 2.

If capital is limited, all alternative uses for money should be examined before you decide to buy a machine. Capital should be put to some other use in the business if it promises a greater return than adding more or better machinery. However, the farmer with limited capital usually can justify the purchase of a tractor, a plow, a cultivator, and the other basic tillage tools. These implements typically have a high annual use and frequently are not available on a custom basis. On the other hand, justifying the purchase of harvesting machines is more difficult because these require a greater outlay of capital and are used less each year. Furthermore, they can be hired on a custom basis successfully in almost all communities.

Problems

1. On how many acres do you use a combine on your home farm each year? What would be the cost per acre of combining if you owned the machine? How would this cost compare with hiring the work done?

2. Compare the relative costs of picking corn with a one-row picker and a two-row picker on your home farm.

3. Determine the approximate number of hours of use per year for the tractor on your home farm. Estimate the amount of fixed cost that would be added by maintaining another tractor.

4. Make a list of the new machines that you think are needed on your home farm. Arrange it with the ones you consider most necessary at the top. How would purchasing these machines add to farm income? Where else could additional capital be profitably invested on your home farm? Should money be spent for these purposes instead of buying more or better machinery?

References

Case, H. C. M., and Paul E. Johnston, *Principles of Farm Management*, Chapter 10, J. B. Lippincott Co., Chicago, Philadelphia, New York.

Day, C. L., "Hay and Ensilage Harvesting Costs," *Missouri Agr. Expt. Sta. Bull.* 561, 1951.

Frick, G. E., and S. B. Weeks, "When to Hire and When to Own Farm Equipment on New England Dairy Farms," *New Hampshire Agr. Ext. Serv. Circ.* 302, Mar. 1951.

Forster, G. W., *Farm Organization and Management*, Chapter 14, Prentice-Hall, New York, 1953.

Hopkins, John A., and William G. Murray, *Elements of Farm Management*, Chapters 20 and 21, Prentice-Hall, New York, 1953.

Lamborn, Ellis W., "Labor Used and Cost of Harvesting Hay in New York," *Cornell Expt. Sta. Bull.* 855, 1949.

Malone, Carl C., *How to Make Your Farm Pay*, Chapter 5, Iowa State College Press, Ames, 1950.

Rickey, C. B., "Cost per Hour of Using Farm Machinery," *Ohio Agr. Ext. Serv. Bull.* 221 (revised), May 1943.

Robertson, Lynn S., and Ralph H. Woods, *Farm Business Management*, Chapter 6, J. B. Lippincott Co., Chicago, Philadelphia, New York.

Weeks, S. B., and G. E. Frick, "How to Make Money Doing Custom Work," *New Hampshire Ext. Circ.* 303, July 1951.

CHAPTER

14

Using Budgets in
Farm Planning

A budget is a summary of the production, prices, receipts, expenses, and income expected from a farming program. A budget is a means of looking forward into the future. Its primary purpose is to aid in choosing among alternative farming plans by estimating the amount of income that each will yield. Its secondary purpose is to estimate the quantities of inputs such as feed, labor, and cash operating expenses that will be needed during the year. Thus budgeting is essentially a tool to be used in making farming plans. Often the budgeting process involves a comparison of the present plan on the farm with one or more proposed changes. For beginning farmers, the purpose of the budget may be to compare two or more proposed plans that appear to fit the resources of the farm. The procedure followed is similar in both these situations since alternative farming programs are compared in both.

In the previous chapters, we have discussed only segments or departments of the farm business. This was necessary because of the complexity of studying the entire business all at once. But farm managers are interested in getting the highest possible return from the whole farming unit instead of from one or two parts of the business. Working with complete farm budgets will give you a better understanding of the interdependence of different enterprises on the farm. For example, making out a budget may demonstrate how overinvesting in machinery reduces crop and livestock income by diverting capital from them. Or it may show that feeding dairy cows high rates of grain is unprofitable where there is only a limited grain supply and it is diverted from hog production. Budgeting will also make the interdependence of the cropping system and livestock program more evident to you.

You may have observed that few farmers go through the formality of preparing a carefully organized, written budget. Does this mean that farmers do not use budgeting in their planning? Budgets can be very simple and be regarded only as "figuring" by farmers. I have watched farmers and farm management workers make simple budgets on cardboard boxes, shingles, and even granary doors. Even though it is well to go about budgeting carefully and systematically, budgets that are simple and informal may serve a highly useful purpose. Often the process of thinking through and analyzing the alternatives involved in budgeting may be more valuable than the final budget itself.

Many proposed changes in farming plans may seem at first to be relatively limited in scope; on closer examination they involve almost the entire farm business. For example, a change from cattle feeding to dairying usually requires a shift toward more forage in the cropping system also. In addition, the power and machinery setup may have to be changed to provide for putting up more forage. In order to compare the change in income that can be expected from a far-reaching shift such as this, it is best to prepare complete budgets for both the present and the proposed plans.

Management Problems

1. Analyzing the resources of the farm.
2. Choosing the alternatives to be compared.
3. Estimating crop production.
4. Estimating feed requirements.
5. Balancing feed requirements with crop production.
6. Selecting the prices to use.
7. Estimating expenses.
8. Evaluating products used in the household.
9. Summarizing receipts and expenses.
10. Refining the budget.
11. Interpreting the results of the budget.
12. Making out a partial budget.

In order to make our discussion more realistic, we will work out a budgeting problem that was presented to a group of Iowa State College students by a central Iowa farmer. You should follow through the budgeting example carefully. You can duplicate the forms we have used for your own purposes if you care to.

Analyzing the Resources on the Farm

The budget should start with the inputs the operator has to put into the farm business. Often the amount of land and working capital he has or can acquire are limiting factors. Other factors such as buildings, the farmer's own managerial skills, and available markets may also be relatively fixed. It is important to start with these fixed elements in planning a budget.

To get a better idea of how to begin, let us consider the resources of the farmer whom we studied. His farm contained 197 acres of land, 180 acres of which were tillable. The operator, whom we shall refer to as Mr. Brown, was in his late forties, in good health, and a good worker. He owned the farm although he had a small mortgage loan against it. He had two sons, one of high school age, and one several years younger. All the work on the farm was done by the operator and his family, with the exception of hay baling, which was custom-hired.

At the time the farm was studied, its principal livestock enterprises were dairying and hog production. These two enterprises were supplemented by a sizable laying flock. In order to provide pasture for hogs and enough forage for the dairy herd, a CCOMM rotation was being followed. Unfortunately the only outlet available for dairy products was a cream market. There were few other dairy herds in the area and prospects for improving the market for dairy products were not good. Although the herd contained a number of registered Brown-Swiss cows, no attempt was made to sell young stock for breeding purposes. The farm had a conventional stanchion-type dairy barn and was fully equipped for hog production. In addition Mr. Brown had a full line of machinery with the exception of the hay baler.

Choosing the Alternatives to Be Compared

Generally there are many farming programs that can be compared in the budgeting process. However, you should narrow the number down to a few of the most promising before attempting to make out a budget. You will understand why this is necessary when you see how much work preparing a budget involves. In the previous chapters on crop and livestock programs, we have studied how to go about choosing the most promising crop and livestock programs. To do this you must (1) have an understanding of the economic principles involved, (2) know the characteristics of the different livestock and crop enterprises, (3) make a careful evaluation of the resources you have available, and (4) consider the markets available.

Several weeks prior to the time the student committee first met Mr. Brown, he had watched a television program in which crop rotation principles were discussed. The principles presented during the television program were the same as those discussed in Chapter 6. As a result, the operator had been analyzing his own cropping system. He wondered if he were not sacrificing too much grain production in having his level, highly productive land in a CCOMM instead of a CCOM rotation. In addition, he was interested in finding some way to reduce the amount of work on the farm.

One of the plans Mr. Brown wanted to compare was the one he was using. This is usually the situation on a farm where a program is already established. There was a wide variety of alternative plans that Mr. Brown might have considered. However, his knowledge of

Figure 111. Budgeting may be used as an aid in planning the livestock program. (Courtesy Union Pacific Railroad)

rotation principles and a hastily prepared budget of the cropping system similar to the one shown in Chapter 6 led him to conclude that his land should be cropped on either a CCOM or a CCOMM rotation. If he were to change to the four-year rotation, he would need to adjust his livestock program to one requiring less forage. Since he was also interested in reducing his work load, he had to find an enterprise that required less labor as well as less forage. Total grain production would be increased if the rotation were changed from CCOMM to CCOM. Therefore, more grain would be available to feed. Cattle feeding seemed to fit in best with the proposed change in the feed supply and the desire for a lighter work load. A calf feeding program was given first consideration because of the high-quality forage available and the lower risk involved.

Therefore, the problem to be analyzed was this: How would the income from the present system compare with the income from a CCOM rotation if the dairy herd were dropped and feeder cattle added? Since we were interested in comparing incomes that could be expected in the future, we had to estimate the income the present plan was likely to yield in the future rather than what it had returned in the past. We were interested in the past performance of the present program only because it would help us estimate future income. It is important that you understand this point. One of the most common mistakes students make in budgeting is to compare past income from the present plan with expected future income from a proposed plan.

Estimating Crop Production

As we mentioned above, one of the crop plans to be compared on the Brown farm was the existing CCOMM rotation. The other was a CCOM rotation. Agronomic estimates indicated that long-run grain and hay yields would be somewhat lower on a per-acre basis under the latter rotation, but total grain production would be greater. Although less total forage would be produced, this would fit in with

Figure 112. In estimating the crop yields to use in budgeting, you should employ the average yields you can expect for the next 4 or 5 years. You should guard against the temptation to make plans on the basis of unusually high crop yields.

Form I. The Cropping System

Crop	Present Plan Acres	Present Plan Production Per acre	Present Plan Production Total	Present Plan Production Operator's Share	New Plan Acres	New Plan Production Per acre	New Plan Production Total	New Plan Production Operator's Share
Corn	72	62 bu	4,464 bu	4,464 bu	90	60 bu	5,400 bu	5,400 bu
Oats	36	47	1,692 bu	1,692 bu	45	45	2,025 bu	2,025 bu
Soybeans								
Wheat								
Alfalfa-brome hay	36	2½	90 tons	90 tons	20	2½	50 tons	50 tons
Red-clover hay	36				25			
Rotation pasture	3	3	9*	9*	3	3	9*	9*
Permanent pasture								
Lots	4				4			
Farmstead roads waste	10				10			
Total acres	**197**				**197**			

* Animal unit months.

297

the lower forage requirement in changing from dairying to cattle feeding.

In estimating yields, you should guard against the temptation to make plans on the basis of years of unusually high crop yields. Because students are inclined to think in these terms, they have a tendency to overestimate yields. If you intend to follow the plan for some time, you should use the average yields you can expect for the next four- or five-year period. If you are making major changes in the cropping system, acreages and total production may be highly irregular during the transition period. If this is true, you must plan how you will make the transition from your present program to the proposed long-run plan. This will involve a series of year-to-year or short-run budgets. The year-to-year fluctuations in grain and hay yields that will occur after you are following the long-run plan can be evened out by carrying supplies over from good to poor years. Grain, hay, and pasture production under both the old and the new plans for the Brown farm have been summarized in Form I.

Estimating Feed Requirements

Determining feed requirements already has been discussed in some detail in Chapter 8. Few farmers keep sufficiently accurate feed records to enable them to base their estimate of feed requirements on their past feeding performances. In addition, budgeting frequently involves the consideration of livestock enterprises with which the operator has had no previous experience. Therefore, the only practical alternative is to use standards derived from records kept by experiment station workers and by other farmers. Feed requirements for the major livestock enterprises were given in Chapter 8.

Balancing Feed Requirement with Crop Production

Generally it is best to start with the available hay and pasture in balancing the feed requirements with the supply. There usually is no alternative use for pasture; hay is costly and difficult to market.

It is not necessary that the plan make provisions for utilizing all the grain on the farm. Often the livestock program may fit the available labor, capital, and buildings better if part of the grain is sold for cash. In other cases, a plan in which some of the grain is purchased may fit best.

To return to Mr. Brown's problem, he had the capital, the labor, and the equipment for a heavy hog program and a sizable poultry flock. For him, making full use of the feed produced on the farm was a good goal.

The amounts of feed required to support the livestock program on the Brown farm under the present and the proposed plans have been entered in Forms II and III. At the bottom of these forms, requirements have been balanced against the supply. Arriving at the totals involved some trial and error. The size of the calf-feeding program had to be adjusted to make full use of the forage produced. In addition, it was necessary to feed a higher proportion of oats relative to corn than indicated in the feeding standards shown in Chapter 8. Therefore, oats were partially substituted for corn in feeding young pigs on a pound-for-pound basis. If this substitution had not been made, there would have been an even greater excess of oats and not enough corn.

Selecting the Prices to Be Used

In making the budget, it was necessary to predict what prices would be during the period for which the plan was being prepared. The need to formulate expectations concerning future prices is not peculiar to making plans with the aid of a formal budget. All plan-

Figure 113. Budgeting may be an informal process of "figuring" the costs and returns that would accompany such minor changes as increasing the level of feeding grain to the dairy herd, or it may be a careful estimate of the expected costs and income for several different complete farming programs. (Courtesy Soil Conservation Serv.)

Form II. Livestock System and Feed Requirements (Present Plan)

Kind of Livestock	Number of Animals	Corn, bu	Oats, bu	Milk, lb	Skim Milk, gal	Protein Supplement, lb	Legume Hay, tons	Other Roughage, tons	Silage, tons
Dairy cows	16	176	304			2,288	56		
Young dairy stock	11	33	55		834		9		
Bull	1	15	30	3,000			3		
Spring pigs (22 litters)	132	1,936	339		7,000	4,540			
Fall pigs (18 litters)	108	2,041	321		6,250	4,690			
Laying flock	300	186	213			7,050			
Replacement flock	400	72	76			1,500			
Total feed required		4,464	1,338				68		
Total seed required			108				..		
Total requirement		4,464	1,446				68		
Production (from Form I)		4,464	1,692				90		
Amount to be purchased							..		
For sale or carry-over			246				22		

Form III. Livestock System and Feed Requirements (New Plan)

Kind of Livestock	Number of Animals	Corn, bu	Oats, bu	Skim Milk, gal	Protein Supplement, lb	Legume Hay, tons	Other Roughage, tons	Silage, tons
Beef calves:								
Wintering phase	34	250	150		...			
Feeding on pasture	34	1,224			2,240	49		
Spring pigs (22 litters)	132	1,827	527		11,540			
Fall pigs (18 litters)	108	1,841	671		10,940			
Laying flock	300	186	213		2,400			
Replacement flock	400	72	76		1,500			
Total feed required		5,400	1,637			49		
Total seed required			135			: :		
Total requirement		5,400	1,772			49		
Production (from Form I)		5,400	2,025			50		
Amount to be purchased						: :		
For sale or carry-over		0	253			1		

ning must be based on some assumptions of what prices will be. When a farmer plans to farrow pigs, he expects the price of hogs to be high enough in relation to the price of corn to make it worth while to feed the corn to them. When he uses fertilizer, he expects the price of the added yield he will get to be sufficiently high to more than cover the cost of the fertilizer. Often the farm manager who does not use a budget in planning does not define clearly what he thinks prices will be. He subconsciously bases his estimates on past prices. But preparing a budget brings him face to face with the problem of making a clear-cut decision on what he thinks future prices will be. The plans that he makes on the basis of carefully

Form IV.   Estimated Farm Expenses

Description	Present Plan	New Plan
1. Permanent improvements, upkeep, and insurance	$ 270	$ 280
2. Depreciation on improvements	240	300
3. Farm machinery repairs	210	280
4. Tractor fuel, oil, grease	256	306
5. Depreciation on machinery	620	690
6. Taxes, insurance, cash rent	510	510
7. Miscellaneous		
8. Livestock purchased	228	3,492
9. Feed purchased	1,086	1,861
10. Crop expense, seed, and fertilizer	1,226	1,488
11. Machine hire	409	227
12. Livestock expense, veterinary, etc.	767	511
13. Hired labor		
Total expenses	5,822	9,945

formulated price estimates are more likely to be sound than plans based on haphazard guesses.

The relative prices of farm products are particularly important in making long-run budgets. The relationship of the prices of inputs to each other and to product prices are also important to the farmer. This was emphasized in our study of the best combination of protein and grain to feed hogs, the best amount of fertilizer to use on crops, and the optimum rate of feeding grain to cows. But these are short-run decisions. The long-run plan can be adjusted from month to month and from year to year to take into account any shifts in these price relationships.

Past prices are a good starting place for selecting prices to use in the long-run budget. If plans are being made for only a year or two ahead, more emphasis should be given to present prices and the outlook immediately ahead. Average prices for the most recent 5-year period were used as a basis for preparing the budget on the Brown farm. Using an average of several years helps to even out any unusual and temporary distortions in the relationship among prices. For example, the price of corn may rise temporarily relative to other prices after a year in which the corn crop is abnormally short. A budget based only on prices prevailing during such a period would

Table 64. Prices Used in Budget

Hogs
Spring farrowed, marketed in early October	$20.10 per cwt
Fall farrowed, marketed in March	$19.40 per cwt
Packing sows	$15.60 per cwt
Butterfat	$ 0.74 per lb
Eggs	$ .38 per doz
Feeder calves, early October	$24.00 per cwt
Slaughter cattle, choice, early September	$27.00 per cwt
Cows, culled from herd	$17.50 per cwt
Veal calves	$23.00 per cwt
Hens, culled	$ 0.19 per lb
Corn	$ 1.38 per bu
Oats	$ 0.76 per bu
Soybean oil meal	$ 5.20 per cwt
Linseed oil meal	$ 5.00 per cwt
Meat scraps	$ 6.40 per cwt
Dairy feed (18%)	$ 4.60 per cwt
Laying mash	$ 5.10 per cwt
Starter mash	$ 5.80 per cwt
Baby chicks, Leghorn day-old pullets	$32.00 per 100
Fertilizer	
33–0–0	$86.00 per ton
10–20–0	$82.00 per ton
0–20–0	$48.00 per ton

be distorted. But, over a 5-year period, both high and low corn yields would be reflected in the price relationships.

Prices based on an historical average should be adjusted to conform to the long-run outlook. For example, cattle prices during the 1947 to 1952 period were unusually high relative to the prices of other livestock products. Prospects in 1954 were for heavy supplies of cattle. For this reason, the prices of feeder and slaughter cattle used in the budgeting example were adjusted downward from their 5-year average to bring them in line with the long-run outlook.

The prices of commercial feeds, fertilizers, seeds, and similar inputs tend to change relatively little from year to year. Therefore, prices prevailing for these inputs at the time the budget is made are probably as good a basis as any for the budget.

The prices used in the budgeting example are shown in Table 64. They have been presented to enable you to make the calculations involved in the budgeting example, should you choose to do so. You should not accept these prices as appropriate for your situation. You will want to bring them up to date and fit them to the markets prevailing in your area.

In selecting prices, you must be sure to base them on the quality of the products you plan to sell and to consider the time of year that your products will be marketed. The prices shown in the table are for a specific grade of product at a specific time of the year. For example, prices for good-to-choice feeder calves during early October were used. For hogs, October prices were used for the spring crop and March prices for the fall crop.

Estimating Expenses

The amounts of livestock and feed that would have to be purchased under the present and proposed plan were estimated previously and are shown on the bottom of Forms II and III. The quantities to be purchased were then multiplied by the appropriate price, and the result was entered in the proper expense column in Form IV.

Estimating some of the other expenses such as machinery and building costs and repairs is more difficult. If the program presently followed on the farm is one of the plans to be compared, expenses during the last year are the best basis for making these estimates. However, where a change in the acreages of crops is proposed, as on the Brown farm, machinery expenses also will change. In the example, the acreage of corn increased from 72 to 90 and the oat acreage from 36 to 45 acres. Therefore machinery expenses would increase. But they would not increase in the same proportion as grain acreage. That part of machinery and power costs that represents fixed expense would remain unchanged. Variable-expense items such as fuel cost would increase. These relationships were explained in Chapter 13. Baling hay was the only operation that was custom-hired on the Brown farm, and the new plan proposed a decrease in the hay acreage from 36 to 20 acres. Therefore, there would be a decrease in custom hire in changing from the present to the proposed plan.

The only change in building expenses on the Brown farm would result from converting the barn to serve as shed room for housing the beef calves. It was estimated that the cost of this alteration would be $1,000. However, the entire $1,000 cannot be charged against a single year's expense since the improvement would be serviceable over a period of years. Therefore, the $1,000 original cost should be charged off over a period of years. In the example, it was estimated the improvement would be serviceable for sixteen years, and hence the yearly depreciation was figured at $60 per year.

Crop expenses include such items as seed and fertilizer. These should be estimated on the basis of the acreage planted to each crop and the amount of fertilizer that will be used with the cropping system. Livestock expenses consist of such items as veterinary fees and small items of equipment such as teat cups, milk strainer pads, and small hog troughs that are short lived and can be charged off as current expense. Several items such as taxes and insurance usually are the same, or nearly so, for the present and the proposed system.

In estimating expense items, you should remember that, in both the present and proposed plans, you are interested in what expenses are likely to be in the future. You are interested in what they have been in the past only to the extent that the past serves as a guide to the future. Therefore, if any of the expense items have been unusually large or small over the period on which you are basing your estimates, you should adjust them accordingly.

If the two or more plans being compared are all new plans, there is no past experience on the farm to use in estimating expenses. Under these circumstances, cost studies published by the experiment station can be used. They are particularly helpful in estimating such items as miscellaneous livestock expense and power and machinery expense.

Evaluating Products Used in the Household

A part of the income on most farms comes from using products produced on the farm for household consumption. One way to evaluate these products is to put a price on them in line with what they would cost if purchased. Another method is to use the price for which they could be sold. This latter method is the simplest and for this reason is most often used. Whether the meat, eggs, and dairy products to be consumed on the farm are separated from those sold on the market in making out the budget is unimportant. This is especially true if they are evaluated at market prices. We have estimated their value on the Brown farm on the basis of what they could be sold for. Their total under each plan has been entered in Form V.

Summarizing Receipts and Expenses

Receipts and expenses can be entered and prospective net income estimated in Form V. When this was done for the Brown farm, the estimated income for the present plan was $12,224 and for the new plan $12,296. The anticipated income estimated in this way represents a return to the land, the money invested in machinery, livestock and equipment and the labor of the operator and his family.

The farm we used in the budgeting example was owned by the operator. Therefore, it was unnecessary to set aside a part of the crop for the landlord or to enter a charge for rent. When the farm is rented on a crop-share basis, the crop can be divided between the tenant and landlord in Form I. Landlord receipts are not entered in the income summary. Only the expense items borne by the tenant are entered in Form IV, the expense summary. The income estimate reached in this way is a return on the tenant's labor and capital.

Refining the Budget

Even though you have used care in formulating the plans to be compared, you may not be completely satisfied with the most promising plan, once you have completed the budget. Usually some adjustments are necessary. For example, instead of abandoning dairying completely, you may be interested in knowing what would happen to income if a 4- or 5-cow herd were maintained along with some feeder cattle. Or you may be wondering how income would be affected if a one-litter hog program with May or June farrowings were followed instead of a two-litter system.

One way of estimating the effect of these changes would be to make a completely new budget. However, it is usually possible to make minor adjustments by altering the budget that has already been prepared. In following this procedure, you must be careful not to overlook any important changes in expense items.

Interpreting the Results of the Budget

In the budgeting problem we analyzed, the expected income from the new plan was only $72 more than the income anticipated from the existing plan. Moreover, the income under the dairy program (the present plan) could be expected to be somewhat more stable

Form V. Estimated Yearly Receipts and Farm Income

Products to Be Sold	Present Plan			New Plan		
	Quantity	Price	Total Receipts	Quantity	Price	Total Receipts
Beef steers	5,500 lb	$17.50 per cwt	$ 962	323 cwt	$27.00 per cwt	$8,721
Cows (5)	1,440 lb	$23.00 per cwt	$ 331			
Veal calves (8)						
Poultry, culled pullets and hens	1,240 lb	19¢ per lb	236	1,240 lb	19¢ per lb	236
Hogs						
Spring	253 cwt	$20.10 per cwt	5,085	253 cwt	$20.10 per cwt	5,085
Fall	246 cwt	$19.40 per cwt	4,772	246 cwt	$19.40 per cwt	4,772
Sows	88 cwt	$15.60 per cwt	1,373	88 cwt	$15.60 per cwt	1,373
Egg sales	4,480 doz	38¢ per doz	1,702	4,480 doz	38¢ per doz	1,702
Dairy products	4,640 bu	74¢ per lb	3,434			
Corn						
Oats	246 bu	76¢ per bu	187	253 bu	76¢ per bu	192
Wheat						
Other crops						
Labor off farm						
Custom work						
Other income						
Value of products used in household			200			160
Total estimated receipts			18,046			22,241
Total estimated (from Form IV)			5,822			9,945
Estimated farm income			12,224			12,296

than the income from calf feeding. Would this very small increase in income justify the operator's changing to the new plan? To answer this question, we must return to our early discussion of the goals of the farm family. In this case, one of the reasons the operator was interested in changing his farming operations was to lighten his work load. Although expected income under the new plan is not significantly higher, the amount of labor required per year is reduced from about 5,050 hours under the present plan to 4,151 hours under the new plan. Would the family prefer the lighter work load and the greater amount of leisure time to the more stable income available from continuing to dairy? This is a decision that only the farm family can make for itself.

Year-to-year adjustments

Although complete budgets usually involve long-run plans, it is impossible to take into account, when the long-run plan is made, abnormal weather conditions, disease problems, or changes in prices that will occur from year to year. For this reason, short-run adjustments must be made from year to year to bring the plan into line with these changes. For example, a crop failure may necessitate a sharp reduction in hog numbers, or an outbreak of contagious abortion may force a reduction in the size of the dairy herd.

You can also do a better job of predicting what prices will be 3 months in the future than 5 years hence. Therefore, the long-run plan should be altered periodically to fit short-run price expectations. If it appears that the seasonal drop in hog prices will come unusually early, you may be justified in marketing hogs in advance of the usual marketing period, or, if the outlook for poultry is unusually favorable, it may be wise to keep 350 pullets instead of the usual 300 birds.

Thus the long-run plan arrived at on the basis of a budget should not be regarded as hard and fast, but only as a guide to be adjusted to short-run conditions.

Making a Partial Budget

Sometimes planning on the farm involves only a small segment of the business. This would be true of many of the short-run adjustments mentioned in the previous section and some long-term plans. Partial budgets can be used in making decisions of this type. With partial budgets, all costs and returns that would be the same, or nearly so, under the alternative plans being compared, do not enter into the budget.

Suppose you were choosing between selling eggs on the market or selling them for hatching purposes. How would you determine which would be the most profitable? This decision is not interrelated with other phases of the farm business. Therefore, a partial budget is sufficient. The best way to approach this problem is to estimate the returns and costs for each marketing method. However, only those costs that are different under the two methods of selling eggs would enter into our budget. The final product of our budgeting procedure would not be an estimate of net income from each method of selling eggs. Instead it would be a figure telling us how much the income from one marketing outlet exceeded or fell short of income from the other.

Under what conditions will use of a partial budget lead you to the same conclusion as a complete budget? Let us consider a corn-belt farmer who owns and operates 160 acres of land, all of which is tillable, and who has been selling most of the grain he raises. A corn–corn–oats–meadow rotation is followed on the farm, a small beef cow herd of 10 cows is kept, and the calves are fed out. No hogs are raised. Each year some forage goes to waste since the beef cow herd does not make full use of it. The operator is considering adding 10 litters of pigs to the livestock program and is interested in the effect this change will have on income. Sufficient housing is available for the swine enterprise. A summary of a complete budget is shown in Table 65. This summary compares the income that could be expected from the present and the proposed farming program. Changes in receipts arise under the new plan from selling less corn and oats and more hogs. Feed purchases, livestock expenses, and livestock equipment expenses are increased by the addition of hogs. The results of the budget indicate that yearly income would be increased by $590 if he changed from the old to the new program.

In order to prepare the complete budget, all receipts and items of expense had to be estimated. This involved a great deal of work. Could this work be reduced by using a partial budget?

A summary of a partial budget of the same "present" and "new" plans worked out above is given in Table 66. You will notice that the income advantage of the new plan over the present plan is exactly the same for both the partial and the complete budgets. In the partial budget, no attempt was made to estimate cattle receipts

Table 65.   Summary of a Complete Budget

Present Plan

Receipts

Corn	$ 5,879
Oats	1,398
Cattle	2,250
Total receipts	$ 9,527

Expenses

Feed purchases	$ 75
Livestock equipment	50
Livestock expenses	30
Other expenses	3,850
Total expenses	$ 4,005
Expected Net Income	$ 5,522

New Plan

Receipts

Hogs	$ 2,773
Corn	4,292
Oats	1,284
Cattle	2,250
Total receipts	$10,599

Expenses

Feed purchases	$ 427
Livestock equipment	100
Livestock expenses	110
Other expenses	3,850
Total expenses	$ 4,487
Expected Net Income	$ 6,112
Advantage of the new plan over the present plan	$ 590

and expense items (labeled other expenses in the complete budget summary), such as building depreciation and repair, crop expenses, machinery expense, and taxes. It was possible to ignore these items because they were not altered by the addition of the swine enterprise. This emphasizes the chief advantage in using the partial budget; it saves computing many items, especially expense items, that are difficult to estimate.

However, in using this procedure you must be careful not to overlook income and expense items that are significantly different under the two plans being compared. By way of illustration, livestock expenses under the new plan were $50 more than under the present

Table 66.   Summary of Partial Budget

Present Plan

Corn	$ 5,879
Oats	1,398
Partial receipts	$ 7,277
Feed purchases	$ 75
Livestock equipment	50
Livestock expenses	30
Partial expenses	$ 155
Comparative Income	$ 7,122

New Plan

Hogs	$ 2,773
Corn	4,292
Oats	1,284
Partial receipts	$ 8,349
Feed purchases	$ 427
Livestock equipment	100
Livestock expenses	110
Partial expenses	$ 637
Comparative Income	$ 7,712
Advantage of the new plan over the present plan	$ 590

plan. If we had ignored this increase and left miscellaneous livestock expenses out of our budget, we would have exaggerated the advantages of adding hogs by $50. Changes in plans that involve many segments of the farm business should not be budgeted on this basis because of this danger.

The partial budgeting procedure is useful only for comparing the difference in expected income from two or more plans. It does not provide an accurate basis for estimating the amount of feed, cash expenses, and other inputs that will be required for the whole farm business.

Problems

1. Using the budgeting example given in the text, estimate what would happen to income if (1) the Brown farm continued on a CCOMM rotation, (2) the hog and poultry program remained the same, and (3) calves were substituted for dairy cows. Assume that a sufficient number of calves were fed to consume the forage and that added grain was purchased.

2. Make a copy of Forms I and II. Enter on the form last year's crop production on your home farm. Would you consider the yields and cropping

pattern typical? If you were adjusting them to represent the present system in the budget, what adjustments would you make?

3. Make a copy of Form III. Draw up a typical livestock program for your home farm based on the present system. Estimate the amount of feed required yearly, and balance this against the expected feed supply.

4. Calculate the estimated prices received by farmers for the different products produced in your area during the last 5 years. Be sure they reflect local market conditions and seasonal prices that are in line with the time products would be marketed under your present typical plan. Adjust any prices that appear to be out of line with the long-run outlook. Estimate the price of farm supplies (other than purchased livestock and feed grains) on the basis of their current prices. Use 5-year averages for purchased livestock and feed grains.

5. Make a copy of Form IV. Estimate the expenses you would expect in the future under the present typical plan you have outlined in 4 above.

6. Copy Form V from the text. Make a summary of receipts and expenses for your present farming plan. Estimate the long-run yearly income expected under the present plan.

7. What alternative farming plans do you think would fit on your home farm? Be sure to take into account the resources available on the farm. Select the most promising alternative, and repeat the process that you have just gone through for the present plan. Which program promises the greatest income, the present program or your new plan? In view of the goals of your family, do you think you would be justified in changing to the proposed plan?

References

Cunningham, J. B., P. E. Johnston, and M. L. Mosher, "Planning the Farm Business" (examples, blank forms and basic data on which to formulate the plan), Illinois Agr. Ext. Serv.

Efferson, J. Norman, *Principles of Farm Management*, Chapter 18, McGraw-Hill Book Co., New York, Toronto, London, 1953.

"Farm Management Facts and Figures," *Mich. State Coll. Agr. Econ. Mimeo. Rept.* 529.

Forster, G. W., *Farm Organization and Management*, Chapters 6, 7, and 8, Prentice-Hall, New York, 1953.

Hopkins, John A., and William G. Murray, *Elements of Farm Management*, Chapters 8, 14, and 17, Prentice-Hall, New York, 1953.

"Planning the Farm Business," *Purdue Agr. Ext. Serv. Division Agr. Econ. Rev. Pub.* 7.

Planning the Farm Business, prepared by Univ. Nebraska Ext. Serv. and Dept. Agr. Econ.

15

Using Farm Labor Efficiently

Even though much of the labor used on the farm is supplied by the operator and his family, it is typically a scarce resource. Economizing on its use may be fully as important as using land and capital efficiently. Farmers who must depend on hired labor have a continuing reminder of the need to use labor efficiently when they pay the wage bill, but the need for economy also is present where no hired labor is used. Using the existing labor supply more efficiently may make possible an expansion in the livestock program or may provide more time to do some jobs more thoroughly and carefully during busy seasons of the year.

Management Problems

1. Planning the work schedule.
2. Simplifying the chore routine.
3. Managing hired labor efficiently.
4. Deciding how much to invest in labor-saving equipment.

Planning the Work Schedule

Allocating labor among competing uses

During some seasons of the year, particularly during spring and summer, there frequently is not sufficient time to perform every job that should be done. The manager must learn to select the jobs that are most important and give them priority. The principle of alternative returns applies in allocating labor among competing uses, just as it applies in deciding how to use limited capital. If profits are to be maximized, it is not enough for you to use your time and that of your hired workers just doing jobs that should be done. Before undertaking each task, you must always ask yourself if there is any other work that should be given a higher priority.

Oftentimes deciding what to do first is not easy. For example,

I once visited a midwest farm during June where a spell of rainy weather had made it difficult to keep the work up to schedule. As a result, the corn needed cultivating. Some alfalfa that had been cut the previous week and had been rained on several times had to be put up. A June crop of pigs had been farrowed in the cattle

(Courtesy Deere & Co.)

Figure 114. Farm jobs, such as harvesting forage crops and cultivating corn, often compete for the farm operator's attention during the summer months. If both jobs cannot be done at once, the farm manager must decide which job is most important and do it first. (Courtesy J. I. Case Co.)

shed and needed to be moved from the contaminated lots around the farmstead to clean pasture. But before this could be done, some fence had to be built. In addition, the farmstead was in need of a thorough cleaning up, and some fencing materials that had been purchased the previous fall to rebuild a line fence lay unused near the machine shed. Which of these jobs should the farm operator do first? It is quite apparent that cleaning up the farmstead and building the line fence could be postponed without decreasing farm income. But the choice among moving the pigs to clean ground, putting up hay, or cultivating corn first was not an easy one. The operator in this case decided to give priority to putting up the hay.

Seasonal distribution of labor requirements

The fact that the work load on the farm is not evenly distributed through the year complicates planning the work schedule. On some types of farms, such as wheat farms, most of the work for the year must be squeezed into only a few months. On livestock farms, particularly where dairying is important, labor needs through the year

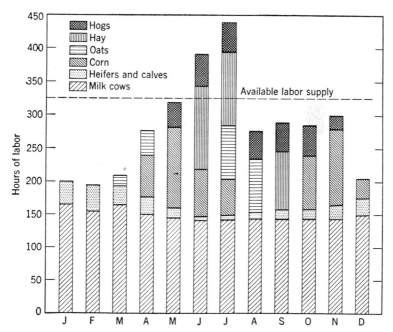

Figure 115. Monthly distribution of labor requirements for crop and livestock production on a small cornbelt dairy farm.

are more stable. A graph showing the hours of labor used during each month of the year on a small cornbelt dairy farm is presented in Figure 115. You will notice that the amount of labor used during the spring and summer months was approximately twice that used during the winter months.

How can farmers best deal with the problem of seasonal labor peaks? One way is to work longer hours themselves during the planting, cultivating, and harvesting seasons. On some farms, housewives or other family members who ordinarily do not participate in the farm work help out for a few days during the busy seasons. In the past, many farmers counted on hiring day labor to take care of peak labor loads, but this is becoming increasingly difficult. Since the peak labor load tends to come at about the same time on all farms in the same area, there is keen competition for what little day labor is available. Some farmers have found that hiring certain operations on a custom basis is one of the best ways to secure additional labor during the busy periods.

Leveling out seasonal labor peaks

Another way to ease the pressure on the labor supply during the spring and summer months is to even out the seasonal distribution of labor requirements as nearly as possible. This can be done in part by selecting the time at which pigs are farrowed, baby chicks started, and cows freshened to avoid conflicts with the field work.

Figure 116. One of the most difficult decisions in managing farm labor is deciding which jobs to do first. Hauling manure is a low-priority job. It should be done at times when field work is not pressing. (Courtesy Union Pacific Railroad)

In addition, there is some flexibility in the time at which certain jobs can be done. For example, manure can be hauled, fences built, and buildings repaired during periods when other work is not pressing. Certain jobs such as planting, cultivating, and harvesting crops must be done at fixed periods during the year. If they are not done then, yields and hence income are likely to be reduced. Lower priority work such as hauling manure and repairing fences and buildings should be fitted around jobs where timing is critical. One rule of

Figure 117. Farmers can prepare for busy seasons when getting jobs done on time is highly important by checking and repairing machinery during slack periods. (Courtesy Wallaces' *Farmer and Iowa Homestead*)

thumb that is useful in planning the work schedule is as follows: During slack periods never put off until later any job that can just as well be done now. But do no work during rush periods that can just as well be put off until later.

It is well to plan ahead so that high-priority jobs can be done with a minimum of delay. For example, you can inspect farm machines and make needed repairs during the winter months instead of waiting until it is time to use the machines. Fences can be constructed ahead of the time when the pigs should be moved to clean ground.

The following check list suggests what jobs might be done during each month of the year. It was designed as a guide for the work program on a general farm. Although the schedule must be modified to fit any one farm, it illustrates the type of planning ahead that leads to efficient use of labor and equipment.

January

Finish income tax work.
Plan budgets for the coming year.
Check all machinery and arrange for necessary repairs.
Purchase all seed, fertilizer, and inoculation material.
Select boar for spring breeding.

February

Order baby chicks.
Test seed oats.
Check housing and brooding equipment for spring pig crop.
Assemble self-feeders, watering equipment, and sun shades for spring pig crop.
Order spray materials.

March

Check all seeding and fertilizing equipment.
Finish any fencing as soon as the frost is out of the ground.
Lay out contours and terraces.
Clean and repair tile outlets.
Begin seeding oats if weather permits.

April

Complete all fencing work during the days when it is too wet for field work.
Begin spring plowing as early in the month as possible.
Earmark gilts from best litters.
Vaccinate and castrate spring pigs.
Arrange for a supply of water for livestock on pasture.

May

Prepare seed bed, and plant corn.
Breed sows for late August and September pigs.
Move young chicks to range.
Begin cultivating corn.

June

Cultivate corn.
Put up hay.
Spray and cut weeds on rainy days.
Arrange for any repair work to be done on buildings during late summer and early fall.
Check grain bins for needed repairs.

July

Complete cultivation of corn.
Harvest small grain.
Put up hay.
Select boar for fall breeding.

August

Fill ditches, and establish grassed waterways.
Make building repairs.
Haul manure.
Prepare for fall farrowing.
Select and separate breeding gilts from spring pigs.
Cull and sell old hens as they molt.

September

Haul manure.
Check corn storage facilities.
Castrate fall pigs.
Clean up around the farmstead.
Harvest soybeans.

October

Harvest corn crop.
Prepare buildings for winter.
Haul and spread limestone and rock phosphate.
Build temporary fence for next year's hog pasture.
Cull late maturing pullets.

November

Check winter watering facilities.
Order seed corn for next year.

December

Take inventories, and close record books.
Analyze outcome of past year's business.

Coping with unfavorable weather

Planning the work schedule on the farm is always complicated by the threat of unfavorable weather conditions. It is necessary to make allowances for the possibility of field work being slowed down by rainy weather. Because timeliness is so critical, it is better to have too much rather than too little labor on hand for such operations as planting and harvesting.

In addition, even if your work program usually is not crowded during busy seasons, you should plan as though it might be. For example, if only a few days are available for planting corn, you should be in a position to take full advantage of them. This means having everything in readiness for the planting operation ahead of time.

Simplifying the Chore Routine

On most farms, livestock chores consume more time and labor than any other job. Studies have shown repeatedly that chore work often takes `considerably more time than necessary because it is done inefficiently. The operators spend too much time in travel. They go through too many unnecessary motions and do their work the hard instead of the easy way.

Once the chore routine is established on the farm, it usually undergoes no major rearrangement but is revised from season to season to include new jobs. For example, when pigs are farrowed or baby chicks purchased, the job of taking care of them is added to the chore routine already being followed. It is easy to make the mistake of adding these jobs to your program without sufficient planning to fit them in smoothly with the routine already being followed.

What steps should be taken to reduce the time and energy needed to do chores? The existing chore routine should be carefully studied and a new one that eliminates as much wasted effort as possible developed. Many industrial plants place a great deal of emphasis on analyzing their operations to see if they can find ways of improving them. These analyses are called time-and-motion studies. In agriculture, this process of analyzing the work routine is called "farm work simplification."

Improving the work routine is a different problem on every farm. It is also a problem that is never solved once and for all because the jobs to be done on the farm are always changing. It is important that you concentrate on developing a questioning attitude toward work routines and learn how to analyze and improve them. To what extent are present work methods dominated by habit and tradition? Have other farmers developed an easier, more economical way of doing a job? It is important that you approach the problem of utilizing man labor just as analytically as you would the problem of using feed, land, machinery, or any other farm resource.

Examples of reduction in chore time

The savings possible through a careful analysis of the chore routine are often striking. For example, a Minnesota farmer with a herd of 13 cows and 14 other dairy cattle reduced his dairy chores from 3 hours and 39 minutes to 2 hours and 45 minutes through study and planning. Much of the savings on this farm came through reduction of the amount of walking by 37%, or a total of 138 miles a year. In addition, the time required for machine milking was reduced, and hand stripping was eliminated. A cart was substituted for pails in feeding grain to cows, the location of the feed supply was changed, and drinking cups were installed. A summary of the savings in time and travel that were achieved are shown in Table 67.

Figure 118. One method of reducing chore time is to make use of feed carts. This reduces the number of trips and the amount of travel. (Courtesy *Farm Journal*)

Chore travel was reduced from 906 to 656 miles, or a total of 250 miles per year, on an Iowa farm where beef feeding, sheep production, and a laying flock were the major livestock enterprises. At the time the study was made, beef cattle were being fed chopped hay which was stored in round cribbing 40 feet from the hay bunk. By arranging the hay racks close to the supply, much of this travel was eliminated.

On this same farm, the feed for the poultry flock was stored 120 feet from the laying house. Under the revised plan, a small bin that

Table 67. Daily Savings in Time and Travel from Improving Work
Methods on a Minnesota Dairy Farm*

	Hours per day			Miles per day		
Jobs	Before	After	Savings	Before	After	Savings
Milking utensil care	2.1	1.5	0.6	0.3	0.3	0.0
Feeding, caring for cows, calves, and other cattle	1.1	0.8	0.3	0.7	0.3	0.4
Cleaning stable, bedding, letting cattle in and out	0.5	0.4	0.1	0.4	0.2	0.2
Total	3.7	2.7	1.0	1.4	0.8	0.6

* S. A. Engene and V. A. Dose, "Saving Seconds," *Minn. Farm Business Notes* 266, pp. 203, Feb. 1945.

could be filled through the wall was built in a corner of the laying house, and the feed supply for the laying flock was stored there. This greatly reduced the amount of the travel needed to feed the laying flock.

The grain fed to beef cattle on this farm was carried in baskets from the granary to the feed bunks. Although this distance was not great, many trips were made each week, and heavy labor was required. To cut down the time and work in this operation, feed was loaded on a wagon each week. After the wagon was covered with a canvas to protect the feed from the weather, it was pulled up alongside the bunk. The feed was then shoveled directly from the wagon into the bunk.

The changes made on both the Minnesota and Iowa farms were, without exception, simple and fairly obvious, once the existing chore routine was examined. No one change made possible great savings in time and travel, but, added together, they resulted in large savings. Nor were the changes expensive. The chief expense incurred on both farms was the cost of building feed storage bins close to feeding areas.

Steps in farm work simplification

The steps that should be followed in making a farm work simplification analysis are as follows:

Step I. Observe the present routine and break it down into many small steps.

It is important that you itemize each step that you take in doing

Pattern of travel using a basket

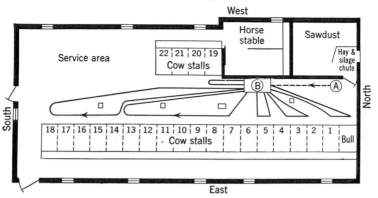

Pattern of travel using a feed cart

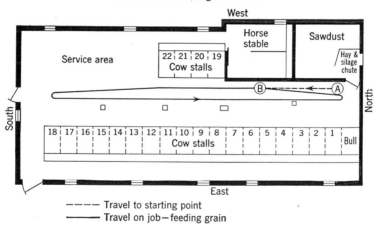

---- Travel to starting point
——— Travel on job—feeding grain

Figure 119. Travel in feeding grain to dairy cows was reduced from 317 to 155 feet by using a feed cart instead of a basket. (From *Vermont Agr. Expt. Sta. Bull.* 503)

a job. Once you have done this, you may be surprised at the number of small details that make up what seemed to be a simple job. In some cases, you may wish to record the amount of time and travel required in each step.

A breakdown of the task of feeding grain and protein supplement to a dairy herd illustrates the many small details involved in doing a job.

1. Go to feed alley at cow no. 1.
2. Get basket.
3. Go to granary.
4. Fill basket by means of shovel.
5. Go to barn, to cow no. 1, with full basket.
6. Feed cows nos. 1 through 10, carrying basket in one hand and using grain scoop with other.
7. Go to granary.
8. Fill basket by means of shovel.
9. Go to barn, to cow no. 11, with full basket.
10. Feed cows nos. 11 through 19.
11. Go to feed alley at cow no. 1.
12. Set down basket.
13. Fill pail with high-protein feed from sack.
14. Pick up pail.
15. Feed cows nos. 1 through 10.
16. Go back past cow no. 1 and across to cow no. 11.
17. Feed cows nos. 11 through 19.
18. Go to feed alley at no. 1.
19. Set down pail.
20. Go to other work.*

A carefully prepared breakdown of a job, such as the one shown above, forms the foundation for a thorough study of the existing routine.

Step II. Question every detail of the existing routine. Why are you performing this detail? Could it be eliminated? If you have convinced yourself that the step is really necessary, you should raise the following questions:

1. Can I do the job in fewer steps and leave out some of the details?
2. Can I combine some of the details or parts of a job or jobs?
3. Can I save time by doing a job at a different place in the chore routine?
4. Are my feeds, supplies, and equipment so located that working and carrying are kept to the minimum?
5. Can I rearrange buildings, or relocate lots, doors, or gates for greater convenience?
6. Is my equipment adequate and suitable for the job?
7. Can hand jobs be made less tiring? †

Step III. Develop the new method, and put it to use.

The new routine can first be planned on paper. But the real test comes when it is applied. It is not unusual to find that some of the

* Reprinted from *Modern Farm Management,* by Boss and Pond, copyright by Webb Publishing Co., 1951, with permission of the publishers.

† From *Farm Work Simplification,* by Lawrence M. Vaughan and Lowell S. Hardin, John Wiley & Sons.

revisions will not work well in practice. However, you should not discard a proposed improvement in the routine too hastily. You may have developed considerable skill in doing your work the old way through repeating the routine many times. For this reason, the new routine may seem awkward the first few times it is followed.

The purpose of work simplification analysis is not to speed up the work. This can be done by working more rapidly or by carrying a heavier load. Instead, its primary goal is to reduce chore time by eliminating and simplifying operations. Even though no savings in time and travel are achieved, changes in the chore routine may still be justified because the work is made less strenuous and disagreeable.

Ways of simplifying the chore routine

Studies of the chore routines on a large number of farms indicate that the most promising ways of saving labor are as follows:

1. *Arranging Work Areas as Close Together as Possible.* Much of the time used in doing chores is spent in walking from one work

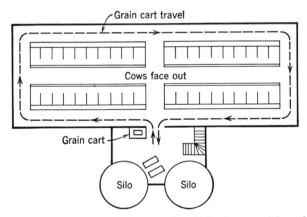

Figure 120. A diagram showing an example of circular travel in a dairy barn. Note that the labor on this task begins and ends at the feed work center. The grain cart is in position for the next feeding. (From *N. Hampshire Agr. Expt. Sta. Bull.* 387)

area to another. For example, you may spend a large amount of time walking from the feed bin to the stanchions, from the hoghouse to the barn or from the milkhouse to the barn. Usually the cost of rearranging large, permanent buildings is excessive, but feed bins can be moved nearer to the feeding area or the milkhouse can be moved closer to the barn at a small cost. Hay can often be stored near the place where it will be fed.

2. Providing for Circular Travel. Travel can be further reduced by providing that something be accomplished on the return trip. Cow stalls and individual hoghouses can be arranged in two rows so that, in feeding or milking, the worker completes the job at the point where he started. This avoids backtracking. In some cases circular travel involves going out of the way a small distance on a return trip to pick up a tool or do a job that would otherwise require a separate trip.

3. Providing an Adequate Number of Small Tools and Locating Them Conveniently. If a shovel is used both in the barn and in the granary, one should be provided for each work area. Tools should also be located close to the area where they will be used. This greatly reduces the walking required to get them and put them back. The cost of having pails, baskets, shovels, and forks readily available to every work area is small compared to the time and effort saved over a period of a year or two.

4. Using Cars, Carriers, or Wheelbarrows Whenever Possible. This serves two purposes; (*a*) it reduces the total amount of travel since a larger load can be taken each time than by hand, and (*b*) it makes the work easier. Carrying feed, water, or manure by hand is not so efficient as transporting them on wheels.

5. Locating Feed Supplies near Feeding Area. Feed bins in the barn, the poultry house, or the hoghouse eliminate much of the travel required in feeding. Feed can be moved periodically from the granary to these storage points with a wagon or truck.

Simplifying other types of farm work

Work simplification analysis is especially useful in analyzing livestock chores which are repeated again and again throughout the year. In addition, a large percentage of the labor utilized on a livestock farm is taken up with doing chores. But this type of analysis is also useful in simplifying other types of operations, particularly those involving hand labor. Studies of tomato picking, for example, have shown that labor requirements can be reduced considerably. The time and work involved in haying operations have also been reduced on farms where a work simplification analysis has been applied.

Managing Hired Labor

It has been difficult to hire capable farm labor in most farming areas since the start of World War II. Farmers have had to compete more and more with other industries for their hired help. As a result, farm wages have risen rapidly, more rapidly than the cost of other farm inputs. The high cost of labor and its scarcity make hiring and keeping a good hired man a major management problem on farms where hired help is needed.

Maintaining good operator-laborer relationships

According to studies, farm workers believe that the following factors are important in maintaining good operator-laborer relationships and in obtaining a high level of performance from hired men.

1. Wages in Line with Those Paid on Other Farms and in Other Types of Employment. Because farmers typically supply their hired help with meat, eggs, milk, and housing, the actual money wages need not be so high on farms as in other industries. Farm workers also stress the importance of wages being paid regularly and on time.

2. Personal Treatment. In an Indiana study of labor-operator relationships, farm laborers rated fair treatment as the factor most important to high worker morale.* They rated this even above good wages. Hired men reported that they appreciated the operator sharing the undesirable jobs and giving them responsibility when their work justified it.

3. Adequate Living Facilities. If the hired worker is married, the type of living facilities that are provided for his family plays an important role in his and his wife's attitude toward the job. In the 1920's most farm workers were single men who lived with the farm family. Since then, farm families have become increasingly reluctant to take workers into the home. The houses provided on many farms at the time the change was made from single to married help were small and poorly built. As a result, poor housing frequently is a serious handicap to keeping hired help.

4. Time Off for Leisure and to Take Care of Personal Affairs. Most workers want some arrangement for regular time-off periods. Workers believe that they should have one day a month or a half a day every 2 weeks for their own use.

* *Purdue Agr. Expt. Sta. Bull.* 546.

Selecting hired men

Because finding a good hired man is so important to the success of the business, the manager should take enough time for the task to make a thorough investigation. In interviewing a prospective hired man, you should determine why the man is interested in working on a farm. He may be a young man who wants to get experience and save money before starting to farm for himself. Young men in this class often make excellent hired men. On the other hand, he may be an older man who lacked the ability or ambition to farm for himself or to find a better nonfarm job. Sometimes individuals who are failures as farm operators make good hired help. They may lack the ability to manage their own time and money wisely but work well when told what to do. In other cases farm workers have never progressed out of the hired-man status because they are lacking in ambition and intelligence. These are factors that count heavily against a prospective hired man. In addition, you will want to find the answer to these questions concerning a prospective hired man: Is he honest? What type of farm experience has he had? Is he a drifter who is constantly moving from one job to another? Why did he leave his last job?

Once a farm operator has found a hired man who is reasonably satisfactory, he should make an effort to keep him. Even though the present man is lacking in some respects, finding a better one often is impossible. The ambitious, intelligent worker who can take responsibility and make decisions on his own is almost impossible to find. Men of this type usually do not spend many years as farm laborers.

Supervising hired labor

Farmers often complain that hired workers do not do their work well. They frequently say that, once their hired man has completed one job, he cannot see anything more to be done. No doubt the fault frequently lies with the worker. But the difficulty can also arise from the failure of the operator to give his hired help proper supervision. The following are some ways of improving the supervision given hired labor:

1. *Give the worker a weekly preview of the work to be done on the farm.* The worker should know several days ahead what the work schedule will be. This will help him know what to do next after he has finished one job. In addition, he is more likely to

take an interest in getting the work out of the way if he understands what must be done.

2. Keep a list of rainy day jobs that need to be done. Unfavorable weather frequently interrupts the work schedule. Because these interruptions often come with little warning, a loss of working time is likely to occur unless plans are made in advance for this contingency. If the operator is not always on hand when these interruptions occur, workers should be given advance instructions on what to do in the event of rain.

3. Make instructions clear and definite. The farm operator should not expect his hired help to know how he wants the work to be done. It is the operator's responsibility to instruct his workers and to be sure they understand the details of a job. Giving instructions clearly is more difficult than most people realize. It is an important part of the manager's job and should not be done hurriedly.

4. Point out the errors the worker makes, but tell him also when he has done a job well. Pointing out a mistake once it has been made will not undo the error. But it will help prevent the worker from repeating the mistake. Few people like to be told they have made a mistake. Therefore, these criticisms should be made tactfully and in a constructive spirit. A worker should also be told when he has done a job well. This helps him to know what you expect and provides him with an additional incentive to do his work well. It also makes it easier for him to accept criticism when criticism of his work becomes necessary.

Wage agreements

Although most workers are hired on the basis of an oral agreement, a written agreement is preferable. As a minimum, the wage to be received along with the "extras" in the form of meat, eggs, milk, and housing should be agreed on. Some farmers have attempted to increase the incentive of their workers by including a bonus arrangement in the agreement.

The simplest and the most widely used bonus plan is to pay the worker a cash bonus at the end of the year, providing he stays through the entire year. This helps to lessen the possibility of hired workers leaving the job in the middle of a busy season. In other cases, the hired man is given a small percentage of the receipts from major enterprises on the farm. For example, one method is to give him one or two dollars for each hog marketed or a small

Figure 121. Some farm operators attempt to give their hired workers a greater incentive to do a good job by letting them share in the earnings of the farm business. The terms of the arrangement should be definite and clearly understood by the worker. (Courtesy *Farm Journal*)

percentage of all hog receipts. On dairy farms, the worker is sometimes given a percentage of the milk check. These arrangements help provide an incentive for hired men to do good work.

The following is an example of a wage agreement containing several incentive provisions. This agreement was made in 1948 between an Iowa farm operator and a married farm employee. Hogs, dairy, and poultry products were the main sources of income on the farm.

    I. Wages per month from March 1, 1948 to March 1, 1949.
        $110 per month. $55 to be paid the fifteenth and $55 to be paid the last day of each month.
    II. Extras:
        Eggs: 3 dozen per week.
        Milk: 2 quarts per day.
        Cream: ½ pint per day.
        Meat: Two 225-pound hogs per year for butchering. One for each 6-month period.
    III. Electricity: Separate meter.
    IV. House, garden, and potato patch large enough for own use.
    V. Chore together every Sunday morning. Chore to be done alone every other Sunday evening.

VI. Bonus:
  A. 5% of egg receipts.
  B. 5% of cream receipts.
  C. 3% of butcher hogs receipts.
     ● 1. Employer reserve right to keep an equal number of gilts
        for sows as in spring of 1948.
       2. Hogs butchered for home use not to be counted in bonus.
       3. Feed purchased will be deducted from gross sales prior to
          figuring bonus.
VII. Bonus will be paid March 1, 1949, providing the employee has stayed
     the full year.
VIII. If any butcher hogs remain to be sold after March 1, 1949, the bonus
      on them will be paid at the time of sale.
IX. The bonus is guaranteed to average $15 per month until March 1, 1949.

Some farmers have attempted to base the bonus on a percentage
of the net income from the farm. This gives the worker an interest
in the outcome of the entire business. Although this method has
much to recommend it, it has several drawbacks. Some farmers object to giving their hired man a full accounting of their business.
In addition, there is an opportunity for misunderstanding to arise
out of the way in which net income is computed. The rate at which
depreciation on machinery and improvements is to be computed is
one source of trouble. The method of evaluating inventories of feed
and livestock is another. If the bonus is based on a percentage of
net income, the methods to be used in computing income should be
agreed on at the time the arrangement is made.

Deciding How Much to Invest in Labor-Saving Equipment and Machinery

Machinery and equipment are partial substitutes for labor. As
we have seen in the previous section, adequate small tools save labor
in the chore routine. There usually is no question of the wisdom
of investing in these small tools because a small investment saves
a large amount of labor. But a number of other types of labor-
saving equipment present more complicated decisions. For example,
should a farmer buy a mechanical barn cleaner or a silo unloader?
Should he install a pressure water system and pipe water into all
of his buildings? These improvements all save labor. But they
also involve considerable quantities of capital.

In deciding how much to invest in labor-saving equipment, the
farm operator must first consider the alternative returns for his

capital. Would buying equipment of this type mean sacrificing a more profitable alternative investment? If this is true, it is usually best to limit the investment in labor-saving devices to those that require a small outlay of capital.

The labor situation must also be considered. If there is heavy pressure on the existing labor supply and more equipment would mean doing a better job, labor-saving devices are particularly advantageous. They are also more likely to be a good investment if they make possible a reduction in the amount of labor that must be hired.

Although we have discussed the problem of labor-saving devices in terms primarily of livestock equipment, the same principles are involved in selecting field machinery. The problem of the best size and type of machine to buy has been discussed in Chapter 13.

Problems

1. Prepare a schedule of the jobs that are done each month of the year on your farm. When does the peak labor load come? Could you suggest any changes in the time at which different jobs are done that would help level out this peak?

2. Have a student repeat a simple job such as folding 10 sheets of paper and placing each of them in an envelope. Time him to see how long it takes. Make a list of each operation that he goes through in doing the job, and analyze the routine. See if you can make any suggestions for doing the job more easily or in less time. Time the revised operation to see how much time it takes. Be sure to let the student doing the job repeat it several times, using his own method, before you begin your study.

3. Draw a map of the chore area on your farm. Walk off the distance between the points where you (or someone else) walk when doing chores. Make a list of all the jobs that are involved in the chore routine in the order in which they are done. Estimate the distance traveled each time the chores are done. How many miles of travel would be required during a year if this same amount of travel were necessary at all other periods of the year? Analyze the routine carefully. Can you suggest ways for reducing the amount of time involved in doing the chores? How large an investment would it require?

4. Draw up what you would consider a good wage agreement on a farm in your community. What extras would you include? What provisions would you include for increasing the incentive of the worker to do his work well?

5. How, if at all, would saving labor increase income on your farm? What additional labor-saving equipment could be used on your farm? How much would each item cost? Which items do you think should be purchased first? Be sure to consider the capital they would require and the labor they would save.

References

Boss, Andrew, and George A. Pond, *Modern Farm Management*, Chapter XXIV, Webb Publishing Co., St. Paul, 1947.

Bradt, C. G., "Are You a Good Boss?" *Cornell Ext. Bull.* 666.

Byers, George B., "Effect of Work Methods and Building Designs on Building Costs and Labor Efficiency for Dairy Chores," *Kentucky Agr. Expt. Sta. Bull.* 589, 1952.

Carter, R. M., "Labor Saving through Farm Job Analysis," *Vermont Agr. Expt. Sta. Bull.* 503, 1946.

Case, H. C. M., and Paul E. Johnston, *Principles of Farm Management*, Chapter 9, J. B. Lippincott Co., Chicago, Philadelphia, New York, 1953.

Dow, George F., "Labor Efficiency in Harvesting Hay," *Maine Agr. Expt. Sta. Bull.* 453, 1947.

Efferson, J. Norman, *Principles of Farm Management*, Chapter 13, McGraw-Hill Book Co., New York, 1953.

Engene, S. A., and V. G. Dose, "Saving Seconds," *Minn. Farm Business Notes* 266, Feb. 1945.

Hopkins, John A., and William G. Murray, *Elements of Farm Management*, 4th Ed., Chapter 19, Prentice-Hall, New York, 1953.

Lloyd, O. G., and Jean C. Evans, "Laborer-Operator Relationships on Indiana Farms (1950)," *Purdue Agr. Expt. Sta. Bull.* 546.

Murphy, Roger G., "Labor in Dairy Barn Chores," *Cornell Agr. Expt. Sta. Bull.* 854, Dec. 1949.

Oberholtzer, J. W., and L. S. Hardin, "Simplifying the Work and Management of Hog Production," *Purdue Agr. Expt. Sta. Bull.* 506, 1947.

Piper, Edward H., "Chore Practices on New Hampshire Commercial Poultry Farms," *New Hampshire Expt. Sta. Circ.* 73, 1946.

Robertson, Lynn S., and Ralph H. Woods, *Farm Business Management*, Chapter 6, J. B. Lippincott Co., Chicago, Philadelphia, New York, 1946.

Vaughan, Lawrence M., and Lowell S. Hardin, *Farm Work Simplification*, John Wiley & Sons, New York, 1949.

16

Planning the Farmstead
and Farm Building Arrangement

The farmstead serves two important functions on the farm. It is the center of business activity; it is the place where the farm family lives. For this reason, the convenience and welfare of the farm family must be given consideration equal to the needs of the farm business in farmstead planning.

One half to three fourths of the working time on livestock farms is

Figure 122. Buildings may contribute to farm income by protecting feed, livestock, and machinery from the weather; by saving labor; or by enabling the dairyman to meet sanitation requirements. Often farm families spend more on buildings than their income-producing functions justify because they like an attractive farmstead. (Courtesy J. I. Case & Co.)

spent at the farmstead. A poorly planned farmstead can increase greatly the labor required to do farm work. The farmstead also constitutes a major investment and an important source of expenses. A study of farmstead costs on 40 Indiana farms showed that interest, depreciation, maintenance and other expense items on permanent buildings and improvements averaged $2,110 at 1947 prices.

How can the farmstead be arranged to serve best its dual function as the center of business activity and family living? How much should be invested in buildings? How can building costs be reduced?

Management Problems

1. Planning the arrangement of the farmstead.
2. Planning farm buildings.

Planning the Arrangement of the Farmstead

One of the difficulties faced in planning the farmstead arrangement is that the buildings are usually already more or less permanently established. Even though a more satisfactory arrangement than the existing one could be worked out, it would be too costly to move the buildings so that they would fit into the new plan. Usually the most constructive step that can be taken toward a well-arranged farmstead layout is to develop a long-time plan. As new buildings are added, they can be located according to the plan. Other less costly improvements, such as windbreaks and drives, often can be made after the plan has been worked out.

Locating the farmstead

Since few people ever have an opportunity to plan the location of a farmstead, we will touch on this problem only briefly. The farmstead itself should be located so that it can be reached easily from the road. Locating it some distance from the highway means that a long lane and the fences that go with it must be maintained. In addition, the long lane wastes land. The farmstead also should be located on a high spot with good drainage. Other things being equal, it is best to have the buildings centrally located in respect to the farm. This reduces travel to and from fields and the amount of fencing required for lanes. If the buildings are placed in the corner of a rectangular-shaped farm, getting livestock to the far end of the farm is difficult.

Factors to consider in located buildings

How should the farmstead be arranged? Where should the buildings be located? The following are the most important factors that should be considered in planning the farmstead arrangement:

1. Efficiency with which work is done.
2. Ease with which the farmstead can be maintained.
3. Appearance of the arrangement.
4. Comfort and convenience of the farm family.

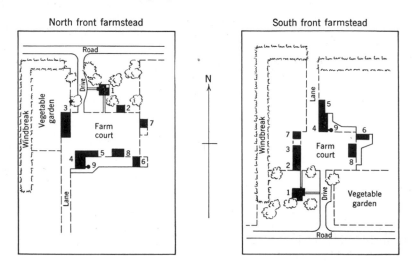

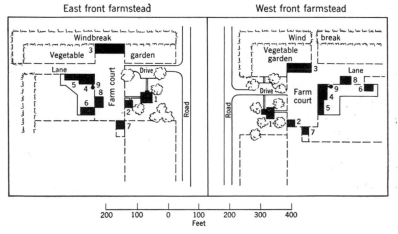

Figure 123. Model farmstead layouts for farmsteads facing different directions.

1. House
2. Garage
3. Machine shed
4. Barn
5. Cattle shed

6. Hoghouse
7. Poultry house
8. Corn crib
9. Silo

The direction in which a farmstead faces influences the way in which it should be arranged. Figure 123 shows four "farmstead layout types": two for north- or south-front farmsteads on an east-west road and two for east- or west-front farmsteads on a north-south road. These layouts follow a simple pattern. Generally, however, it is not feasible to plan an arrangement exactly like one of those shown. However, the model layouts can be used as guides in planning an arrangement that does fit a particular situation.

Figure 124. Windbreaks that are properly placed protect the farmstead from winter winds and reduce the amount of snow collecting around the buildings. (Courtesy Soil Conservation Serv.)

In each of these model layouts, the house is located on a drive approximately 100 feet from the road. Parking space for visitor's cars is provided by the side of the house. The farm buildings are arranged around a rectangular court. Livestock buildings are located on the far side of the court at least 150 feet from the house. Feeding floors are placed on the sheltered side of the livestock buildings. Each of the farmsteads is protected by a windbreak located on the north and west side of the farmstead, about 100 feet out from the area to be protected. This provides sufficient space so that drifted snow will not interfere with farm operations.

Planning Farm Buildings

Farmers can invest an almost unlimited amount of money in buildings. Where should you draw the line? What factors should you consider in deciding how much to spend on buildings? These are the questions with which we are concerned in this section. Let us begin by listing the most important factors you should consider in planning farm buildings.

1. The investment in buildings should be in line with the needs of the farm business and the financial resources of the farm family.

2. The buildings should fit the farming program and farming methods planned for the farm.

3. Where possible, buildings should be designed so that they can be easily adapted to new uses if enterprises or farming methods are changed.

4. Buildings should be so constructed and arranged as to economize on the use of labor.

5. If capital is limited and there is danger of the buildings becoming obsolete, semipermanent instead of permanent structures should be built.

6. Those improvements that promise to be the most productive should be provided first. This is especially important when the amount of capital that can be put into buildings is limited.

Overinvesting in buildings

Farmers frequently make the mistake of putting too much money into buildings. This is understandable, since a good set of improvements is a source of pride for many farmers. Overinvesting in buildings increases taxes, depreciation, and maintenance costs. It also freezes large amounts of capital so that it cannot be used for other investments on the farm. Any investment in building other than the home that will contribute to more income on the farm must be justified in terms of convenience and personal satisfaction, and, therefore, should properly be treated as a luxury. The well-to-do farm family can afford this luxury and is justified in spending its money for a fine-looking farmstead if it chooses. However, the family that is short of capital must take a different view of building investments. Capital invested in buildings often does not yield a return comparable with that from other uses on the farm. It is also poor business to borrow money to build elaborate barns, grain storage, or sheds. Overimproving with borrowed capital has led to financial difficulty for many farmers.

In deciding whether to invest more money in buildings, if you have limited capital, you should always ask yourself in what way such an investment will increase your income. Even if you decide that the annual return would exceed the annual cost, you must still consider alternative uses for the money. Could it be used more profitably in some other investment on the farm?

Fitting buildings to the farming program

In spite of the fact that farming methods have changed greatly in the last half-century, farm building design has changed surprisingly little. There is a tendency for farmers who are constructing new buildings to pattern them after existing structures in the neighborhood. The design of existing buildings may have fitted the farm pattern that was followed at the time they were built, but often it does not serve present-day needs. For example, new hay harvesting methods and grass silage production make the barn with a hay mow out of date on many farms. Present-day sanitation methods in hog production make the central farrowing house a questionable investment.

Although some of the buildings already on the farm may be out of date, it is usually most advantageous to go ahead and use them. Sometimes they can be remodeled at a reasonable cost to increase their usefulness. If they are to be replaced, however, the new structures should be designed to serve best the needs of the future and not those of the past. This may mean replacing a barn with multipurpose sheds and providing hay keepers and silos to store forage, or it may mean substituting portable housing and concrete feeding floors for the central hoghouse.

Flexibility in buildings

Farm buildings usually are built to last for many years. However, the price of one product may decline in relation to the price of another, or the capital and labor position of the farm operator may change. These changes may call for shifts in livestock enterprises. As a result, a building that is designed to serve only a single enterprise may become virtually useless unless it can be extensively remodeled. Many dairy farmers in northeastern Iowa who built expensive dairy barns found them of little value when a declining

Figure 125. Buildings that can be put to many different uses are less likely to become out of date than those built to serve a single purpose. The Quon-

set-type structure shown above can be adapted easily to a variety of uses.
(Courtesy Great Lakes Steel Corp.)

butterfat market led them to change to beef feeding. Changes in farming methods may also cause buildings that are still sturdy and in good repair to become out of date. The change from horses to tractors in recent years has made horse barns obsolete. The increased emphasis being given to sanitation in hog production on many farms has made the central farrowing house less serviceable. Some farmers are wondering currently if artificial drying of corn along with the picker–sheller will make the conventional corn crib out of date in a few years.

What can the farm manager do about this tendency for building needs to change? One possibility is to build low-cost structures designed to last only a few years as there is less chance of short-lived buildings becoming obsolete before they are fully depreciated. Another way is to make the buildings as flexible as possible. Sheds can be constructed so that they can be used for housing livestock or machinery or for storing grains. The pen-type system of housing dairy cows can be adapted cheaply to house other types of livestock.

Much attention in recent years has been given to designing buildings that are adaptable to a number of uses. As a result, a number of plans for buildings of this type are now available. Quonset-type structures, for example, are being used increasingly as multipurpose buildings. The inconvenience and cost of providing flexibility of this type must be weighed against the alternative cost of having to remodel a highly specialized building should the enterprise for which it was designed no longer fit on the farm.

Economy in the use of labor

Most farmers spend more time working around the farmstead than doing field work. Proper arrangement of the buildings around the farmstead is one important factor in achieving efficiency in the use of labor. Because traveling from one work area to another consumes a large percentage of chore labor, buildings should be so located as to reduce travel. Proper design of buildings can also reduce labor requirements. For example, openings on machine sheds should be large enough to permit machinery to be taken in and out easily. If machine sheds are constructed in such a way that getting machinery in and out is difficult, machines often will stand outside during seasons of the year when farmers are busy. Cattle sheds should be built so that the manure can be taken out with a manure loader. Hay-storage facilities should be arranged so that cattle come to the hay instead of the hay being carried to the cattle.

Feed should be stored near the area where it will be fed. Often small bins can be built in barns and laying houses. Feed can then be moved as it is needed from central storage facilities to the smaller bins.

Permanent or temporary buildings

Usually you can choose between buildings designed to last for many years and structures built to last for only a few years. What type should you build?

In the previous paragraph we pointed out that short-lived buildings are less likely to get out of date than permanent structures. The semipermanent building has the added advantage of requiring less capital. What factors should be considered in choosing between semipermanent and long-lived buildings? Let us suppose that you are planning a new barn. You can build a structure with an expected life of 50 years for $8,000, or you can put up a barn expected to last 20 years for $5,000. An estimate of the items of cost per year of each of the barns is shown in Table 68.

Depreciation and repair costs are greater on the cheaply constructed barn, but interest on the money invested is less. In estimating interest on investment, only the average investment over the life of the building has been included. Where the straight-line method of depreciation is used, the average investment over the life of the building is equal to half the original cost.

You will note from Table 68 that the estimate of the yearly cost of the 20-year barn is greater than that of the 50-year barn. Under

Table 68.   Estimated Yearly Cost of a Semipermanent and a Long-Lived Barn

Long-Lived Barn

Depreciation	$8,000 (50 years)	= $160 per year
Interest	4,000 × 5%	= 200 per year
Repairs	8,000 × 2%	= 160 per year
Insurance and taxes	8,000 × 1%	= 80 per year
Total annual cost		$600 per year

Semipermanent Barn

Depreciation	$5,000 (20 years)	= $250 per year
Interest	2,500 × 5%	= 125 per year
Repairs	5,000 × 4%	= 200 per year
Insurance and taxes	5,000 × 2%	= 100 per year
Total annual cost		$675 per year

what circumstances if any would you be justified in building the
semipermanent structure, in spite of its greater yearly cost?   The
answer to this question lies partly in how likely the 50-year barn is
to become obsolete.   If the barn is likely to be out of date in 20

Figure 126. Using temporary or short-lived corn cribs instead of permanent
corn cribs may result in a higher yearly cost of storing corn, but the temporary structure requires a smaller investment. If capital is limited, farm
income may be increased by getting along with temporary cribs and using the
money saved in this way elsewhere on the farm. (Courtesy J. I. Case Co.)

years, it is better to build the short-lived barn. The consequences of investing $8,000 instead of $5,000 in the barn should also be considered in making the decision. In calculating our costs, we have figured the interest on the average investment over the life of the structure at 5 per cent in both cases. This approximates the prevailing interest rate on borrowed money in most areas. But you may be limited in the amount of money you have or can safely borrow. As a result, building the $8,000 instead of the $5,000 barn may mean foregoing other investments in the farm business. Using the $3,000 saved on the cheaper building in other ways may bring a yearly return much greater than $75, the estimated differences in annual cost between the two barns.

We have referred to barns in our example. But you can choose between permanent and semipermanent or temporary structures in nearly every type of building. Corn and hay storage and machinery housing are other good examples.

Making the most important improvements first

Although a few farmers may have sufficient capital to construct every building they need, most farmers do not. They must consider other uses for capital on their farm and make the best use of the limited amount of money they can spend on buildings. In order to do this, they must be sure always to make those improvements first that will contribute the most to the farm business. Under these conditions which improvements should be given priority?

The answer to this question differs among farms, depending on the improvements already available, their condition, and the needs of the farming program. Usually the first money should be used to keep foundations and roofs of buildings already on the farm in good repair. This is true only of buildings that serve a useful purpose. If structures are in very poor condition or cannot be altered to fit the farming program, letting them depreciate without investing more money in them is advisable.

On many farms, remodeling existing buildings is also high on the list. For example, the replacement of horses by tractors has eliminated the need for horse stalls. This space often can be rearranged economically to provide facilities for farrowing pigs or storing hay.

Portable housing for hogs on farms where they are a major enterprise and grain storage facilities should be given high priority. Where labor is in short supply and a heavy livestock program is carried on, money invested in a modern water system is usually a highly profitable investment. On the other hand, housing for many types of machines and paved feed lots are examples of improvements that rank further down the list. Although these improvements can be justified on many farms, it is usually best to postpone them until more pressing needs have been met.

Problems

1. Draw a map to scale of your farmstead, placing each building in its present location. Then locate the buildings on the map in the way you would like to have them. Would such a relocation be practical? How much would it cost? .

2. Are there examples of buildings on your farm that have become obsolete? What changes would be necessary to make these buildings useful?

3. Obtain plans for a semipermanent and a permanent corn crib from your local lumber dealer. Estimate the cost of construction of each crib. How does the cost per bushel of storage space compare? What are the advantages and disadvantages of each type of structure?

4. Make a list of new buildings, improvements on existing buildings, and other improvements that are needed on your farm. Which of these do you think should be given priority?

References

Case, H. C. M., and Paul E. Johnston, *Principles of Farm Management*, Chapter 11, J. B. Lippincott Co., Chicago, Philadelphia, New York, 1953.

"Farm Machinery Housing," *North Central Regional Pub. 31, Illinois Agr. Ext. Serv. Circ. 702.*

Forster, G. W., *Farm Organization and Management*, 3d Ed., Chapter 12, Prentice-Hall, New York, 1953.

Hopkins, John A., and William G. Murray, *Elements of Farm Management*, 4th Ed., Chapter 18, Prentice-Hall, New York, 1953.

"Planning the Electric Water System and Plumbing for Your Farmstead," *USDA Misc. Pub. 674.*

Robertson, Lynn, "Farm Buildings in Relation to Farm Management in Indiana," *Purdue Agr. Expt. Sta. Bull. 435, 1939.*

Robertson, Lynn S., and Ralph H. Woods, *Farm Business Management*, Chapter 10, J. B. Lippincott Co., Chicago, Philadelphia, New York, 1946.

17

Adjusting Production to Prices and Markets

Two centuries ago, production on American farms was aimed largely at supplying products for the household. Only a small part of the output of the farm was sold on the market. The farm family purchased few supplies for consumption and for use in production. As a result, farmers were affected relatively little by changes in prices. But a steady shift away from this subsistence type of agriculture has been under way, until today farmers in some areas sell nearly their entire output and buy many supplies for use in production. Because of his dependence on markets the fortunes of the farmer are closely associated with prices—prices of the products he sells and of the equipment and materials he buys.

Prices of farm products are constantly changing. They rarely remain stable from year to year or even from day to day. What is the nature of these price movements? To what extent should farmers attempt to adjust their business to them? We have already discussed the problem of gearing livestock production to seasonal price changes, and some of the adjustments that are possible in hog, dairy, and poultry production. In this chapter we want to consider adjustments to price changes from the standpoint of the whole farm unit.

Management Problems

1. Adjusting production to long-run price changes.
2. Adjusting production to cyclical price changes.
3. Using outlook and market news information.
4. Adjusting to government price-support programs.
5. Buying farm supplies.

Adjusting to Long-Run Price Changes

If you observe the pattern of farm price movements over the last 100 years, you will see that prices have moved up and down in three

or four great cycles. The long-run changes in the price of farm
products since 1800 are shown in Figure 127, along with the wholesale prices of nonfarm products. The price changes in this graph
are presented in the form of index numbers. The indexes used are
an average of the prices received for all farm products with each
product weighted according to its importance. The indexes show
the relationship of prices each year to those received in the 1909
to 1914 period. For example, if the index is 200 for any one year,
it shows that the average price of farm products that year was twice

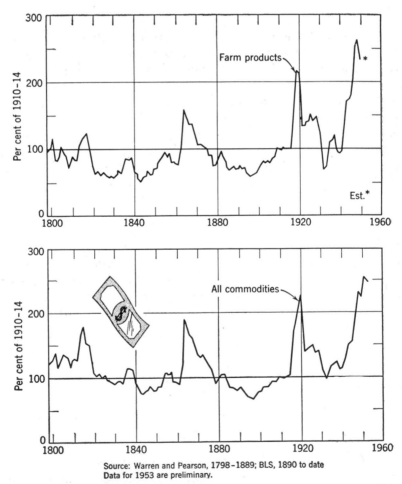

Source: Warren and Pearson, 1798–1889; BLS, 1890 to date
Data for 1953 are preliminary.

Figure 127. Wholesale prices of farm products and of all commodities.
(Bur. Agr. Econ., USDA)

as great as it was in 1909-14; if the index drops to 50, the average price was only half as high as in 1909-14.

Returning again to Figure 127, notice that farm prices reached one peak in the early 1800's, a second during the Civil War, a third after World War I, and a fourth after World War II. After these peaks, farm prices have broken sharply each time. They reached their lowest points in the early 1840's, during the 1890's and in the early 1930's. The upward phase of these long-run movements is usually called an inflation or a boom. The downward phase may be referred to as recession, if it is mild, or as a depression if the price decline is prolonged and severe.

The causes of these ups and down are highly complex. The major inflationary periods are clearly related to wars. But, beyond that, there is no simple explanation for the depression periods that have occurred. It is beyond the scope of this discussion to investigate the causes of depressions and booms. Certainly, to a very large extent, they are due to factors from outside of agriculture and are beyond the control of farmers.

Types of adjustments

During periods of increasing prices, farm product prices typically rise more rapidly than the prices of things farmers buy for use in the farm business (Fig. 128). As a result, farm incomes rise. What adjustments to rising prices should farmers make in their business? During these periods, the margin between the cost of producing products and their selling price widens. For this reason farmers can increase their income by concentrating on a high volume of output. They can afford to sacrifice some efficiency and economy in production in order to have a greater output to sell at high prices. Hog production can be expanded even though the added litters are not cared for as well. Cows that would normally be culled from the dairy herd can be kept in order to increase total output. Fertilizer can be used at higher rates.

On the downward side of the cycle, farm product prices drop more sharply than farm costs, and farm income declines. Under these conditions, the emphasis should be on low-cost production. Enterprises that have been expanded to the point where costs are high, in order to take advantage of favorable price relationships, should be cut back. Dairy herds and laying flocks should be culled more closely. Fertilizer should be used more sparingly.

As we noted in our study of farm credit, falling prices place a

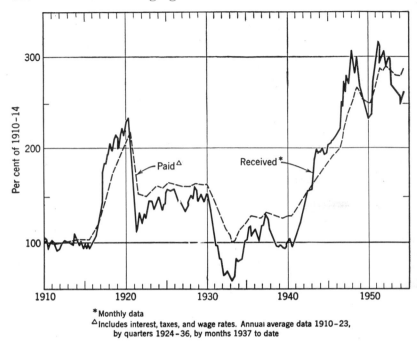

*Monthly data
△Includes interest, taxes, and wage rates. Annual average data 1910-23,
by quarters 1924-36, by months 1937 to date

Figure 128. Farmers' prices. (Agr. Marketing Serv., USDA)

particularly heavy burden on the farmer who uses large amounts of credit. For this reason, credit should be used sparingly when declining prices are in prospect. At the same time, renting on a cash basis is less desirable because cash-rental rates typically do not decline so rapidly as farm prices.

In addition to these adjustments, falling income often forces the farmer to make adjustments that he would prefer not to make. For example, he may have to reduce the amount of hired labor and do more work himself, or, if he has been hiring no labor, he may find it necessary to change to enterprises that can absorb profitably more of his own labor such as dairying and poultry production. Farmers also can reduce their purchases of farm machinery and labor-saving devices during periods of low income. They can spend more time keeping their present machinery in repair and making it do. Major repairs on buildings can be postponed. Like families in other occupations, farm families also can adjust to lower incomes by reducing their living expenses.

Adjusting Production to Cyclical Price Changes

If you examine price changes more closely, you will find that the prices of some farm products have moved up and down in shorter but fairly regular cycles at the same time that broad swings in the level of all farm prices were occurring. Each cycle usually extends over a period of several years. An example of cyclical price movements is the pattern that hog prices have followed over the last 80 years. This pattern is shown in Figure 129. You will notice that prices rise for two or three years, reach a peak, and then decline for a year or two. The cycles are not all alike. Some are shorter

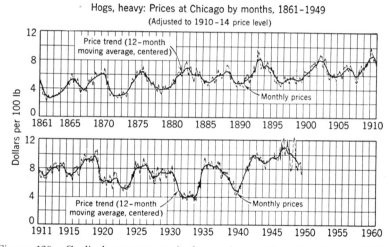

Figure 129. Cyclical movements in hog prices. (Bur. Agr. Econ., USDA)

than others, and some do not rise as high or fall as low as others, but a cyclical pattern is clearly evident.

What is the cause of these more or less regular ups and downs in hog prices? They are closely related to fluctuations in supplies reaching the markets. The supply changes, in turn, seem to arise out of shifts in the relationship between hog and corn prices. This relationship is commonly expressed in terms of the corn-hog ratio. The corn-hog ratio indicates the number of bushels of corn required to buy 100 pounds of pork. It is computed by dividing the price of 100 pounds of pork by the price of a bushel of corn. When the corn-hog ratio is high (corn is cheap relative to pork), converting feed into pork is profitable.

Now let us examine how these cycles seem to come about. Suppose we start with a situation in which there is a relatively large corn crop. Corn prices are low relative to hog prices. Farmers are thus encouraged to feed corn to hogs. They expand hog production, and the larger supply tends to depress the market. That a favorable corn-hog ratio does stimulate hog production is illustrated in Figure 130. In turn, a drop in hog numbers takes place as farmers respond to the less favorable corn-hog ratio. Eventually, as supply dwindles, hog prices rise. The situation once again becomes favorable for processing corn into pork, and the cycle is ready to repeat itself.

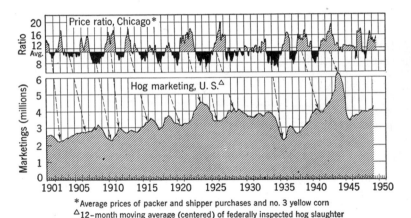

*Average prices of packer and shipper purchases and no. 3 yellow corn
△12-month moving average (centered) of federally inspected hog slaughter

Figure 130.   Relationship between the corn-hog price ratio and hog marketings, 1901-49. (Bur. Agr. Econ., USDA)

Cattle prices seem to follow a somewhat cyclical pattern. However, the cycles are not so regular, and the number of years from one peak to another is greater than with the prices of hogs. The explanation of the cattle cycles is similar to that for hogs. Cattlemen anticipate more favorable cattle prices. As a result, they hold back more young stock for breeding purposes. This tends to reduce supplies temporarily, causing prices to rise, but eventually supplies build up once herds have been expanded, and then the downward phase of the cycle begins. The cyclical fluctuations in cattle numbers are shown in Figure 131.

Farmers clearly create problems for themselves when a large percentage of them tend to increase or decrease their output of a product at more or less the same time. Should the individual farmer try to avoid following the crowd? Should he attempt to adjust his production so that he is producing at full capacity when prices are at the peak of the cycle?

Some good farm managers argue on one side of this question and some on the other. One school of thought contends that it is costly and inefficient to expand and then decrease production in response to expected price changes. They argue that many of the costs of production stay the same (are fixed costs), regardless of the amount one produces. Persons holding this view think that farmers should attempt to find the best combination of products, organize the farm business to fit best the available resources, and then stick to the

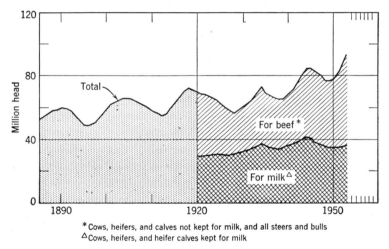

* Cows, heifers, and calves not kept for milk, and all steers and bulls
△ Cows, heifers, and heifer calves kept for milk

Figure 131. Cattle on farms January 1. (Bur. Agr. Econ., USDA)

program. Other farm managers believe it is best to shift the emphasis given to different enterprises from time to time as prospective prices change. For example, when price prospects for hogs seem unusually good, they will increase the number of sows farrowed, or, if prospects for cattle feeding do not look promising, they will reduce their cattle feeding operations or drop out of the market altogether for a year or two.

The question of which plan to adopt is not easy to answer. It depends to some extent on the type of farming being undertaken. Dairying and beef raising are not flexible enterprises; it is not easy to shift in and out of them. Therefore only minor adjustments can be made. For example, as was explained in Chapter 11, the level of feeding grain to dairy cows should be adjusted to changes in the ratio of feed costs to milk or butterfat prices. If part or all of the calves produced by the beef breeding herd are usually fed out, there is an opportunity to make some adjustments in feeding. When price prospects are favorable, all of the feeders can be fed out, but, when the outlook is not so favorable, the calves can be sold instead.

The make-up of the costs involved in production must be considered in deciding whether year-to-year shifts in enterprises should be made. As we have observed before, part of the costs of producing all types of farm products are fixed costs; they continue, regardless of the quantity produced. Housing and equipment costs in all types of livestock production are largely fixed. In hog production and beef raising and feeding, these cost items are not an important part of total costs. They are somewhat more important in dairying and poultry. Other items of cost may also be fixed. If labor is already available on the farm and would become partly unemployed from shifting out of an enterprise, it should be treated as a fixed cost. The same is true of pasture and unmarketable roughages such as corn stalks and straw.

Variable costs consist of such items as feed, veterinary expenses, and electricity. These costs can be avoided during any one year by dropping out of production.

It is best to cut back or drop out of an enterprise during any year (1) if one does not expect to meet variable costs or (2) if a more profitable use can be made of the feed, labor, and housing in some other enterprise. These shifts from one enterprise to another must be planned and carried out several months or even a year ahead of the time the product will be marketed. Farmers who lack skill in forecasting prices run the risk of shifting production at the wrong time. They may reduce hog numbers when price relationships turn out to be the most favorable, or they may shift into cattle feeding during the wrong year. Farmers who maintain a stable program do not run this risk. They are "in" during both good and bad years. To be successful with a flexible program, a farmer must be prepared to spend considerable time in studying outlook information.

Using Outlook and Market News Information

Farmers need information on future prices for two reasons: (1) to help them plan their farming programs as we discussed in the section above, and (2) to help them make short-run marketing decisions.

Many complex forces help determine what the price of farm products will be. The prospective supply is one important factor. On the demand side, the level of employment and the demand from foreign countries have important effects. Actions of the government such as purchases for the military or price-support programs also have had an important influence during the last 20 years.

A farmer is not in a good position to gather information on the many factors influencing prices. He may look around the neighborhood and decide that other farmers are reducing hog numbers, or

Figure 132. The demand and the price for farm products are often influenced by factors far removed from a farmers local vicinity. The level of industrial employment is a good example. Studying outlook reports is an excellent method for farmers to keep in touch with conditions that influence the price of their products. (Courtesy Monsanto Chemical Co.)

he may observe that his city friends are employed at good wages, but he is in a position to gather information about only a limited segment of the whole economy. National trends that finally determine prices may be moving in the opposite direction from those the farmer is able to observe in his local vicinity. To make intelligent estimates of future prices, it is necessary to have information on what is happening in other parts of the country and even in other parts of the world.

The government and state colleges have set up facilities for gathering and analyzing economic trends that influence prices. Specialists interpret and summarize economic information and pass it along to farmers through outlook letters, radio talks, and outlook meetings. Several commercial organizations also perform a similar function.

The science of predicting prices has not developed to the point where predictions can be made with a high degree of accuracy. Usually prices are not predicted directly in outlook reports. The reports provide background information on supply and demand conditions, and often some indication of the direction in which prices are expected to change is also given. The following statement from the *Iowa Farm Outlook Letter*, published by Iowa State College, illustrates the type of economic information on the nonfarm sector of the economy that is often given in outlook reports.

Observers now see more signs of a downturn. Steel output has been below the rate of last spring for some time. Scrap steel has nosedived. Automobile output seems too high to hold up. Housing starts have dropped. Farm machinery output has dropped and the industrial machinery industry expects to cut its output by next year. All these signs point to a slow-up in the durable goods sector of our economy.

Inventories have been mounting. Industrial output has been slowing down.

Yet, personal and business incomes continue at record highs. Prices have been reasonably steady in recent weeks. Retail sales are high. Unemployment is as low as any time since World War II.

However, government spending during the 1954 fiscal year will be less than estimated earlier. The lion's share of this cut will come out of the military. For the first time in several years, we face a future in which we have lower government spending coinciding with other forces which are tending to produce less vigorous business.

Statements of this kind are important in that they give some indication of the demand that is likely to exist for the things that farmers have to sell.

Outlook publications often provide more definite information on the prices farmers can expect. An illustration of this is the following statement from the South Dakota weekly *Farm and Ranch Outlook Letter*, published in August of 1953.

Present prospects indicate that egg prices should continue quite favorable this fall and early winter. In the remaining months of 1953, egg production is likely to be slightly higher than during the fall months of 1952, since the number of laying hens is expected to be the same or somewhat greater and the rate of lay higher. However, part of this increase in output will be offset by the smaller holdings of storage eggs. These supply prospects, therefore, suggest that prices to farmers in the last part of 1953 and early 1954 will be very close to prices received during corresponding months a year earlier.

This discussion was preceded by a more detailed analysis of the factors likely to influence the supply of eggs. Information of this kind is of aid in helping farmers decide how closely to cull the pullet flocks and how many of last year's hens, if any, to hold over.

Even though you make a careful study of all the information available, you still will not be able to predict price trends with absolute accuracy. Studies of the accuracy of price predictions in outlook publications show that the economic analysts preparing them have a good record for being right, but they occasionally have been badly in error. You must be content with doing a better job of judging prices and markets through studying outlook information than you could by guessing.

Market news information

To do a good job of marketing, you should study market news information in addition to outlook information. In contrast to outlook material, market news information concentrates on the short run—the next few days ahead. It tells you what products of different grades are currently selling for on various markets. It provides information on current and expected receipts of livestock and grain. Knowledge of these conditions will help you to choose the best time and place to market.

The differential among markets in the prices paid for livestock of the same quality is usually about the same. But occasionally, owing to local supply or demand situations, sizable spreads of a temporary nature may develop. Market news information can help producers take advantage of these price spreads in their selling.

The U.S. Department of Agriculture has reporters at all major markets. These men observe and report the activities of those buying and selling on the market, including the prices asked by sellers, the bids made by buyers, and the prices that finally result. The information the reporter collects at the market is sent to newspapers and radio stations, by whom it is passed along to the farmer. Some news agencies have reporters of their own located at market centers to supplement the information supplied by the market news services.

If you have grain or livestock to sell, you can keep in touch with the market through general newspapers, the radio, and special market newspapers. In addition, you should check prices at local dealers or small packing plants located close by. Prices available at these outlets usually are not reported through the market news services.

Adjusting to Government Price-Support Programs

Since 1933, the prices of many farm commodities have been supported either directly or indirectly by the government. These supports often determine the price a farmer will get for his product.

Figure 133. Government programs frequently require that farmers make difficult decisions. For example, corn producers must decide whether to qualify for a government loan on their corn crop by participating in an acreage control program. (Courtesy Wallaces' *Farmer and Iowa Homestead*)

Frequently they also create added problems for the farm manager. Sometimes he must decide whether to participate in an acreage control program, or he must weigh the advantages of storing his grain under a government storage program or selling it on the open market.

The details of price-support measures change from year to year. For this reason, we will not attempt to examine the exact provisions of the current programs. Instead, we shall look briefly at the history of governmental price-support activities and examine how they function.

Although several attempts were made during the 1920's to bolster sagging farm prices by government action, the present methods of support had their origin with the passage of the Agricultural Adjustment Act of 1933. This Act declared that it was the policy of Congress to seek a balance between the production and consumption of agricultural commodities that would give farmers "parity" prices for their products. Since the parity concept has become the central theme of price-support measures, let us see what it means and how it is computed.

The 1933 Act declared that the period from August 1909 to July 1914 should be used as the basis for determining when the prices of the things that farmers sold were in balance with the prices of the items they bought. They defined this balance as parity. The parity price of a commodity, using corn as an example, was to be computed as follows: The average price of corn on farms in the United States during the August 1909 to July 1914 period was 64 cents per bushel. The prices paid by farmers for consumption and production items was 3 per cent higher in June of 1933 than in the base period. Thus, if the purchasing power of corn was to be in line with the 1909–14 period, it would be necessary that the price of corn also be 3 per cent higher than during the base period. Thus, the parity price of corn in June of 1933 would have been 64 cents × 1.03 or 65.9 cents per bushel. Actually the price at that time was only 56 cents per bushel.

Essentially the same procedure has been used to arrive at parity prices since then. Adjustments have been made from time to time, with the major change coming in the early 1950's. At this time the method was changed so that the parity prices of a number of important products would reflect market price relationships of the most recent 10-year period.

At no time have attempts been made to support prices at 100 per cent of parity. In the early days of the program, prices on basic crops (corn, cotton, peanuts, rice, tobacco, and wheat) were supported from 52 to 75 per cent of parity. Since that time, the level at which prices should be supported has been the subject of much controversy among farm leaders.

Storage of nonperishable crops has been one of the principal methods of supporting prices. The government, through the Commodity Credit Corporation, offers nonrecourse loans at the support level.

The crop is given as security. However, since the loan is a non-recourse loan, the government accepts the grain instead of the money in case the farmer decides not to repay the loan. It will be to his advantage to let the government take the grain if the market price does not rise above the loan rate. Of course, if the market price does rise above the loan rate, the producer will be ahead by repaying the loan and selling the grain on the market. Farmers must provide suitable storage for the crop. One of the difficult decisions farmers sometimes face is whether to invest in additional storage facilities in

Figure 134. Government price-support programs play an important role in determining the prices farmers can expect for their products. One method that the government uses to support prices is to store grain after years of large crops and to release it when supplies are short. (Courtesy Wallaces' *Farmer and Iowa Homestead*)

order to take advantage of the loan privilege or to sell at a lower price on the market. The amount by which the loan rate exceeds the market rate is the most important factor in determining whether additional storage is justified.

In order to prevent the accumulation of excessively large stocks of stored products, provisions were made in the price-support legislation for acreage control and marketing quotas. To qualify for commodity loans, producers are required to cooperate with the acreage control program when supplies become large enough so that acreage reduction is considered necessary. Marketing quotas provide that only the output produced on allotted acres can be marketed without a tax penalty. However, producers are given the opportunity to vote on whether or not they want marketing quotas when supplies reach a certain level. To be put into effect, the quotas must be approved by two thirds of the producers who vote. In the event that producers do not approve marketing quotas, the level at which prices are supported is reduced.

Acreage control measures usually allow each producer to decide if he wants to participate in the program. If he chooses not to reduce his acreage, however, he forfeits the opportunity of participating in the commodity loan program. This creates another important problem for the farm manager. For example, should he reduce his corn acreage to conform to his allotment, or should he follow his usual cropping pattern? The answer for any one farm depends on the past cropping pattern and how the acreage shift will affect the livestock program. In some cases, owing to the complementary relationship between forage and grain crops, the reduction in corn acreage may increase rather than decrease total corn production over a period of years. This might happen if the farm operator had been following an exploitive cropping pattern and the reduction in corn acreage led to more grasses and legumes being included in the rotation. Farmers in this position undoubtedly would profit by cooperating in the acreage reduction program.

The answer is not as clear-cut for the cash-grain farmer who has been following a rotation that maximizes his total output of grain. If he participates in the program, he will reduce total production, but he will get a somewhat higher price for his product. It should be pointed out, however, that the nonparticipant also receives some of the benefits from the acreage reduction and the storage programs. These measures tend to bolster the market price for the corn he sells. In the final analysis, whether he would be ahead by not reducing his acreage and as a result sacrificing his loan privileges depends on the spread that develops between the market and the support price.

The livestock farmer who has organized his farm to feed all of the grain and forage he raises would benefit by participating in acreage reduction only by sealing his own corn and buying corn on the market. Typically, he can buy corn at a somewhat lower price than the support level. Again, the wisdom of participating in the program depends on how great this spread turns out to be. Sealing your own grain and buying feed requires some additional storage space to accommodate the purchased grain.

Satisfactory methods of supporting prices of products that are not easily stored have not been worked out. Attempts have been made to bolster the price of potatoes, butter, and eggs through storage, but they proved costly since storage costs were high and large quantities spoiled or were destroyed. Other efforts have been made to support the prices of these products through government purchase for the school lunch program, public relief, and public institutions.

When prices are supported by government purchases through regular marketing channels, the farmer has no direct decisions to make on his participation in the program, but he will want to know what commitment the government has to support prices and how prices will be supported. He will need this information before he can do a good job of judging future price trends and planning production and marketing.

Buying Farm Supplies

Today many farm families buy nearly all the items they consume, as well as many of the inputs used in the farm business. The change from horses to tractor power has resulted in farmers buying tractors instead of raising colts on the farm. Tractor fuel has replaced farm-raised feeds as a source of energy. Commercial feeds are now used in livestock production to supplement feed grains grown on the farm. Fertilizer, baby chicks, seed corn, and electricity are among

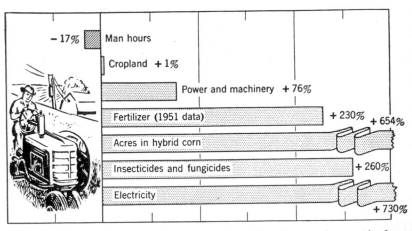

Figure 135. The quantity of inputs purchased by farmers for use in farm production has increased greatly since pre- World War II years. As a result, buying farm supplies has become increasingly important in managing the farm business. (Bur. Agr. Econ., USDA)

the other items that farmers now purchase. The volume of these purchases has increased by leaps and bounds during the last three or four decades. For example, a 1952 study showed that the value of inputs purchased in Iowa (measured in terms of 1950 dollars) has increased twenty-fold in the last 40 years.

This rapid expansion in the use of purchased inputs has increased the importance of the farm manager's purchasing activities. Farm accounts of 160 farmers in southeastern Minnesota show that they purchased an average of $8,932 worth of livestock, feed, machinery, fertilizer, and other items used in production during 1952 (Table 69). What can the farm operator do to improve this phase of his business? How much time can he afford to spend in purchasing activities? These are some of the problems we will consider in this section.

Important factors in buying

One of the skills basic to doing a good job of buying is the ability to evaluate what you are buying. This is a difficult task because many improvements are taking place in farm supplies and equipment. Antibiotics have made the evaluation of feeds more complicated. New forms of fertilizer have appeared on the market. Ma-

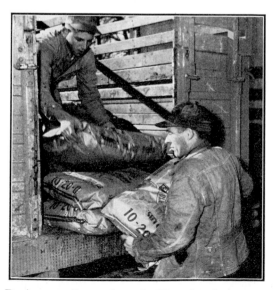

Figure 136. Buying supplies such as fertilizer has become an increasingly important function of the farm manager. (Courtesy Wallaces' *Farmer and Iowa Homestead*)

chinery design has been changing rapidly. You must keep abreast of these developments in order to buy inputs that best fit the needs of your farm. This is fully as important as buying the inputs at a reasonable price.

Intelligent buying also requires that you keep informed on the going prices of the things you are buying. The selling price of many farm purchases are arrived at through a bargaining process. This is true of farm machinery and livestock and to a lesser extent of other items such as feed and fertilizer. You will be at a disadvantage in bargaining if you do not keep informed on values. The seller of most of the items that farmers buy is a specialist in that he deals in them everyday. He is more likely to be in close touch with the market than the typical buyer. If you offer to pay more than the

Table 69. Average Purchases on 160 Southeastern Minnesota Farms, 1952 *

Livestock	$1,418
Miscellaneous items used in livestock production	323
Feed	2,383
Machinery	1,628
Machinery repair and service	566
Gasoline and oil	1,021
Building and fencing materials and labor	1,349
Miscellaneous items including insurance	244
Total	$8,932

* Adapted from *Univ. Minn. Dept. Agr. Econ. Rept.* 209.

going price for an item, you can be sure the dealer will accept your offer. But, if your bid is below the going price, the well-informed dealer will not agree to make the sale. Thus, a poorly informed buyer will err only in the direction of paying more than an item is worth.

You must be careful to make a distinction between major and minor items in your buying activities. The savings possible through careful buying in making a $1,000 purchase are likely to be much greater than on a $100 item. You should also give greater emphasis to those purchases for which the price is arrived at through a bargaining process. The price on some items tends to be established by the dealer and to be the same from one dealer to another. Usually there is little advantage in trying to get a better buy on items sold in this way.

Sources of information on prices

There are several ways that you can get information on the prevailing market for different items.   One is to check with neighbors who have made similar purchases.   A second method is "to shop around" and contact a number of sellers to see how their prices compare.   For feeder cattle, information on the prices of various weights and grades is available through the livestock market news services.

Figure 137.   Many farmers buy feeder cattle at livestock auctions.   Buying in this way requires experience and skill of the buyer because in a short time he must judge the quality of the cattle and decide how much he will pay.
(Courtesy Union Pacific Railroad)

Many farmers find that attending farm auction sales and livestock auctions, in addition to providing entertainment, helps them keep in touch with the market.   Farmers' wives sometime complain that their husbands have attended auction sales for years without buying anything.   However, the time used in this way still may have been well spent if it helped the farmer keep in closer touch with current prices.

When to buy

Because a wide variety of purchases must be made on most farms, keeping sufficiently well informed to do a good job of buying is time-consuming. One of the things the farmer must guard against is spending too much time in purchasing activities. He must be careful that he does not lose more by neglecting work on the farm than he saves by doing a good job of buying. This is especially important during busy seasons of the year.

These conflicts can usually be avoided by making major purchases during slack periods. Such items as farm machinery, fertilizer, and seed can be bought in the winter when sufficient time can be devoted to the transactions without neglecting farm work. Similarly, fencing and building materials can be purchased during the late summer and fall months when field work is not pressing.

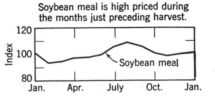

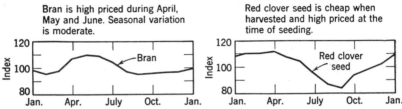

Figure 138. Seasonal price pattern of soybean meal, bran, and red clover seed. Based on prices prevailing from November 1946 to October 1950. Yearly average = 100.

Seasonal price movements are also an important factor in buying some inputs such as commercial feeds and legume and grass seed. Soybean oil meal prices are typically highest in the summer and lowest from November until April, the period of heaviest production; red clover seed is cheapest in September, at the time of harvest, and rises to a peak in the early spring months at the time of seeding (Fig. 138).

The extent to which a farmer should attempt to adapt his buying to seasonal price movements depends on the storage facilities he has available and his capital position. Buying feeds and seeds when prices are low for later use requires that suitable facilities be available for storing them so that their quality can be maintained. In addition, this practice uses up capital so that it cannot be utilized elsewhere on the farm. As a minimum, the farm operator should keep only a small inventory of commercial feeds on hand during the season of the year in which the price trend is downward and build up his inventory when prices are at their seasonal low. Generally it is advantageous to buy grass seed in the fall because of the sharp seasonal rise in price in the winter and the relative ease with which the seed can be stored.

Obtaining help in buying

Buying is so important to the success of cattle and lamb feeding that many feeders seek the help of specialists. One must be able to judge quality in order to do a good job of buying livestock. Many inexperienced buyers lack this ability. Order buyers who specialize in helping feeders with their buying are available at most feeder markets. The farmer tells the buyer the type and quality of livestock he wants, and the buyer attempts to fill his order. In return, the farmer pays the buyer a commission for this service. Other feeders purchase through local buyers who ship feeder lambs and cattle in from the range.

Buying through an order buyer does not insure that feeder animals will be bought right. The farmer himself must make the decision concerning the best time to buy. At the best, all the order buyer can do is to insure that the feeders are bought in line with the current market price and that the farmer gets the quality for which he pays. There is always the possibility that the order buyer's judgment will be in error or that he will not be reliable. Hence care must be exercised in selecting the order buyer.

Many experienced feeders would rather trust their own judgment and do their own buying. In this way they save the commission charged by the order buyer. Which is the best practice to follow depends on the ability of the farmer to analyze the market, to judge quality, and to bargain.

Problems

1. Bring the hog cycle shown in Figure 129 up to date. In which phase of the cycle do you think prices are now?

2. Determine the present corn-hog price ratio, using prices you could get for corn and hogs at local markets. Do you think the ratio is favorable for hog production?

3. Examine all the sources of outlook information available in your school library. After studying the outlook for hogs and eggs, predict what you think the prices of eggs will be 2 months from now. Arrange a contest among a number of fellow students to see who can come the closest to the actual prices. Be sure you agree definitely on the quality, weight, and market you are using in your prediction.

4. Examine the sources of market news information available to you. Are any publications available that are devoted primarily to market news information? Which newspapers furnish the most complete information? What are the advantages of radio market news over that found in daily papers?

5. Find out from the publication *Agricultural Prices* what the current parity prices are on the chief farm products sold in your community. Are present prices above or below parity?

6. Make a list of the items purchased for use in the farm business on your home farm. Rank them according to their importance.

References

Boger, L. L., "Seasonal Price Changes of Major Michigan Farm Products," *Mich. Agr. Expt. Sta. Spec. Bull.* 355.

Case, H. C. M., and Paul E. Johnston, *Principles of Farm Management*, Chapter 13, J. B. Lippincott Co., Chicago, Philadelphia, New York, 1953.

Cox, Clifton B., H. A. Stuckenschneider, and Don Paarlberg, "Marketing Hogs in Northeastern Indiana," *Purdue Agr. Expt. Sta. Bull.* 561.

Efferson, J. Norman, *Principles of Farm Management*, Chapter 10, McGraw-Hill Book Co., New York, Toronto, London, 1953.

Forster, G. W., *Farm Organization and Management*, Chapter 21, Prentice-Hall, New York, 1953.

Hopkins, John A., and William G. Murray, *Elements of Farm Management*, Chapter 11, Prentice-Hall, New York, 1953.

Paarlberg, Don, "Seasonal Variations in Indiana Farm Prices," *Purdue Agr. Expt. Sta. Bull.* 566.

"Price Programs of the United States Department of Agriculture," *USDA Misc. Pub.* 683.

Robertson, Lynn S., and Ralph H. Woods, *Farm Business Management*, Chapter 11, J. B. Lippincott Co., Chicago, Philadelphia, New York, 1946.

18

Adjusting to the Risks in Farming

No doubt you have heard farming referred to as a big gamble. Farmers say this because they must put their money and labor into enterprises without knowing for sure what they eventually will get in return. The following are some of the risks in farming:

1. Price changes.
2. Unfavorable weather.
3. Disease.
4. Human failings.
5. Insect damage.
6. Actions of the government.

Prices

Price changes are the most troublesome uncertainty in farming. When a farmer makes production plans, he never can be sure of the price he will get for what he produces. For example, cattle prices often change sharply from the time feeder cattle are purchased until the fattened animals are sold, or hog prices may decline severely from the time sows are bred until the pigs are raised to market weight. Government price-support measures have partially stabilized the prices of some farm products, but they have not effectively stabilized livestock prices, particularly those for cattle and sheep, enterprises that involve a high degree of price risk.

Weather

Farm production is subject to many kinds of weather hazards. During some years, a lack of rainfall reduces crop yields and shortens the supply of pasture. During other years, too much moisture drowns crops or reduces ultimate yields by delaying field operations. Early frost and hail are also hazards in some areas. Windstorms sometimes also destroy buildings and crops.

Figure 139. Farming involves weather and disease risks as well as price risks. Farmers must pay out most of the cost of producing a crop of corn without knowing how much corn they will finally harvest in the fall. (Courtesy Wallaces' *Farmer and Iowa Homestead*)

Disease

Disease takes its heaviest toll in livestock production. All classes of livestock involve some disease hazard, but it is a particularly serious problem in hog, sheep, and poultry production. Although measures can be taken to reduce the chance of disease, they are often costly, and there is always the danger that they will not be effective. Plants also are susceptible to a wide variety of diseases. This is especially true of truck crops and small grains.

Human uncertainties

Production must be guided and carried out by human beings, and farmers must deal with many individuals in managing their business. Human beings are often unpredictable and sometimes make mistakes. A creditor may become uneasy and press for premature payment of a loan, or the landlord may become disgruntled and threaten to terminate the lease. Farm machinery can be damaged severely by a careless operator. Sometimes a hired hand may decide to quit during a critical season. Illness or injury to the operator, a member of his family, or a key hired worker during a critical period may handicap farming operations.

Insect damage

A wide variety of insects interfere with farm production. Worms sometimes destroy corn as it is coming up. Chinch bugs, grasshoppers or cornborers may seriously damage or destroy growing crops.

Actions of the government

Since 1933, actions of the government have played an important role in farming. Farmers can never be sure how acreage control, marketing quotas, and price-support measures will affect their operations from one year to another. Dairymen producing grade-A milk often face the risk that changes in sanitary regulations will either put them out of the market or necessitate changes in their barn and equipment.

Management Problems

1. Deciding how much risk to take.
2. Selecting methods of adjusting to risk.
3. Planning the farm insurance program.

Deciding How Much Risk to Take

In discussing farming goals in the first chapter, we pointed out that, almost without exception, farmers are interested in making money. Most of them also prefer to keep the risks they must take to a minimum. There are exceptions, however. Some people enjoy taking risks. We commonly refer to them as gamblers.

Let us turn to a highly imaginary situation to illustrate the typical attitude toward risk and the consequences of this attitude. Suppose you have shipped to Chicago a carload of cattle worth $20 per hundredweight on the current market. Imagine further that there is a buyer who stands ready to flip a coin with you. If it comes up heads, he will pay you $50 per hundred pounds for the cattle, but, if it comes up tails, he will pay you nothing. We will not inquire at this point why the buyer is willing to make such an offer, but we will assume, for the sake of the illustration, that you know he is honest. If you sold your cattle on this basis, you would return from the market either with a large check or with nothing.

If you repeated this procedure year after year, you would average $25 instead of $20 per hundred for your cattle over a period of years. Would you be willing to sell cattle on this basis? If you are like most farmers, you would prefer the smaller but surer return to taking a chance on a greater return.

This same attitude carries over into organizing the farm business. Some managers plan their operations primarily to avoid risk, and are willing to sacrifice income to do so. They tend to pass up opportunities that are usually profitable but involve some risk of loss, in order to concentrate on other enterprises that are more certain.

How much risk should a farmer take? The answer depends largely on his financial position and family responsibilities. He should place the protection of his business from bankruptcy ahead of higher profits. If a large loss would seriously handicap his operations and make it difficult for him to support his family properly, he should not risk it. Beginning farmers are frequently in this position. They often are hard pressed financially. In addition, they frequently have heavy family responsibilities. On the other hand, the well-established farmer with a financial backlog is in a position to take risks. He can suffer a loss one year and still "make it back where he lost it" the next year. However, it is not unusual to find that older farmers who are financially secure are reluctant to take risks. Frequently they have accumulated enough to see them through their old age. They often feel that, if they gambled and lost heavily, they would be too old to work their way back again to financial security. Although farmers can never hope to eliminate all risks, there are several methods they can use to reduce them. Because a reduction in risk is often obtained at the cost of reduced income, planning the farm business to avoid all the risk possible is not a good goal. Instead the individual must weigh the desirability of lowering risk against its cost.

Selecting Methods of Adjusting to Farming Risks

The following are a number of methods that farmers can use to adjust to the risky environment in which they must operate:

1. Learning more about the future.
2. Selecting low-risk enterprises.
3. Diversifying enterprises.

4. Diversifying the marketing program.
5. Hedging.
6. Maintaining reserves.

In addition, the farm operator can insure against a number of the hazards involved in farming. The use of insurance is discussed in the next section.

Learning more about the future

Price changes are a source of risk when they are unexpected. If you know that a price decline is forthcoming, you usually can adjust to it and reduce the harmful effect it will have on income. For example, if you correctly anticipate a sharp decline in the price of slaughter cattle, you can restrict your feeding operations or sell the animals before the break comes, or, if you expect the seasonal decline in hog prices to come unusually early, you can arrange to farrow pigs earlier and get them on the market before the sharp decline begins. There is no way that you can predict price changes with absolute accuracy, but a constant study of expected changes can help improve your accuracy and reduce the risk to you of fluctuating prices. We have already discussed sources of information on price outlook and the factors influencing price changes in Chapter 17.

The further into the future that you must look, the more uncertain your estimates of future events become. For example, it is easier to predict what prices will be a month ahead than a year ahead. Sometimes one of the best ways to obtain better information on which to base a decision is to postpone making the decision. Suppose, for example, that you were wondering how many litters of pigs you should farrow the next spring. You could make the decision at the time the sows are bred. But, if you breed the maximum number of sows that you think you will keep, you can wait until farrowing time to make a final decision on the number to save. Or, if you raise the maximum number of pullets that you can house, you can wait until fall to decide on the exact number to keep over winter. Then you will be in a better position to make an estimate of the price relationships that will prevail during the laying season.

Farmers often feel uncertain about going into enterprises or adopting farming methods with which they have had little experience. Usually the best way to guard against severe losses from lack of know-how is to embark on new ventures on a small scale. For example, if you are interested in lamb feeding but lack experience, you should feed only a small lot of lambs the first year. This will give you a chance to learn how to deal with disease hazards and buying and selling problems, but, if you make serious mistakes and run into trouble, losses will not be heavy.

Selection of enterprises

Farmers can also reduce risk by selecting low-risk enterprises. As we pointed out in Chapter 8, there are important differences in the amount of risk involved in various livestock enterprises. The same is true of the crop enterprises to a lesser degree. Soybeans are somewhat surer than the other major crops. On the other hand, the speciality crops such as truck and fruit crops involve the greatest amount of risk.

Diversifying enterprises

Farmers are often advised not to put all their eggs in one basket. This is a simple way of saying that concentrating on a single enterprise is risky. One of the best ways of reducing risk is to diversify farming enterprises and produce several different products.

There are several areas of the country where the farming program is built around a single crop. For example, in parts of the Great Plains area, wheat is the only crop produced on many farms. In some areas of the South, cotton is almost the sole crop raised. The operators of these one-crop farms are dependent entirely on the outcome of this one crop for their income. This causes their income to fluctuate considerably from one year to another. Farm leaders in these areas have repeatedly urged farmers to shift part of their resources to other types of production to give more stability to their income.

There are other reasons for diversifying production in addition to reducing risk. For example, raising several different crops each year may help increase crop yields and distribute labor and machinery requirements. Raising more than one type of livestock helps in fitting livestock to the feed supply. We have discussed these advantages of diversification in the chapters on planning the cropping system and the livestock program.

Diversifying production helps to reduce both price and weather risks. If you raised only corn and the weather were particularly unfavorable for corn production, your farm income would be reduced sharply. However, during the same year the weather might be somewhat more favorable for producing oats. If you raised both

corn and oats, the effect of the poor corn crop on income would be
cushioned somewhat by better oats yields. Raising several crops
reduces risk from low prices in the same way.

Diversifying livestock enterprises affords even more protection
against risk than raising several crops. This is particularly true
when feeder cattle are one of the major enterprises. For example,
price declines in 1952 and 1953 resulted in many cattle feeders not

Figure 140. Specializing in the production of a single crop such as potatoes
involves more risk than a diversified farming operation. (Courtesy Union
Pacific Railroad)

meeting feed costs. However, price relationships were somewhat
more favorable for hog production during these years. Farmers who
both fed cattle and raised hogs were affected less adversely by the
drop in cattle prices than those who specialized in cattle feeding.

This protection against price risk resulting from diversification is
lessened somewhat by the tendency of prices to move up and down
together. This is particularly true of changes in farm prices that are

associated with drops in the general price level such as occur during depressions. There is also a tendency for crop yields to move up and down together. Soybean yields, for example, are closely related to corn yields.

Although diversifying the farming program helps to stabilize income, it should not be carried too far. If too many enterprises are kept, each is likely to be too small to be efficient. Small enterprises typically require more labor and a larger investment in equipment and housing per unit of output. In addition, diversification often involves raising crops or types of livestock that are not the best suited for the resources of the farm.

Diversifying the marketing program

You no doubt have heard farmers complain that they have an uncanny ability to sell their products at the wrong time, that the price always is higher before and after they sell. Dairy products and eggs must be marketed many times during the same year. As a result, there is no hazard of a substantial loss from selling them on the wrong day. On the other hand, cattle, hogs, and grain are often sold at one or two times during the year. There is danger of severe loss from picking the wrong day to market these products. This risk can be lessened by diversifying the marketing program. Cattle feeders, for example, can divide a lot of cattle into four groups and market each group a week apart. Cattle prices frequently vary enough from one week to another to make the difference between a good profit and a loss. A cattle feeder who markets at four different times would not be likely to pick a bad day every time he sold. Instead he would be more likely to sell some of his cattle on a good market and some on a poor market, but the price he would receive for the entire lot would average out fairly well. You will recall that one of the advantages of the two- and three-litter systems of hog production over the one-litter system is that hogs can be marketed at several different periods of the year. The hog marketing program can be diversified still more by marketing each crop of hogs at several different times.

Selling at several times does not guarantee that you will get more for your product. If you sold all of your cattle at one time and happened to select the right day, you would get more for them. Instead, the purpose of marketing at several different times is to reduce the risk of selling the entire output on a poor market.

Hedging

Some livestock producers, particularly those who plan to feed purchased grain, make use of a process known as hedging. Suppose you had decided to feed cattle and planned to buy the feed needed for the operation. If you did not know in advance what your feed would cost, you would have two sources of price uncertainty, namely, changes in the price of cattle and changes in the price of feed. You could remove any doubt concerning how much you would have to pay for feed by buying all of it at the start of the feeding period. However, it is sometimes impossible or inconvenient to do this because of limited storage facilities or lack of capital. Nevertheless, you can protect yourself against fluctuations in the price of feed by buying "futures" or contracts for grain to be delivered in the future on the grain exchange. The grain exchange is a highly organized market where contracts both to buy and to deliver grain are purchased and sold. If you needed to buy grain in December, March, and May, you would buy December, March, and May futures equal to the amount of grain you expected to buy. When the time came to purchase feed, you would buy it in the usual way and sell your future contract for that month. If the cash price of grain for feed had gone up 10 cents per bushel, this higher feed cost would be offset by a gain on the futures that were sold. On the other hand, a hedge would also prevent you from profiting from a decline in feed costs since you would lose a corresponding amount on the sale of your futures.

The purpose of hedging is not to make money but to serve as a form of insurance. It removes the element of uncertainty in feeding purchased feed that arises from possible changes in the price of feed.

Maintaining reserves

Maintaining reserves as a method of protecting against risk can be illustrated most simply as it applies to feed inventories. Livestock producers in areas where crop yields fluctuate widely from year to year run the risk of a feed shortage during poor years. If they do not take measures to insure an adequate feed supply, they sometimes are forced to liquidate part of their herd during drouth years. This can be especially costly with beef and dairy herds. Having to sell part of the herd often involves a financial sacrifice because other farmers also are likely to be in a forced selling situation. This tends to depress the market. Once the herd has been partially liquidated, several years may be required to rebuild it.

There are two ways to meet this situation. One is to maintain a reserve of cash or credit that can be drawn on. Feed can then be purchased to tide the herd over a poor year. The disadvantage of this system is that purchased feed, especially hay, is usually costly in drouth areas. The short supply causes prices to increase. In addition, the buyer must pay the cost of transporting the feed from feed surplus areas.

A second and better method of averting the risk of a short feed supply is to carry over a feed reserve from more favorable years. Several stacks of hay or a supply of grass silage may mean the difference between financial trouble and holding one's own. Of course, carrying over feed reserves involves some cost. Either additional storage space must be provided or else some hay will spoil as it is kept from year to year. But bearing these costs in high-risk areas may be preferable to taking the risk of running short of feed during a severe drouth.

This same method may be used as a protection against unexpected financial difficulties. Many farmers make it a practice to maintain a reserve of readily available cash. The reserve is drawn on when unexpected financial difficulties arise, so that the farm business is not disrupted. For example, if unexpected losses occur, the farm operator with a cash reserve will not be forced to sell cattle or hogs prematurely. He will not have to reduce his farming operations for lack of capital.

Planning the Farm Insurance Program

Farmers can protect themselves against a number of risks by buying insurance. This is true of losses due to fire, wind, and hail. In addition, with a liability policy the farmer can insure his automobile and can protect himself against law suits resulting from accidents or injuries that occur on his farm. Insurance programs do not eliminate these losses but reduce them to a known cost. The fundamental principle on which the typical mutual insurance company functions is as follows: A large number of people organize and agree to pay any losses members of the group suffer. When a great many cases are considered, it is possible to predict fairly accurately what percentage of policy holders will experience a loss and hence how much money must be paid by each member to cover the losses of the entire group. Thus each individual pays a small amount each year for the losses of the entire group. In return, he is spared the uncertainty of having to pay for a large loss falling on him alone.

Mutual companies, which write a large share of the wind and fire insurance on farms, operate on a nonprofit basis. This means that the policy holders in the company pay the cost of the losses plus the cost of administering the program. For example, suppose experience has shown that, on the average, there will be a $5 loss from fire per $1,000 insurance each year in a certain area. If insurance for $4,000

Figure 141. Farmers can insure against some risks such as hail damage to crops or fire or wind damage to farm buildings, but they cannot insure against losses due to floods, droughts, insects, or disease. (Courtesy *Successful Farming*)

is written on a $5,000 house in this area, the "loss cost" would be $20 per year. If the company is to break even, it will have to charge $20 each year plus enough more to cover its own operating expenses.*

Some farmers carry their own risk. Instead of taking out insurance, they pay their own losses as they occur. In this way, they pay none of the expenses involved in administering an insurance program. Whether this is a good idea depends on how badly the individual needs protection. If one or two severe losses would cripple his business or mean hardship for his family, he needs insurance. On the other hand, a farmer in a strong financial position who would

* From *USDA Farmers Bull.* 2016.

not be handicapped by a severe loss may save money over a period of years by not buying fire, wind, and hail insurance, but he can never be sure that he will come out ahead in the long run by not insuring against these risks.

Fire and windstorm insurance

Most fire insurance policies are written by small mutual companies. A standard policy, giving protection against fire and light-

Figure 142. Fire is one of the risks with which farmers must deal. They can reduce this risk to a known cost through insurance. (Courtesy Soil Conservation Serv.)

ning, generally is used by all companies within a state. Other types of coverage, in addition to fire and lightning, may be written into the policy. The most common rider is known as extended coverage. It provides protection against damage from vehicles, explosion, riots, smoke, and aircraft.

Most mutual companies have an assessment provision in their policies. This permits them to assess their members or policy holders an extra amount when unusually heavy losses occur. However, if the company has built up strong reserves by charging somewhat more than costs, it may draw on them instead of making a special assessment.

Some mutual insurance companies write both fire and wind insurance, whereas others offer only windstorm protection. Small localized companies are not in a good position to deal with wind losses, because a high proportion of their members may experience losses from a single windstorm. When a severe storm occurs, causing widespread losses in the area in which the company operates, financial disaster for the company or an extremely high assessment on its policy holders or both can result. If the company is large enough so that it operates throughout an entire state or in several different states, this hazard is eliminated. Small insurance mutuals writing wind insurance sometimes reinsure their losses in a larger company. Under this arrangement the company with which they are reinsured protects them against unusually heavy losses.

Keeping insurance policies effective

Farmers may think that they are insured, only to find after a loss that they are not. A number of factors can keep a policy holder from getting a full settlement on a fire damage claim. Any action that increases the risk of a loss usually renders the coverage ineffective, unless special provisions are made in the policy. For example, any of the following can release the insurance company from its obligation to pay a loss:

1. Leaving the property vacant beyond a specified period of time, usually 60 days.

2. Increasing the risk by storing gasoline in or near a building, operating a corn drier, or running a stove pipe through a partition.

3. Taking out additional insurance without notifying the first company with which you were insured.

4. Changing the title to the property without notifying the company.

Determining the amount of coverage

The amount of insurance carried on a building should be based on what it would cost to replace the structure. The insurance company will then depreciate the replacement cost to bring the value in line with the age and condition of the structure. The replacement instead of the original cost of the building should be used in deciding how much insurance to carry, since costs change over time.

In basing the insurance coverage on present replacement costs, you should think in terms of the cost of a replacement building that will perform the function equally as well. For example, if a large expensive barn is being used to house cattle and to store hay, you should base your insurance coverage on what it would cost to replace the barn with well-designed, cheaper cattle sheds and hay storage facilities. If the building is completely obsolete and really serves no useful purpose on the farm, there is no justification for paying money to insure it.

When building costs are increasing, as they were during the 1940's and early 1950's, there is a danger of letting insurance coverage lag too far behind replacement costs. For this reason, plus the fact that buildings become obsolete and new structures are added, the fire and wind policy should be reviewed regularly every year or two to see that it is up to date.

Crop insurance

In most areas, the only insurance available on crops is protection against hail. In specialized fruit-producing areas, insurance against frost damage is also available. Protection against hail damage has been developed by mutual and private companies to the point where it is dependable and effective. Farmers in North Dakota, Colorado, and Montana may also obtain hail insurance through state-operated insurance companies.

Whether a farmer should carry hail insurance depends on his financial position. If losing a crop through hail will severely handicap his farming operations and he is farming in an area where hail is a hazard, he should take advantage of the protection provided by hail insurance. Often credit agencies insist on their farm borrowers insuring their crop if the borrower's financial position is doubtful.

Hail damage lends itself to insurance coverage much better than other types of weather damage such as drouths. Usually the amount of hail damage can be estimated reasonably accurately, and losses tend to be confined to relatively small areas. On the other hand, determining losses from drouth is often difficult. The condition of the soil and the manner in which the crop was planted and cared for play an important part in determining how severely the crop will be affected by drouth. This makes adjusting losses difficult. In addition, drouths often cover a wide area. Few companies would have sufficient financial resources to pay losses and survive a year or two of widespread drouth.

However, the federal government is now experimenting with "all-risk" crop insurance. The purpose of this program is to offer protection against crop losses due to hail, wind, flooding, and drouth. Federal crop insurance guarantees the farmer an amount per acre that is approximately equal to his cash expenses. Premiums collected from farmers are expected to balance payments to them over a period of years; the costs of administering the program are borne by the federal government. If you are interested in finding out more about federal crop insurance, you should contact your county agent.

Liability insurance

Sometimes visitors to the farm, hired help, or neighbors are injured by animals, machines, trucks, or automobiles belonging to a farmer. Under some circumstances, the injured party may go to court and obtain a court judgment against the farmer by proving negligence. If someone succeeds in establishing that the farmer is liable, the settlement granted by the court may be large enough to cause financial hardship. Even if the party bringing suit is not successful in establishing liability, defending against the lawsuit may be costly.

Insurance companies offer personal liability policies which protect farmers against lawsuits of this type. Such a personal liability policy protects a farmer against suits arising from injury caused by any farm animals, as well as from personal acts of the farmer or members of his family while on or off the farm.

It does not protect the farmer from lawsuits resulting from work accidents to hired help. To obtain this type of protection, he must take out employer's liability insurance or workmen's compensation insurance. Both types of insurance protect the farmer, but, with employer's liability insurance, the employee, in case of injury, must prove negligence by the farmer and obtain a judgment against him in court if the employee is to receive payment from the insurance company.

Workmen's compensation protection insures an injured employee that he will receive certain benefits or payments set up by law, if he agrees not to sue his employer. It offers the same protection to the farmer as employer's liability. It is usually preferable from the standpoint of the worker, since the question of who is negligent is not considered by insurance companies in making settlements. Workmen's compensation insurance usually costs no more than employer's liability insurance.

The most widely used form of liability insurance is for personal injury or property damage caused by automobiles. The three types of automobile liability insurance commonly sold are (1) bodily injury, (2) property damage, and (3) medical reimbursement. The first type protects you in the event that you or a member of your family injures someone else while driving a car. The second type (property damage) protects you if, when driving your car, you cause damage to someone else's property including his car. The third, medical reimbursement, protects the driver against any medical and hospital expense arising from an accident.

Usually property damage and bodily injury coverage are purchased together. Medical reimbursement is a broader type of coverage since the car owner, his family, and any passengers are covered, regardless of who is responsible for the accident. If you have liability insurance, the company will defend you and pay any judgments that may be obtained against you up to the limits of your policy.

Problems

1. Plot on a graph the crop yields in your township or county over a 25-year period. For which crop do the yields fluctuate the most? To what extent do the yields of different crops tend to move up and down together? For which crops do the yield fluctuations seem the most closely related? Using crop production costs in Chapter 6 and yearly prices for crops, calculate the yearly net income from the three most important crops in your area for the last 20 years.

2. List the sources of income on your home farm and the approximate percentage of gross income that comes from each source. To what extent are the principal enterprises high-risk enterprises? Would you consider your farm business a diversified or a specialized operation?

3. Secure the market quotations on choice slaughter steers weighing 1,000 pounds for August for the last 4 years. What price would you have received each year if you had sold cattle on the 14th of the month? What average price would you have received each year if you had sold one fourth of a lot of cattle of this weight and quality on the 1st, 7th, 14th, and 21st of the month? If one of these dates falls on a day when there is no market, use the next day instead. In how many years would selling some cattle at several different times have resulted in a higher average price than selling all the cattle on the 14th of the month?

4. On the basis of the analysis you made in the first exercise above, would you consider your locality a high-risk area? What caused the low yields during the years in which they occurred? How large a feed supply do you typically have left over when you begin to harvest the new crop?

Do you think there is sufficient danger of a short crop to justify carrying a larger feed reserve than you normally do?

5. Find what types of insurance are carried on your home farm. Examine the policies to see if all buildings are covered. Are any buildings insured that should not be? Do you think the coverage is adequate?

6. Ask a local insurance agent what percentage of farmers in your locality insure their crops against hail damage. Determine the cost of hail insurance in your area. Under what circumstances do you think a farmer is justified in incurring the cost of insuring against hail?

References

Botts, Ralph R., "Insurance for Farmers," *USDA Farmers Bull.* 2016, 1950.
Efferson, J. Norman, *Principles of Farm Management,* Chapter 19, McGraw-Hill Book Co., New York, 1953.
Heady, Earl O., and Russell O. Olson, "Substitution Relationships, Resource Requirements, and Income Variability in the Utilization of Forage Crops," *Iowa Agr. Expt. Sta. Bull.* 390, 1952.
Hopkins, John A., and William G. Murray, *Elements of Farm Management,* 4th Ed., Chapter 8, Prentice-Hall, New York, 1953.
Johnson, Glenn R., and Cecil B. Haver, "Decision-Making Principles in Farm Management," *Kentucky Agr. Expt. Sta. Bull.* 593, 1953.
Robertson, Lynn S., and Ralph H. Woods, *Farm Business Management,* Chapter 14, J. B. Lippincott Co., Chicago, Philadelphia, New York, 1946.
Thair, Philip J., "Federal Crop Insurance: Should You Take It Out in 1952?" *N. Dakota Agr. Exp. Sta. Reprint* 290, from Bimonthly Vol. XIV.
Thair, Phillip J., "Stabilizing Farm Income against Crop Yield Fluctuations," *N. Dakota Agr. Expt. Sta. Bull.* 362, 1950.

CHAPTER

19

Planning the Size
of the Farm Business

It is not unusual to find a farmer with a good rotation, high crop yields and feed returns, and a high production per dairy cow, but with a disappointing income. This situation of a seemingly good manager with a low income often is the result of the farm business being too small. In analyzing farm businesses, students tend to overlook the importance of volume of production in their eagerness to appraise crop yields, individual livestock enterprises, and the

Figure 143. Many farmers in the United States lack sufficient land and equipment to make efficient use of their labor. Though they may work hard, their labor frequently is not used to good advantage and their productivity is low. As a result they have low incomes. (Courtesy Monsanto Chemical Co.)

physical appearance on the farm. Often they overlook the most important "yield" of all, the volume of production per farm operator. Inadequate farm size and the low income resulting from it are a common problem in the United States. In some sections of the country, a high percentage of farms are too small. One study of low-producing farms showed that, in some areas of the South, 75 per cent or more of the farms had gross earnings of $2,500 or less in 1950. Although the greatest concentration of low-income farms is in the Southern States, some of them can be found in all sections of the country. The distribution of low-producing farms over the United States is shown in Figure 144. The basic cause of low productivity on these farms is a lack of land and capital resources to combine with the labor of the operator and his family. It is difficult to make up for a lack of business volume by high efficiency. If adequate land and capital resources are not available for use in the farm business, satisfactory earnings are impossible.

Management Problems

1. Measuring the size of the farm business.
2. Choosing the best size of business.
3. Selecting ways of increasing the size of the farm business.

Measuring the Size of the Farm Business

The size of a farm business can be measured in several different ways. Acquainting yourself with the most widely used measures will serve two purposes: (1) It will help you in studying farm management reports. State colleges emphasize different measures of size in their farm management studies. You can better compare the size of the business on your home farm with the results of these analyses if you understand the measures of size of business used in them. (2) It will impress on you the limitations of using acres of land in the farm as the only measure of size of business.

Let us consider how we might go about describing the size of a nonfarm business. This will help point up the ways in which we might measure the scale of a farming operation. Suppose a new shoe factory were coming to a city. How could the local newspaper go about describing the size of the new business to its readers? First, the paper might tell its readers the total amount of floor space the plant would cover. Although this would be somewhat parallel to describing the size of a farm business in acres, it would give the readers only a hazy idea of the size of the operation to be

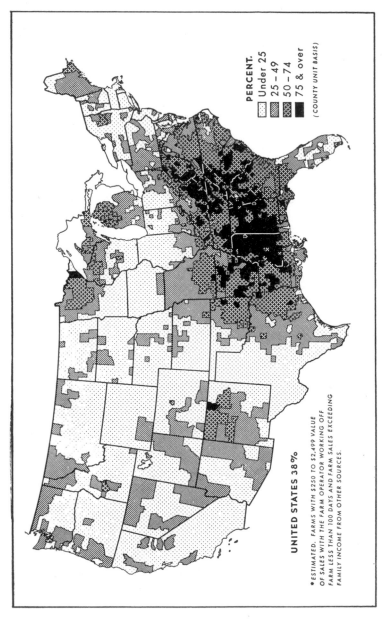

UNITED STATES 38%

*ESTIMATED. FARMS WITH $250 TO $2,499 VALUE OF SALES WITH THE FARM OPERATOR WORKING OFF FARM LESS THAN 100 DAYS AND FARM SALES EXCEEDING FAMILY INCOME FROM OTHER SOURCES.

PERCENT.
- Under 25
- 25 – 49
- 50 – 74
- 75 & over

(COUNTY UNIT BASIS)

Figure 144. Distribution of low-production farms over the United States. (Bur. Agr. Econ., USDA)

carried on at the shoe factory. The paper could move a step closer by reporting the number of men the plant would employ. Still another possibility would be to report the total investment the company would have in plant equipment and inventory. All of these are measures of the quantity of one or more of the inputs going into the business. The size of the shoe factory could also be measured on the basis of its output: the number or value of the shoes it would produce.

Similarly, the size of a farm business can be measured in terms of the land, labor, or total capital being used in the business, or in terms of its output. The most commonly used method of describing the size of a farm business is the total acres in the farm. However, the other measures of size are also employed sometimes. What are the strong and weak points of each of these measures?

Total acres

This is such a common method of describing farm size that students are often surprised to discover that there are other methods. Total acres at best is only a rough measure of the size of a farm business. It is more useful in areas where the land is uniform in quality and about the same proportion of all farms is tillable. Its chief limitation is its failure to reflect differences in the volume of livestock production among farms. Two farms both may contain 160 acres. Using acres as a measure of size of business, we would say they were the same size. However, one may be strictly a cash-grain farm. The other may process all the crops raised through livestock. Obviously, the latter farm has the larger business. Total acres loses meaning as a measure of size when the farms being compared contain widely different land resources and carry on different types of farming.

The inadequacy of acres as a measure of size of business is illustrated by a comparison of farms containing the same number of acres located in eastern and southern Iowa. Eastern Iowa is an area with highly productive soil resources and intensive livestock programs. Southern Iowa has poorer soil resources and raises less livestock. A much smaller percentage of the land is in rotated crops. Notice that in the 140–199-acre group, for example, the gross value of production on farms in southern Iowa was $7,793. But in eastern Iowa on farms with the same number of acres the gross value of production was $11,824. There were similar differences in net income (Table 70).

Table 70.   Acres as a Measure of Farm Size in Southern and Eastern
Iowa, 1952 *

Number of acres

	0–139	140–199	200–259	260–359	360 and Over
Southern Iowa					
Acres in rotated crops	78	111	157	196	288
Man-months of labor	13	15	16	18	21
Gross value of farm production	$5,693	$7,793	$10,334	$11,531	$15,047
Net farm income	2,550	3,795	6,048	5,588	7,174
Eastern Iowa					
Acres in rotated crops	98	137	188	260	369
Man-months of labor	14	15	18	22	31
Gross value of farm production	$9,434	$11,824	$15,829	$22,155	$32,278
Net farm income	4,568	5,723	7,600	11,702	14,985

* Data from *Iowa Farm Business Assoc. Records.*

Crop acres

In some areas, a sizable proportion of the farm may consist of
waste land, unproductive timberland, or blue grass pasture. Where
this is true, total acres is a particularly poor indicator of the volume of business on the farm. Using crop-acres partially overcomes
this difficulty. Crop-acres usually include all the land that is in
rotated crops.

Man-work units

This measure of farm size is based on the amount of work necessary to raise the crops and take care of the livestock on the farm.
A man work unit is the amount of work that could be accomplished
by an average man working a 10-hour day. Standards for the
amount of time required to do different jobs have been developed
from detailed studies of labor used on farms. These standards are
stated in terms of work units. The standards used by farm management workers at the University of Minnesota to estimate the number
of work units on a farm are shown in Table 71. To estimate the size
of a business in terms of work units, you must itemize crop and
livestock production and multiply each item by the appropriate
work-unit standard (Table 72).

You may wonder why the amount of labor actually required on

Table 71. Number of Work Units for Each Class of Livestock and Each Acre of Crops*

Item	Number of Work Units	Item	Number of Work Units
Dairy and dual-purpose cows	14.0 per cow	Small grain	0.7 per acre
Other dairy and dual-purpose cows	4.0 per animal unit†	Sugar beets	3.0 per acre
Beef breeding herd	5.0 per animal unit†	Sweet corn	2.3 per acre
Feeder cattle	0.35 per 100 lb	Corn husked	1.1 per acre
Sheep, farm flock	1.8 per animal unit†	Corn, hogged	0.7 per acre
Sheep, feeder	0.4 per 100 lb	Corn, shredded	2.2 per acre
Hogs	0.3 per 100 lb	Corn, silage	1.7 per acre
Turkeys	0.7 per 100 lb	Corn, fodder	1.0 per acre
Hens	22.0 per 100 hens	Alfalfa hay	0.9 per acre
Canning peas	2.0 per acre	Soybean hay	1.4 per acre
Soybeans for grain	0.7 per acre	Other hay crops	0.6 per acre

* From *Southwestern Minn. Farm Management Serv. Ann. Rept.* 1952. *Univ. Minn. Dept. Agr. Econ. Rept.* 209.

† Animal unit represents 1 dairy cow or bull, 2 other dairy cattle, 1¼ beef cows or bull, 1 feeder steer or heifer, 3⅓ other beef cattle, 7 sheep, 14 lambs, 2½ hogs, 5 pigs, 50 hens, or 1,100 pounds of turkeys produced.

the farm is not used as a measure of work units. Such a procedure does not permit comparison of farms because of differences among them in the efficiency with which labor is used. Farms on which labor was used inefficiently would appear to be larger than those on which labor was used efficiently. Using a standard man work unit for each job eliminates this difficulty.

Total capital managed

The total capital employed in a farm business may also be used as a measure of its size. The value of all inputs of land, machinery,

Table 72. Example of How Total Man Work Units Can Be Estimated on a Typical Midwestern Farm

Enterprises	Number	Work Units	Total Work Units
Dairy cows	20	14.0 per cow	280
Other dairy cattle	20	4 per animal unit	80
Hogs	20,000 lb	0.3 per 100 lb	60
Corn, husked	60 acres	1.1 per acre	66
Corn, silage	5 acres	1.7 per acre	8.5
Oats	30 acres	0.7	21
Alfalfa hay	30 acres	0.9	27
Total man work units			542.5

livestock, feed, and equipment are added together to determine total capital managed. Usually an average of the opening and closing inventory is used. All inputs should be included, regardless of whether they are supplied by the tenant or landlord. This makes possible comparison of farms on the basis of the total capital managed in the business, regardless of whether they are rented or owner-operated.

Although not often used, total capital managed does permit a meaningful analysis of the relationship between size of business and earnings. It has the drawback of being somewhat difficult to compute because of difficulties involved in placing a value on some items of farm capital.

Gross production

Just as the size of a shoe factory could be described by the number of pairs of shoes it produces, so can the scope of a farming operation be measured in terms of its output. On specialized farms producing only a single product, the output could be stated in physical quantities. For example, number of bushels could be used as the measure of the gross production and size of a wheat farm. However, most farms produce a wide variety of crop and livestock products. There is no one physical unit that can be used in adding together all kinds of crop and livestock products. For this reason, it is necessary to use dollar values in totaling the volume of production on farms producing several products.

Usually purchases of feed and livestock are deducted from sales and inventory increases in estimating gross production. This procedure is necessary in order to put farms buying large amounts of feed and livestock on the same basis as farms that raise all the feed and livestock they eventually sell.

Value of gross production is probably the most useful measure of the size of a business, but it has two important limitations: (1) Gross output will vary among farms of the same type employing the same quantity of land, labor, and capital because of differences in weather. (2) Comparisons of year-to-year changes in volume of output are difficult because of shifts in the farm price level.

Choosing the Best Size of Business

Studies have shown repeatedly that larger farms tend to have higher incomes. These results emphasize that one of the necessities for a high farm income is a sufficient volume of business. We have already presented in Table 70, one illustration of the tendency for incomes to increase as the number of acres farmed increases. A similar illustration of the relationship between income and the number of tillable acres in the farm is shown in Figure 146. Notice how the earnings tend to increase as the number of tillable acres increases. Notice also that there is a wide range in earnings even among farms with the same number of tillable acres. This is due partly to the limitations of number of tillable acres as a measure of size of business. Some farms do a greater volume of business than

Figure 145. Abandoned farmsteads are often found in areas where small farms are being consolidated into larger farms. Although letting these farmsteads run down may seem wasteful, over the long run it may result in greater economic efficiency because machinery and labor are often used more efficiently on larger farms. (Courtesy Soil Conservation Serv.)

others with the same number of tillable acres. Differences in management efficiency and in weather may also account for some of the variation among farms within the same size range.

A study of operators' earnings from 1928 through 1937 on Minnesota farms showed that earnings increased steadily with increases in both acres and work units. The operator's earnings is the income that can be credited to the operator's labor and management. However, the relationship was closer when the work-units measure was used. This tendency was reversed only during the depression years of 1931 and 1932 when the small farms lost the least. There was little, if any, relationship between size and earnings in 1930.

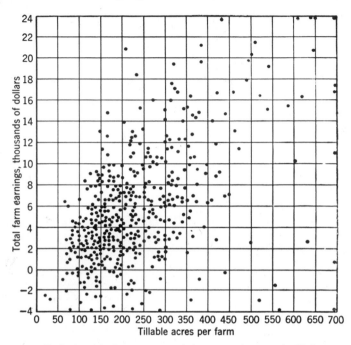

Figure 146. Relationship between total farm earnings and tillable acres per farm on northern Illinois farms in 1952. From *Illinois Farm Bur. Farm Management Serv. Ann. Rept.*, 1952; data relate to farms having a soils rates from 56 to 75.)

Why do earnings tend to increase?

How can we account for the tendency for income to increase as the size of the business increases? Perhaps the first and most obvious explanation is that the farmer with the larger business has more resources working for him. He has more acres of land and more livestock to earn income; he produces a greater output. A second reason is that the resources employed on larger farms are often used more efficiently. As a result, cost per unit of output may be lower on large farms.

Sources of increased efficiency on larger farms

The principal sources of increased efficiency and lower production costs on larger farms are as follows:

1. Increased efficiency and fuller utilization in the use of labor.
2. Lower machine cost as a result of greater annual use.

3. Greater efficiency in field operations because of larger fields.
4. Lower building cost per animal housed or per bushel of grain stored.
5. Economies in buying farm supplies and selling farm products.

1. Labor Efficiency. When the farm is small, labor may be used inefficiently because of a lack of land, machinery, fertilizer, and livestock to combine with it. Often the operator and his family do not have sufficient work on the farm to keep them fully employed. In other cases the family may work hard but have a low income because their labor is not used productively. On such farms, the operator and his family may spend much of their time doing jobs that add little to income.

Often a large increase in the size of a business results in only a small increase in the amount of labor needed on the farm. Notice in Table 70 that 13 man-months of labor were used on farms in the 0–139-acre group in southern Iowa. A man-month of labor is the equivalent of one man working for one month. The gross value of production on these farms was $5,693. On the other hand, the farms in the 200–259-acre group used 16 months of labor but had a gross value of production of $10,338.

Livestock enterprises typically are larger on larger farms. As we pointed out in Chapter 8, less labor per animal is required with large-scale enterprises. Usually the percentage drop is most noticeable when small enterprises are expanded. Also, though the improvement is usually less striking, labor efficiency usually continues to increase until the scale of the enterprise becomes very large. This is illustrated by the decrease in man-hours of labor required per cow on large-scale dairy enterprises in New York State (Table 73).

2. Machinery Costs. Small farms have a problem in keeping machinery costs low. As we pointed out in Chapter 13, an important part of the cost of machine service is fixed costs. On larger farms, fixed costs can be spread out over more acres, making machine

Table 73.   Cows per Farm and Labor Efficiency*
151 Large Dairy Farms, New York, 1949–50

Cows per Farm	Cows per Man	Man-hours per Cow
40–54	16	124
55–69	18	114
70–99	19	106
100 or more	20	104

* Adapted from *Cornell Agr. Expt. Sta. Bull.* 887.

service more economical. Often farmers can operate a 240-acre cornbelt farm with the same basic machinery required for a 160-acre farm. As we saw in Chapter 13, operators of small farms can keep down machine costs by custom hiring, cooperative ownership of machines, and exchanging machines. But even these alternatives are not likely to bring costs down to a level as low as those enjoyed on larger farms.

Operators of large farms also have the advantage of being able to

Figure 147. One of the advantages of larger farms is that large machines can be used economically. Using high-capacity machines reduces the amount of labor required. (Courtesy International Harvester Co.)

employ high-capacity machines economically. Although these machines may reduce machine costs per acre, their chief economy arises through saving labor. For example, cultivating corn with a four-row instead of a two-row cultivator saves nearly 50 per cent of the operator's time. Similar savings are possible through using four-row planters, three-bottom plows, two-row corn pickers, and high-capacity combines.

3. *Larger Fields.* Larger fields give farms containing more acres a further advantage. A smaller percentage of the land is used for

fence rows and unproductive end rows. Less time is consumed in turning in doing field operations because fields are longer.

4. Building Economies. Livestock housing and grain storage can be provided more economically when built on a larger scale. The cost of building a corn crib that will hold 6,000 bushels of corn is less than twice as great as the cost of building a 3,000-bushel crib. Less material is required per bushel of storage provided; proportionately less labor is needed to construct the larger crib. As a result the cost per bushel of storage space in the 6,000-bushel crib is lower. Much the same is true of dairy housing. One can build loose housing facilities for 30 dairy cows at less than twice the cost of a similar arrangement for 15 cows. The cost of milking stalls and milk cooling equipment as well as housing is lower on a per-cow basis for

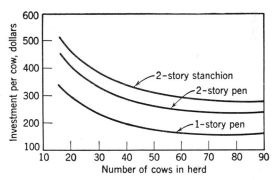

Figure 148. Building and equipment investment per cow by size of herd for both stanchion and pen-type barns, 1945–49 price level. From *Mich. Agr. Expt. Sta. Spec. Bull.* 375)

large herds. The relationship between the investment per cow in buildings and equipment and size of herd reported in a Michigan study is shown in Figure 148. Notice the sharp drop in investment per cow as the size of the herd is increased from 15 to 30 cows.

5. Buying and Selling. Large farms enjoy a further advantage in buying and selling. In buying some types of supplies, a reduction in price is possible through large-volume purchases. For example, commercial feeds usually can be bought more cheaply by the ton than by the bag. Electric power rate structures are arranged so that high-volume users pay less per kilowatt-hour of electricity than low-volume users.

On the selling side, the principal economies are likely to come in transportation. In addition, the manager of a large farm business

Figure 149. Large-scale enterprises frequently enjoy cost advantages in the buying of farm supplies. Bulk handling or commercial feeds reduces costs and labor requirements where large quantities are fed. (Courtesy *Successful Farming*)

can afford to spend more time in attempting to do a good job of buying and selling. His time is used more economically when he buys or sells a large volume. Economies in marketing are more likely to be important for truck crops, fruits, and other specialty crops than for products raised on general farms.

How large a business?

Can the farm business be too large? The answer to this question is tied in with the goals and capabilities of the farmer. As the size of business increases, some of the resulting economies discussed in the previous section tend to be offset by inefficiencies. As farms expand beyond a certain size, the operator must depend increasingly on hired labor. This adds supervision of labor to his managerial job. Organizing and getting the work done become more difficult as the size of the farm increases. This is just as true of expanding the size of the business by adding livestock as by increasing the number of acres farmed. Indeed, some farm management specialists think it takes more managerial skill to expand the business through livestock than by farming more acres. Individuals differ in their ability to deal with these problems. Thus, a 120-acre farm with a 10-cow dairy herd and a small hog enterprise may be large enough

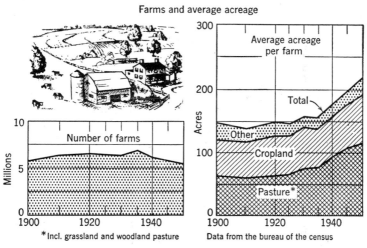

Figure 150. The average number of acres per farm in the United States has increased from 146 in 1900 to 215 in 1950. (*Bur. Agr. Econ.,* USDA)

for the farmer who finds it difficult to organize his work and supervise hired labor.

The advantage of lower machine costs per unit of output also grows less important as the size of the farm increases. You will recall from Chapter 13 that machine costs per acre first decline rapidly but then begin to level out as the machine is used on more and more acres. As the number of acres farmed with one set of machinery is increased, timeliness of operations also becomes a problem. The best time for planting corn may have passed before all of the crop is planted. Cultivating and harvesting part of the crop may be postponed too long. As a result, yields are likely to suffer if one set of machinery is spread over too many acres. These problems can be overcome by duplicating machinery or buying larger machines. Having to buy a second set of machinery increases fixed costs and nullifies the advantage of the lower cost that was achieved through a high annual use. Larger machines may decrease costs up to a point. But there is a definite limit to how large machines can be and still do good work. Studies show that, under cornbelt conditions, the economies arising from lower machine costs are not important as farm size is increased beyond 320 acres of tillable land.

It should be emphasized that increasing the size of the farm business offers no guarantee that earnings will increase. A business producing a larger volume provides the opportunity for increased earnings. If it is not managed efficiently, large losses can also occur.

Selecting Ways of Increasing the Size of the Farm Business

Expanding acres

Suppose you have decided that your farm business is too small. How can you increase its size? One common way is to farm more land. Sometimes this may involve selling the present farm and buying another. If you are renting, you may rent a larger farm.

Often a farmer who has worked many years to improve his farm is reluctant to sell it in order to buy a larger one. Instead, he tries to add to the farm he has by purchasing land near by. If he finds himself fenced in because adjoining farm land is not for sale, he frequently must buy land several miles away from his present farmstead. Farming land this far away creates problems in using pasture land, hauling hay, and carrying on farming operations. However, rubber-tired equipment has greatly simplified this type of operation.

Many owner-operators of comparatively small farms find that renting near-by cropland is an excellent way to increase the size of their unit. This practice is sometimes referred to as field renting. They can farm the added acres while they are young and willing to work longer hours and have help from their youngsters. Later, when they wish to slow down, they can confine their operations to their own farm. Often the added land can be farmed with little added investment in machinery.

Field renting offers the farmer with money enough to buy only a small farm the security of ownership and the opportunity to improve his own farm buildings and home as he wishes. At the same time he can enjoy some of the economies arising out of operating a larger unit.

Increasing acres in rotation

On some farms a large percentage of the land consists of unproductive permanent pasture or areas that are not farmed because of poor drainage. Often the number of acres under cultivation can be increased by bringing these areas into the rotation. To do this, it may be necessary to clear scattered trees and underbrush from the land and perhaps fill gullies that cannot be crossed with machinery. In some cases the land originally was left in permanent pasture because it was considered too steep to farm. If this is the situation, it may be protected against erosion through contouring and terracing. Often deciding whether land can be put under cultivation profitably is a complicated problem. In every case the added cost must be weighed against the added returns.

In addition to increasing crop output, bringing land into rotation may have the secondary effect of increasing the size of the livestock program. This is particularly true when livestock production has been restricted by a low volume of home-raised feed and the operator has been reluctant to buy feed.

Raising more livestock

One widely used method of expanding the size of the business is to raise more livestock. This means putting more capital and labor into the business. Often a heavier livestock program can be handled with the labor already available on the farm by working longer hours and distributing labor requirements more evenly throughout the year.

Table 74. Comparison of Gross Production and Net Income on a Cornbelt Farm That Does Not Buy Feed with one That Does, 1952

Farm A

Livestock sales	$17,629
Total value of feed fed to livestock	10,393
Total value of feed purchased	2,056
Total value of feed raised on the farm fed to livestock	8,337
Gross value of production on farm	12,471
Net farm income	5,982

Farm B

Livestock sales	$29,318
Total value of feed fed to livestock	16,404
Total value of feed purchased	7,886
Total value of feed raised on the farm fed to livestock	8,518
Gross value of production on farm	19,406
Net farm income	9,037

On farms where part of the feed being raised is not fed, the live-stock program can be expanded without buying feed. However, if capital is available to buy feed, there is no reason why the amount of feed raised on the farm should limit the size of the livestock program. Buying feed, particularly feed grains, provides a good opportunity for the skilled livestock farmer on a small farm to expand the size of his business.

The opportunities for increasing income by expanding the volume of livestock production through purchased grain is illustrated by

Figure 151. One way of increasing income on small farms is to perform additional marketing services. The young farm couple in this picture are candling and packaging eggs which will later be delivered to local stores to be sold as premium eggs.

the comparison of two-160 acre cornbelt farms shown in Table 74. Both farms are organized around cattle feeding and hog raising. However, on farm *A* the livestock program is limited to the feed raised on the farm, with the exception that commercial protein and mineral feeds are purchased. Farm *B* buys between $4,000 and $5,000 worth of feed grains in addition to commercial feeds to carry on an expanded livestock program. Notice the greater livestock sales and gross value of production on farm *B*. Notice also that the larger volume of business is reflected in a higher net income on farm *B*.

Changing enterprises

A larger volume of production also may be achieved by changing the types of livestock or crops produced. If the feed raised on the farm is fed to dairy instead of beef cows, the volume of production will be increased. Likewise, shifting part or all of the acreage from grain and hay production to potatoes or other truck crops will expand the size of the business. Both these changes require greater inputs of capital, labor, and management.

Working off the farm

Some farm operators who do not have enough livestock and land to make full use of their labor, increase their income by working off the farm. They may drive a school bus or do trucking or some other type of custom work, or they may sell fertilizer, feed, seed, or insurance. One of the disadvantages of this method of increasing income is that it takes the operator away from the farm. This may lead to neglecting work at home.

Problems

1. Obtain a recent Farm Business Association report from your area if one is available. What measures of size of business are used in this report? What relationship do you find between size of business and income?

2. Do you think that the number of acres of land in the farm is a good measure of size of business in your area? Why or why not?

3. Compute the size of business on your home farm, using all of the measures discussed in the text. How does its size compare with the average of those shown in the Farm Business Association report? Do you think its size should be increased? If so, how?

4. Visit one of the farms with the largest volume of business in your community. What economies can you see arising out of large-scale operations? Can you see any evidence of inefficiency resulting from operating on a large scale?

References

Case, H. C. M., and Paul E. Johnston, *Principles of Farm Management*, Chapter 17, J. B. Lippincott Co., Chicago, Philadelphia, New York, 1953.

Efferson, J. Norman, *Principles of Farm Management*, Chapter 11, McGraw-Hill Book Co., New York, 1953.

Forster, G. W., *Farm Organization and Management*, 3d Ed., Chapter 11, Prentice-Hall, New York, 1953.

Hoglund, C. R., "What Size Farm or Ranch for South Dakota," *S. Dakota Agr. Expt. Sta. Bull.* 387, 1947.

Hopkins, John A., and William G. Murray, *Elements of Farm Management*, 4th Ed., Chapter 10, Prentice-Hall, New York, 1953.

McElveen, Jackson V., and Kenneth L. Bachman, "Low-Production Farms," *USDA Agr. Inf. Bull.* 108.

Robertson, Lynn S., and Ralph H. Woods, *Farm Business Management*, Chapter 7, J. B. Lippincott Co., Chicago, Philadelphia, New York, 1946.

20

Keeping Farm Accounts

How much income has the farm business made during the year? How much financial progress has the farm family made? These are questions that can best be answered by keeping a systematic set of farm accounts. The farm manager's accounting task includes selecting an accounting system, following through the mechanics of keeping records, and analyzing and interpreting farm accounts.

The most important reasons for keeping farm accounts are as follows:

1. To check on the financial position of the farm family and to measure its financial progress from year to year.

2. To aid in analyzing the performance of the farm business.

3. To aid in filing income tax reports.

4. To help divide the income on farms operated by partnerships.

5. To help in making plans and budgets for future farming operations.

Management Problems

1. Making out a net worth statement.
2. Making out a net income statement.
3. Using farm accounts for filing income tax reports.
4. Keeping project records.

In the next chapter, we will consider how accounts can be used to improve the farm business and to plan future farming operations.

Making out the Net Worth Statement

Differences between a net worth and net income statement

What is a net worth statement? How does it differ from a net income statement? It is important that you get a clear understanding of the difference between these two at the beginning of your study of accounting. The net worth statement is a picture, a snap-shot, of the farmer's financial position at any one point in time. It is always an accounting of how a business stands financially as of a specific date, usually the beginning of the year. A net income statement is an accounting of financial transactions that take place over a period of time. It is comparable to a motion picture of the incoming and outgoing payments that have taken place over the time period the statement covers. Usually net income statements for farms extend over a period of a year, beginning with January 1 and ending with December 31.

To prepare a net worth statement, you must total up your assets and liabilities. Your assets are the total value of what you own, the money you have on hand, and what you are owed by others. Liabilities are your obligations to other people or businesses such as debts and unpaid accounts. Net worth is the excess of your assets over your liabilities.

The net worth statement provides a means by which you can check on your financial position. If you compare your net worth from one year to the next, you can tell the extent to which you are making financial progress. In addition, net worth statements are useful from the standpoint of both the borrower and lender in making arrangements for credit.

Taking inventory

Net worth statements require that an inventory be taken of livestock, machinery, feed, and equipment on the farm. An inventory is simply a listing of the types, amount, and value of these items that a farmer has on hand. We shall see later that this is also an essential step in computing net income, if accounts are to be kept on an accrual basis. Taking inventory involves two steps: (1) making a physical count or measure of the items on hand, and (2) placing a value on them.

Grain, silage, and hay stocks can be estimated accurately enough

Table 75.   Cubic Feet in a Ton of Hay

	Settled 1–3 months	Settled Over 3 months
Alfalfa hay	485	470
Clover hay	510	500
Timothy hay	640	625
Wild hay	600	450
Chopped hay	250	250
Baled hay, piled	250	250

for inventory purposes by measuring their physical volume and converting this to tons or bushels. The following rules will help you estimate the quantities of grain and feed crops you have on hand.*

1. To find bushels of grain or shelled corn in a bin, multiply length by width by depth (all in feet) and multiply by 0.8 (eight tenths).

2. To find bushels of shelled corn in a crib of ear corn multiply length by width by average depth (all in feet), and then multiply by 0.4 (four tenths). If the crib is round, multiply distance around crib by diameter by depth of corn (all in feet), and divide by 10.

3. To find tons of hay in a mow, multiply length by width by

Table 76. Estimated Weight of Settled Corn Silage One Month or More after Filling*

	Inside Diameter of Silo, feet				
Depth of Silage, feet	10	12	14	16	18
2	2 ton	4 ton	5 ton	6 ton	8 ton
4	5	8	10	13	17
6	8	11	16	20	26
8	11	16	21	28	35
10	14	20	27	35	44
12	17	24	33	43	54
14	20	29	39	51	64
16	23	33	45	59	75
18	26	38	51	67	85
20	29	42	58	75	95
22	33	47	64	84	106
24	36	52	70	92	116
26	39	56	77	100	127
28	43	61	83	109	138
30	46	66	90	118	149
32	49	71	97	126	160
34	53	76	103	135	170
36		81	110	144	181
38		86	117	152	192
40		90	123	161	203
42			130	169	214
44			136	178	225
46			144	186	236
48			151	195	247

* If the corn silage is unusually dry when put in, deduct 10 to 15%. If corn was unusually rich in grain, add 5 to 10%. Deduct 10%, if very little grain was present. This table was adapted from *Mich. State Coll. Ext. Folder* F-154.

* From *Mich. State Coll. Ext. Folder* F-154.

height (all in feet), and divide by the number of cubic feet in a ton of hay.

4. To find tons in a stack, multiply the overthrow (the distance from the ground on one side over the top to the ground on the other side) by the length by the width (all in feet), multiply the result by 0.3 (three tenths), and then divide by the number of cubic feet in a ton of hay (Table 75).

Once you have measured your cribs, silos, and hay mows, you should keep a record of their capacities. Then you can estimate quickly the amount of feed you will have on hand in following years.

If market quotations are available, feed and crops can be valued in line with their current market price. Since there is no established market on corn silage, it presents a special problem (Table 76). Usually there is enough alfalfa hay sold to establish a market price for it. Corn silage can be valued at about one-third the value of alfalfa on a ton-for-ton basis.

Hogs, feeder cattle and sheep, lambs and poultry should be valued on the basis of current market prices on the farm. Dairy, beef, or sheep breeding animals should be inventoried at cost if they were recently purchased. If raised on the farm, they should be inventoried at what they would bring on the market.

Depreciation

Improvements, buildings, machinery, and equipment are valued on the basis of their original cost minus depreciation. How should we go about depreciating machinery and equipment? Suppose, for example, we wished to put a value on a tractor. We start first with its original cost. Then we estimate how many years it will last. The next step is to divide the original cost of the tractor by the number of years we expect the tractor to last in order to get the amount of depreciation per year. If the original cost of the tractor were $1,800 and we expected it to last 12 years, we would have $1,800 depreciation to distribute over the 12-year period. Thus the depreciation each year would be $150. Therefore, when the tractor was one year old, it would be valued at $1,650; at the end of 2 years, it would be worth $1,500, and so forth.

We can refine our estimate of the yearly depreciation charge arrived at above by taking into account the salvage value of the machine at the end of its useful life. For example, the tractor referred to above might be worth $50 for salvage at the end of 12 years of service. To estimate the yearly depreciation, we would

MACHINERY DEPRECIATION SCHEDULE

Machinery	Year Bought	Cost	Est. Years Life	Accumulated Depreciation	1944 Depreciation	1944 Value End of Year	1945 Depreciation	1945 Value End of Year
Manure Spreader	1940	200 00	10	80	20	100	20	80
Harrow	1945	75 00	15				5	70
Tractor	1938	1200 –	10	720	120	360	120	240 Trade on
Tractor	1946	1060 –	10	Paid $820 difference on trade. Thus $820 + $240 depreciated value of old tractor = $1060				
Mower	1938	120 –	14	54	9	57	9	48

Machinery	Year Bought	Cost	Est. Years Life	Accumulated Depreciation	19__ Depreciation	19__ Value End of Year	19__ Depreciation	19__ Value End of Year

Totals—Machinery

MACHINERY DEPRECIATION SCHEDULE

1946 Depreciation	1946 Value End of Year	1947 Depreciation	1947 Value End of Year	1948 Depreciation	1948 Value End of Year	1949 Depreciation	1949 Value End of Year	1950 Depreciation	1950 Value End of Year
20	60	20	40	20	20	20	–		
5	65	5	60	5	55	5	50	5	45
new tractor									
106	954	106	848	106	742	106	636	106	530
10	70	rebuilt ($48 plus $32 for rebuilding = $80—New Est. years of life 8)							

19__ Depreciation	19__ Value End of Year	19__ Depreciation	19__ Value End of Year	19__ Depreciation	19__ Value End of Year	19__ Depreciation	19__ Value End of Year	19__ Depreciation	19__ Value End of Year

Figure 152. Machinery depreciation schedule. (From *Continuous Depreciation Schedule, Better Farm Accounting Book,* Iowa State College Press, Ames, with permission of the publisher)

subtract the salvage value from the original cost and divide by the estimated years of life. Thus, in this case, the yearly depreciation would be $1,800 − $50/12, or $146 per year. Either way of estimating depreciation is satisfactory. Taking the salvage value into account is somewhat more accurate, but it involves additional work.

The method of depreciation that we have just illustrated is called the straight-line method. This is the simplest and the most widely used method. You will notice that under this system the tractor is depreciated by the same amount each year. Some persons have criticized the straight-line method, because they believe that it depreciates the item too little while it is new and too much when it is older. Although the straight-line method is subject to this weakness, it is not serious when machinery, equipment, and buildings of all ages are included in the inventory. Whereas a newly acquired item is being depreciated less rapidly than it should be, another older item is being depreciated at too rapid a rate. Thus, when the entire inventory is considered, one inaccuracy tends to offset the other.

An example of a depreciation schedule is shown in Figure 152. Once an item has been entered in the schedule, it can be carried along from year to year with the new depreciated value entered each year.

Land and buildings

When the farmer owns the farm he is operating, he must include the value of the land and buildings assets in the net worth statement. As we pointed out before, a depreciation schedule should be set up on buildings. Therefore, land should be valued separately from the buildings.

Land should be valued on the basis of what comparable land is selling for in the community. Once farmers have put a value on their land, they usually prefer to use the same inventory value from year to year. Whether this is a good procedure depends on the use to be made of the net worth statement after it has been computed. If the statement is to be used to estimate financial progress from one year to the next, keeping land values constant from year to year is usually the best procedure. Moving them up and down as land prices fluctuate makes any evaluation of financial progress difficult. Any increase in net worth that occurs during the year may be caused by rising land prices rather than by good financial management. The same problem exists to a lesser extent with other inventory items such as crops and feeds. But, since these items usually make up a smaller percentage of all assets, changes in their inventory value do not influence net worth to the same degree as changes in land values. When the net worth statement is being computed for credit purposes, land should be entered at its current market value.

Other items

Household items should be included, in addition to farm inventory items, if a complete personal net worth statement is desired. Usually, only major household equipment is included. It should be appraised on the basis of what it could be sold for. Accounts receivable that you eventually expect to be paid should be included as assets. They are, as the name implies, bills outstanding that are due you. Of course, bills that you have no prospect of ever collecting are not assets and consequently should not be entered in the net worth statement. Life insurance should be entered at its cash-surrender value, and bonds and stocks at their market value. In addition, the money in the bank and cash on hand should be listed under assets.

Liabilities are usually not difficult to itemize. They include farm mortgage debt, notes at the bank or from other credit institutions, and unpaid bills at stores and dealers. Both the principal and any unpaid interest on debts should be entered as liabilities.

Interpreting the net worth statement

A convenient form for computing net worth is shown in Table 77. It provides space for a statement at both the start and the close of the year and for determining the change in net worth during the year. Many farm account books contain a similar form.

Suppose you have computed the change in your net worth during the year and find that it is decreasing. How would you go about discovering the cause? What changes should you make? Let us look first at the relationship between net income and changes in net worth. This relationship may be stated as follows: Net farm income (computed on the inventory basis) plus nonfarm income minus money used for family living, gifts, and other nonbusiness purposes equals change in net worth. Therefore, a decrease in net worth results when people spend beyond their income. Sometimes the root of the difficulty lies in unsatisfactory farm earnings. However, in years of unusually unfavorable prices and weather, earnings may be low and decreases in net worth may take place in spite of good management.

Decreases in net worth also can result from high family living expenses. Sometimes this is unavoidable if unusual medical expenses have been encountered or if the family is at a stage when expenses are high. The latter may be the case, for example, if several youngsters are in high school and college. Decreases in

Table 77. Net Worth Statement*

ASSETS (What is Owned)	Jan. 1, 1954	Jan. 1, 1955	LIABILITIES (What is Owed)	Jan. 1, 1954	Jan. 1, 1955
Total household furnishing and supplies	$ 1,200	$ 1,200	*Farm Mortgages* Principal, balance due	$13,550	$12,900
Automobile	950	800	Interest due	360	350
Farm Inventory			*Chattel or Crop Liens*		
Land & buildings	48,000	47,500	Principal, balance		
Livestock	7,550	7,150	due	2,000	0
Machinery and equipment	8,100	7,800	Interest due	50	0
Feed crops and supplies	5,600	6,300	*Other Notes Payable* Principal, balance due		
Investments			Interest due		
Stocks & bonds	0	0	*Other debts*		
Life insurance, cash value	3,400	3,525	Store bills	75	65
Mortgages or notes receivable	0	0	Feed bills	275	350
Other real estate	0	0	Doctor, dentist, etc.	50	0
Cash			Installments, balance due	0	0
On hand	25	30			
Checking account	1,200	1,400			
Savings account	0	0			
Notes and accounts receivable	50	0			
Total Assets	$76,075	$75,705	Total Liabilities	$16,360	$13,665

Beginning of year
    Total assets $75,075 minus total liabilities $16,360 equals net worth $59,715
End of year
    Total assets $75,705 minus total liabilities $13,665 equals net worth $62,040
      Change in net worth for the year: Increase $2,325, or Decrease $_____

* Adapted from *Mich. Agr. Ext. Serv. Folder* F-154.

net worth arising from these causes need not give rise to alarm because the condition is usually temporary. Sometimes net worth may decline because the family is living beyond its means, even though there are no unusual expenses. This is a more serious problem. Unless the family has an unusually large net worth, it cannot continue this pattern long and remain financially solvent. Arrangements must be made either to reduce family living expenses or to increase farm income.

It is particularly important for the young farmer to check up on changes in his net worth. He cannot draw on his past experiences in adapting his living expenses to his income. Because he typically has a low net worth and limited capital, he cannot afford to live beyond his means. A close check on changes in net worth is his best guide to the financial progress he is making.

Making out a Net Income Statement

How do you compute net income for the farm business? We will concern ourselves at this point only with the income statement which takes into account changes in inventories. Later, we will explain the cash method of accounting which is widely used for income tax purposes. It should be pointed out that the inventory income statement, also called the accrual method, is also acceptable for income tax reporting. Indeed, many farmers prefer it to the cash basis for this purpose. In addition, the accrual method has the advantage of giving us more information on what actually happened in the farm business during the year.

Parts of an income statement

The net income statement includes the following parts:

1. Opening inventory of livestock, feed, and supplies.
2. Closing inventory of livestock, feed, and supplies.
3. Depreciation on buildings, machinery, and equipment.
4. Receipts.
5. Income from other sources.
6. Expenses including purchases of feed and livestock.

Farm account books may be arranged differently, but they all contain provisions for entering and summarizing the information listed above. In addition, most farm accounts provide space for summarizing the value of food and fuel from the farm that was used in the household.

Opening and closing inventories

Why is it necessary to calculate opening and closing inventories? Suppose you had 1,000 bushels of corn on hand at the start of the year but that the supply had increased to 5,000 by the end of the year. This represents an inventory increase of 4,000 bushels. If you did not take into account this increase in corn on hand through inventories, it would not be counted as income. Yet it was produced on the farm during the year, and the costs involved in producing it are charged against the year's business. It is income to the farm business during the year just as surely as it would be if you had

Figure 153. In computing net farm income on an inventory basis, corn on hand at the end of the year is credited to the past year's business. (Courtesy Union Pacific Railroad)

decided to sell it before the end of the year. By failing to account for the increase in the corn supply through changes in inventory, you would underestimate the true net income for the farm business. On the other hand, if you did not take into account decreases in inventories when they occurred, you would tend to overestimate the amount of income earned by the farm business during the year.

Depreciation

If you have computed opening and closing net worth statements, you are already familiar with the process of depreciation. Exactly the same methods should be used in depreciating items for the net income statement. Usually items that are depreciated are not included in the opening and closing inventories of the net income statement. Instead, the amount the item is depreciated is treated as an expense.

One problem that arises in setting up a depreciation schedule is determining the original cost of the machine. If the item is purchased outright for cash, no difficulty arises since the original cost is simply the purchase price, but most farmers trade in an old machine when they buy a new one. How should you figure the original cost under these circumstances?

When one machine is traded in for another, the cost of the new machine for accounting purposes is the cash difference paid plus the depreciated value of the machine traded in. You can obtain the depreciated value of the machine traded in from the depreciation schedule in your account book. Neither the list price of the new machine nor the trade-in allowed on the old machine is used directly in arriving at the original cost figure. Although we have used a machine in our example, exactly the same procedure would be involved in determining the original cost of a hog feeder, a tank heater, or any other piece of farm equipment where a trade-in might be involved.

Receipts and other income

Usually, the treatment of receipts does not present serious problems in computing net income. Many account books make provisions for entering and totaling the income from each class of livestock separately. This is often useful in analyzing the performance of different enterprises on the farm.

In the inventory or accrual method of income accounting, all items that have been sold are treated as sales during the year, regardless of whether payment was actually received. Suppose, for example, that you sold a thousand bushels of corn late in December but had not received the check; you should count the sale as income during the year in which the corn was actually sold. The only exception to this rule occurs when you have definitely established that you will be unable to collect the money due you from the sale.

Whether off-the-farm income should be included in arriving at net income depends on the use to be made of the income figure after it has been computed. If you are interested in using the income statement to check on the performance of the business, you will want to leave out income from sources not related to the business.

For example, if you own stocks and bonds, the income from them should not be included. Of course, these items must be included in your income tax statement. Most farm account books make provision for entering and summarizing off-the-farm income separately from farm income. On the other hand, income from custom work, gasoline tax refunds, and conservation payments should be included as receipts to the farm business.

Products used in the household

On most farms, some of the products of the farm business are consumed by the family. If the net income statement is to reflect accurately the performance of the farm business, the value of these products should be entered as receipts. One must be careful, however, not to spend too much time in keeping a record of these items. It could become a major accounting project in itself.

Usually the consumption of such items as milk and eggs can be estimated at the end of the year. However, it is well to keep a record of the quantities consumed for a week or two several times during the year to serve as a guide in making the estimate. Usually, the farmer has no difficulty in remembering the number of hogs and cattle that were butchered for home use.

Once you have estimated the physical quantities of these items, you must also place a money value on them. The simplest and perhaps the best basis to use is the price you would have received for them on the market.

Expense items

Which items should be treated as farm expenses and which as household expenses? How should joint household and farm expense items be handled? Obviously, expenses such as tractor fuel and seed corn are farm expenses, and clothing, furniture, and entertainment are personal or household expenses. However, you will find that many other items are not easily classified. For example, groceries used for the family are household expenses, but groceries used to board hired farm workers can logically be treated as a farm expense. Telephones are typically used partly for business and partly for the convenience of the family. The same is true for the family automobile. For this reason, car and telephone expenses should be divided between the farm and the household. Since it is impractical to keep a record of the use made of telephones and automobile for business purposes through the year, the farm operator usually estimates the proportion of these expenses that should be charged to the business.

Repairs

Repairs are another troublesome item. When should they be entered as ordinary expenses? How should they be treated when they improve or extend the life of a machine or building, thus

Figure 154. One of the difficult problems in accounting is to decide whether the cost of building alterations should be treated as repairs or as a capital improvement. Repairs are entered as an expense against the current year's business. The cost of capital improvements must be entered as depreciation over the life of the improvement. (Courtesy Wallaces' *Farmer and Iowa Homestead*)

benefiting the farm business for several years? The entire cost of repairs of this latter type logically cannot be charged against the single year in which they are made. A new depreciation schedule should be set up for the machine or building and the cost reclaimed over a period of several years. For example, suppose a tractor were depreciated in the depreciation schedule until it was worth $300 and had only 2 years of expected life remaining. Then $200 was spent in giving it a major overhaul. After the overhaul, it was worth

$500 and had an expected life of 5 years. A new depreciation schedule should be set up on the tractor, depreciating it $100 per year for the remaining 5 years of expected life.

What about repairs that are necessary to maintain a machine or building? These can be treated as regular expenses. The line between repairs and improvements that should be depreciated is a narrow one. Since there is no hard and fast rule that can be followed in making the division, the farmer must be guided by his own judgment.

Calculating net farm income

You should make periodic entries of receipts and expenses in the account book during the year. At the end of the year, you must close the account and determine net income for the year. In order to do this, receipts and expenses must be summarized. In addition, the depreciation schedule shown in Figure 152 must be brought up to date. This involves extending it for one more year on items already appearing in the schedule. Any new machines and buildings must be entered and the schedule revised to take into account items on which major repairs have been made.

One other accounting chore that must be done at the end of the year is to take an inventory of feed, supplies, and livestock. We have already discussed this problem in connection with working out a net worth statement. Although both an opening and a closing inventory enter into the calculation of net income, only one inventory is taken each year, because the closing inventory of one year becomes the opening inventory of the following year.

Although you will find that account books differ somewhat in the forms they provide for summarizing income, the general procedure followed in all of them is the same. A simplified net income statement containing all the information needed to arrive at net income is shown in Table 78.

You will notice that the income statement is divided into credits and debits. To arrive at net income, debits are subtracted from credits. Usually it is not difficult for students to see why all sales and income are treated as credits and why expenses and depreciation are entered as debits. However, it is more difficult to understand why the closing inventory is treated as a credit and the opening inventory as a debit. If you look at the closing inventory items as supplies that could be converted readily into sales, their treatment as credits is less confusing. Similarly, you will find it helps to

Table 78. Income Statement for Brown Farm, January 1, 1954, to January 1, 1955

Credits		Debits	
Closing inventory		Opening inventory	
Feed	$ 4,000	Feed	$ 5,000
Supplies	800	Supplies	500
Livestock	5,200	Livestock	5,500
Livestock sales	8,500	Crop expenses	1,300
Crop sales	1,000	Livestock expense	700
Miscellaneous income	300	Depreciation	1,800
Value of home-used products	300		
	$20,100		$14,800

Total credits ($20,100) minus total debits ($14,800) equals net farm income ($5,300)

look on the opening inventory as items purchased by this year's business from last year's business.

Some farm record keepers prefer to work only with inventory increases or decreases instead of entering the complete opening and closing inventory in the income summary. For example, if you had 2,000 bushels more corn on hand at the end than at the start of the year, you could enter the value of the 2,000 bushels of corn as a credit. On the other hand, if you had a decrease in the inventory, you would enter it as a debit. You will arrive at exactly the same result by using this procedure as you would by entering the complete opening and closing inventory in the income summary.

Accounts on partnership farms

If you are farming in partnership with someone else, you may want to use accounts to divide the income from the farm business. The basis of division should be worked out in detail at the time the agreement is made. This problem has already been discussed in Chapter 2. Usually little extra effort is required to make farm accounts serve this purpose.

The partnership can maintain a joint checking account from which the day-to-day expenses of the business are paid. In addition, receipts from the sale of farm products can be deposited in the joint account. The partners may make withdrawals from the account from time to time during the year.

Even with a joint account, it may be more convenient for the partners occasionally to pay certain minor expenses in cash with their own money. If this is done, a notation showing by whom the bill was paid should be made when the item is entered in the account book. If the accounts have been carefully kept, a final division of the year's income is not difficult when the accounts are closed at the end of the year.

It may be advisable on rented farms, particularly those leased on a livestock-share basis, to keep the accounts of both the tenant and landlord in the same account book. Combined accounts may be advantageous, even though receipts are divided at the time of each sale and each party pays his share of the expenses as they arise during the year. Keeping both tenant and landlord entries in the same account books aids in summarizing the performance of the whole farm business.

Keeping Accounts for Income Tax Purposes

Current income tax regulations require that farmers who have a gross farm income of $600 or more file an income tax return. As a result, nearly every farmer must keep some type of records on which to base his return. In this section we will focus our attention on farm accounting from the standpoint of income tax reporting.

Comparison of the accrual and cash basis

Farmers may keep accounts and report their income for tax purposes on either the accrual or the cash basis. The accrual method uses inventories. It is the method we have just described in the previous section on making out the net income statement. On the cash basis, farm income includes all cash or value of merchandise or other property received during the year. It does not include value of products sold or of services performed for which payment was not received during the year. On the expense side, all expenses that were paid during the year, regardless of when they were incurred, are deductible. The other principal way in which the cash differs from the accrual method is that no inventories are involved in the income statement.

Most farmers file their report on the cash basis. This preference for the cash basis no doubt is due to the fact that the accounting procedure is somewhat less complicated than the accrual method. Over a period of years, the accrual basis usually results in a more uniform pattern of income from year to year. This is an advantage because tax rates become higher as income increases. Therefore, individuals with a highly variable income are likely to pay more total tax than those who have the same average income over a period of years with a stable income pattern. Farmers reporting on a cash basis must plan their marketing program with one eye on the markets and the other on their tax position. Occasionally they find themselves in the position of having to sell two crops in one year in order to take advantage of favorable markets. This tends to push tax rates into the higher brackets for this year and, as a result, increases the total amount of income tax to be paid. Reporting on an accrual basis largely eliminates these difficulties.

If you have never filed an income tax report, you can start by using either the accrual or cash basis. However, once you have selected a method, you must continue to use it, unless you receive written consent from the income-tax authorities to change.

Forms for income tax reporting

Farmers are required to make a preliminary report of their last year's income on or before January 15, if they report on a calendar-year basis. In this preliminary report, they are required to estimate their receipts, expenses, and net income for the previous year. In addition, the amount of tax due must be computed on the basis of the estimated income and paid at the time the preliminary report is filed. A final report is due on April 15. If the amount of tax due on the final reports turns out to be greater than the tax already paid on the basis of the original estimate, the added tax must be paid. On the other hand, if the amount of tax was overestimated in the preliminary report, the government will refund the difference. Filing a preliminary report can be eliminated by preparing and filing the final report before January 15. A carefully kept set of farm accounts can help in meeting this deadline.

Information required

Farmers must file two basic forms in reporting their income; Form 1040F and Form 1040. We will concentrate our attention on 1040F, because it shows the type of information that must be supplied from farm accounts.

Farmers reporting on the cash basis use pages one and two of Form 1040F and those reporting on the accrual basis use pages two and three. A reproduction of this form is found in Figures 155, 156, and 157. Page one of the form requires a summary of all sales. You will notice that section four of the form is a separate section for entering the income from the sale of purchased items. This is used primarily for reporting the sale of purchased livestock, since

FORM 1040 F
U.S. Treasury Department
Internal Revenue Service

Attach This Form to Your
Income Tax Return Form
1040 and File it With the
District Director of Internal
Revenue for Your District.

SCHEDULE OF FARM INCOME AND EXPENSES
For Calendar Year 1953

1953

If Your Accounts Are Kept on
a Cash Basis, fill in Pages 1
and 2.
If You Keep Books on an
Accrual Basis and Desire to
Use This Form, Fill in Pages
2 and 3 instead.

Or taxable year beginning _____, 1953, and ending _____, 195__

Name _James and Jane Farmer_
Address _Jonesville, State_
Location of farm or farms _2 miles south Jonesville_
Number of acres in each farm _200_

FARM INCOME FOR TAXABLE PERIOD COMPUTED ON CASH RECEIPTS AND DISBURSEMENTS BASIS
(See Instructions on Schedule D (Form 1040) for tax treatment of certain livestock held for draft, breeding, or dairy purposes)

1. SALE OF LIVESTOCK RAISED			2. SALE OF PRODUCE RAISED			3. OTHER FARM INCOME	
Kind	Quantity	Amount	Kind	Quantity	Amount	Items	Amount
Cattle *		$	Grain wheat	725	$ 1,250	Mdse. rec'd for produce	$
Horses			Hay			Machine work	
Mules			Cotton			Hire of teams	
Sheep			Tobacco			Breeding fees	
Swine *	60	2,330	Potatoes	15	25	Rent rec'd in crop shares	
Calves	10	450	Sugar beets			Work off farm	25
			Vegetables			Wood and lumber	
Chickens			Fruits			Other forest products	
Turkeys			Nuts			Agricultural program	
Ducks			Dairy products		5,548	payments	40
Goats			Eggs		292	Patronage dividends, re-	
Bees			Meat products			bates or refunds, if	
Other			Poultry, dressed			not reported elsewhere	
(specify):			Wool and mo-			in return	20
			hair			Other (specify):	
			Honey			Gas tax refund	18
			Sirup and sugar			Feed bags	12
			Other (specify):				
TOTAL		$ 2,780	TOTAL		$ 7,115	TOTAL	$ 115
(Enter on line 1 of summary below)			(Enter on line 2 of summary below)			(Enter on line 3 of summary below)	

Cash Basis (handwritten diagonally across section 1)

4. SALE OF LIVESTOCK AND OTHER ITEMS PURCHASED

1. Description	2. Date acquired	3. Gross sales price (contract price)	4. Cost or other basis	5. Depreciation allowed (or allowable) since acquisition or March 1, 1913	6. Profit (column 3 plus column 5 minus column 4)
20 head cattle	1952	$ 5,000	$ 2,775	$	$ 2,225
** chickens	1953	154	50		104

Cash Basis (handwritten diagonally)

TOTAL (enter on line 4 of summary below) .... $ 2,329

SUMMARY OF INCOME AND DEDUCTIONS COMPUTED ON A CASH RECEIPTS AND DISBURSEMENTS BASIS

1. Sale of livestock raised	$ 2,780	6. Expenses (from page 2)	$ 6,250
2. Sale of produce raised	7,115	7. Depreciation (from page 2)	1,082
3. Other farm income	115	8. Other deductions (specify):	
4. Profit on sale of livestock and other items purchased	2,329		
5. GROSS PROFITS	$ 12,339	9. TOTAL DEDUCTIONS	$ 7,332

10. Net farm profit (or loss) (line 5 minus line 9) to be reported in Schedule C Summary, Form 1040 ... $ 5,007

16—60201-1

* 4 cows, 1 bull, and 2 sows sold, reported on Schedule D.
** If the sale of this item is reported in Sec. 1, page 1, the cost of the chicks may be reported as farm expense on page 2.

Figure 155. Schedule of farm income and expenses. (*Iowa Agr. Ext. Serv. Pamphlet* 209)

FARM EXPENSES FOR TAXABLE YEAR (See Instructions)
(Do not include personal or living expenses or expenses not attributable to production of farm income, such as taxes, insurance, repairs, etc., on your dwelling)

Page 2

1. Items	2. Amount	3. Items (Continued)	4. Amount (Continued)
Labor hired	$ 1,215	Rent of farm, part of farm, or pasturage...	$
Feed purchased	1,760	Freight, yardage, express, and trucking...	
Seed and plants purchased	155	Automobile upkeep (farm share)	125
Machine hire	25	Amortization of grain storage facilities (attach statement)	
Supplies purchased	50		
Cost of repairs and maintenance		Other farm expenses (specify):	
Breeding fees	60	Farm papers	10
Fertilizers and lime	585	Accounting service	30
Veterinary and medicine for livestock	75	Building and fence repair	295
Gasoline, other fuel and oil for farm business	540	Machinery repair	325
		Tractor expense	85
Storage and warehousing		Truck expense	195
Taxes	405		
Insurance on property (except your dwelling)	120	(These expenses are taken from the farm account book.)	
Interest on farm notes and mortgages	35		
Water rent, electricity, and telephone	160		

TOTAL OF COLUMNS 2 AND 4 (enter on line 6 of summary on page 1 (cash basis) or line 7, page 3 (accrual basis)). . . . . $ 6,250

DEPRECIATION (See Instructions)

1. Kind of property (if buildings, state material of which constructed). Exclude land and other nondepreciable property	2. Date acquired	3. Cost or other basis	4. Depreciation allowed (or allowable) in prior years	5. Remaining cost or other basis to be recovered	6. Life used in accumulating depreciation	7. Estimated life from beginning of year	8. Depreciation allowable this year
Barn No. 1	1-5-38	$ 2,400	$ 900	$ 1,500	40	25	$ 60
Barn No. 2	"	750	375	375	30	15	25
*Other buildings	"	3,000	1,130	1,870	—	—	118
Tractors	1-10-51	1,500	300	1,200	10	8	150
Auto (farm share)	1-15-50	400	240	160	5	2	80
Corn picker	7-1-53	1,020	—	1,020	6	—	85
Overhaul tractor	7-11-53	400	—	400	5	—	40
Tires for tractor	4-5-53	160	—	160	5	—	24
*Other machinery	—	4,000	1,200	2,800	—	—	380
3 purchased cows	1-15-50	600	300	300	6	3	100
Bull	1-2-53	140		140	7		20

TOTAL (enter on line 7 of summary on page 1 (cash basis) or line 8, page 3 (accrual basis)). . . . . $ 1,082

16—60201-1

* All buildings and equipment are listed on a detailed depreciation schedule in the farm account book.

Figure 156.

FARM INVENTORY FOR INCOME COMPUTED ON AN ACCRUAL BASIS   Page 3
(Do not include certain livestock held for draft, breeding, or dairy purposes. See Instructions on Schedule D (Form 1040).)

Description (Kind of livestock, crops, or other products)	On Hand at Beginning of Year Quantity	Inventory value	Purchased During Year Quantity	Amount paid	Raised During Year Quantity	Inventory value	Consumed or Lost During Year Quantity	Inventory value	Sold During Year Quantity	Amount received	On Hand at End of Year Quantity	Inventory value
Cows	14	$2,800		$	(2)	$		$		$	16	$3,200
"	4	(800)							4	(785)		
2-yr. heifers	4	600			(4)						6	900
1-yr. "	4	400			(4)						4	400
Heifer calves	4	200			12				10	450	2	100
Herd bull	1	(175)	1	140					1	(300)	1	140
Beef cattle	20	3,500	20	2000					20	5,000	20	2,500
Hens	100	100					30		60	74	100	100
Chicks			220	50			50		80	80	3	250
Brood sows	3	150									3	250
" "	2	(150)							2	(150)		
Boar	1	100									1	100
Pigs	30	600			62		2		60	2,330	30	600
Eggs										292		
Milk										5,548		
Potatoes	10	20			25		10		15	25	10	20
Hay	45	900			80		80				45	900
Corn	1,400	2,100			1,200	1,600			1,000	1,500		
Oats	700	560			800		900				600	540
Silage	50	300			80		85				45	270
Straw	10	100			15		15				10	100
Wheat	150	300			725		100		725	1,250	150	300
Mill feed	2	160									2	200

Accrual Basis (handwritten diagonal)

The values circled are not added in.
These appear on Schedule D.

| TOTALS | | $12,890 (Enter on line 4) | | $2,190 (Enter on line 5) | | $ | | $ | | $15,049 (Enter on line 2) | | $12,120 (Enter on line 1) |

SUMMARY OF INCOME AND DEDUCTIONS COMPUTED ON AN ACCRUAL BASIS

1. Inventory of livestock, crops, and products at end of year... $12,120
2. Sales of livestock, crops, and products during year.. 15,049
2a. Other miscellaneous receipts (specify):
    Work off the farm   25
    PMA 40, Patronage refund 20   60
    Gas tax refund 18, Feed bags 12   30
3.   TOTAL............................. $27,284
4. Inventory of livestock, crops, and products at beginning of year..... $12,890
5. Cost of livestock and products purchased during year............... 2,190   15,080
6. Gross profits (line 3 minus the sum of lines 4 and 5).. $12,204

7. Expenses (from page 2).... $6,250
8. Depreciation (from page 2). 962
9. Other deductions (specify):

10.   TOTAL DEDUCTIONS.. $7,212

11. Net farm profit (or loss) (line 6 minus line 10) to be reported in Schedule C Summary, Form 1040... $4,992

16—69201-1

Figure 157.

Check List of Farm Expenses*

In general, the farmer may deduct from gross receipts all expenditures directly connected with the farm business except those that represent capital investments. The latter most generally may be recovered through depreciation. Many of the expenditures are partly business and partly personal. Only that part which has to do with the farm business is deductible for income-tax purposes.

Labor Hired
Day labor
Season and year labor
Piecework
Cash board

Feed Bought
Grain
Other concentrates
Beet pulp
Feed mixing hired
Hay
Other roughage

Seeds & Plants Bought
Corn
Oats
Rye
Wheat
Other grains
Legumes
Grass
Vegetables†
Seed mixtures
Seed treatment
Plants & vines bought

Machine Work Hired
Tractor
Silo filling
Hay baling   ·
Ginning
Airplane dusting
Other machine work

Supplies Bought
Strainer disks
Washing powders
Leg bands
Stamps and stationery†
Light bulbs & fuses†

Tying Material
Wire
Rope
Twine
Rubber bands

Containers
Bags
Boxes
Egg cases
Poultry and other
crates
Baskets
Cans and pails
Bottles and caps

*Insect and Disease
Control*
Sprays
Dusts
Other materials

Machinery Repairs
Machine-shop work
Repair parts
Blacksmith work
Harness repairs

Farm Bldg. Repairs†
Roofing
Painting
Plumbing
Wiring
Cement
Lumber
Glazing
Nails, screws, bolts
Greenhouse
Coldframes

Livestock Fees
Breeding
Registration, transfer
Cow testing
Exhibition
Sheep shearing

Fertilizer Bought
Mixed fertilizer
Phosphate
Potash
Nitrogen
Lime
Manure

Veterinary
Services
Equipment
Dips
Disinfectants
Fly control
Medicines
Vaccines
Poultry flock treat-
ment
Dehorning

Fuel, Light, Power†
Gasoline
Fuel oil
Oil and grease
Coal
Electricity

Taxes†
Real estate
Other farm property
Auto & truck use tax

Insurance Premiums
Farm buildings†
Livestock
Crops
Accident & liability

Interest Paid
Notes
Chattel mortgages
Real estate mortgage

Rent, Cash
Pasture
Cropland
Buildings

Trucking Hired
Hauling crops
Hauling livestock
Hauling milk
Other hauling†
Freight & express†
Parcel post†

Auto and Truck†
Gas and oil
Antifreeze
Repairs
Tires
Operator's licenses
Insurance

Poultry Bought
Chicks and poults
Other poultry
Hatching eggs
Custom hatching

Miscellaneous
Commissions
Advertising
Storage
Farm papers
Bedding & litter
Small tools and
equipment
Fencing materials
Telephone†
Farm organization
dues
Farm business
travel

* From *Iowa Agr. Ext. Serv. Pamphlet* 209, 1953.
† Particular care should be used with these items to make sure that household expenses are not included.

livestock purchases, unlike other expenses, must be reported in the year in which the livestock is sold. Only the difference between the cost and the gross income from the sale is reported.

Both opening and closing inventories of livestock, crops, feed, and supplies are reported on page three of Form 1040F by farmers using the accrual basis. All purchases and sales of these items are also reported on page three.

Page three of the form provides space for reporting farm expenses and depreciation. The same information is required on this page for both the cash and the accrual method of reporting, with the exception that farmers using the cash basis also enter any depreciation claimed on breeding animals in the depreciation section. Since farmers, on the accrual basis report changes in the value of the breeding herd in their opening and closing inventories, they do not enter depreciation on these animals.

The number and variety of expense items arising out of a farm business is actually much greater than is suggested by the headings provided in the farm expense section. The check list found below shows the wide variety of expenses that are deductible in income tax reporting. It illustrates the difficulty of claiming all deductible expenses without fairly complete farm accounts.

Income is summarized at the bottom of page one for those reporting on a cash basis and at the bottom of page two for those using the accrual method. You will notice that the income summary under the accrual method requires the same information as the income statement shown in Table 78. Thus a farm account book that provides for computing net farm income on an inventory basis contains the basic information needed for filling out 1040F on an accrual basis.

Capital gains and losses

Thus far we have said nothing about one of the most troublesome aspects of income tax accounting—capital gains and losses. Under either system of accounting, gains from the sale of machinery, equipment, and breeding stock (under certain conditions) are called capital gains. The important thing about capital gains is that only 50 per cent of the gains are taxable. Reporting sales as capital gains instead of income thus results in a substantial saving to the taxpayer.

To be eligible for capital gains treatment, the items must have been held for use in the farm business for a period of 6 months or longer (12 months or longer for livestock). The livestock must have been held for draft, breeding, or dairy purposes, and not primarily for sale in the ordinary course of the farm business.

Let us consider several examples to illustrate how the capital gains provisions apply. Suppose you purchased a tractor in 1946 for $1,500 and expected it to last 10 years. Therefore, you depreciated it at the rate of $150 per year. You sold the tractor in 1954 for $500 after you had claimed 8 years' depreciation on it. At the time you sold the tractor, its depreciated value was $300 ($1,500 original cost minus $1,200 depreciation). The amount of capital gains realized on the sale would be $200 (the $500 sale price minus the depreciated value of $300).

With livestock raised on the farm and used for breeding purposes, the entire sale price can be treated as a capital gain in reporting on a cash basis. Only the difference between the inventory value and the sale price is reported when the accrual system is used.

Losses sometimes occur on capital items. For example, in the tractor illustration shown above, you might have sold the tractor for $200 instead of $500. In this case you would have had a capital loss of $100. Total capital losses are subtracted from the total capital gains for the year, and only the difference is reported as capital gains. If capital losses exceed capital gains, the difference up to $1,000 can be subtracted at the full rate from net income.

Capital gains transactions are not reported on form 1040F but are entered in schedule D of form 1040. This is the supplementary form on which all taxpayers compute and report the amount of tax due.

Ordinarily no distinction is made between capital gains and other types of income in computing net income for purposes other than income tax reporting, but most account books make provisions for separating capital gains and losses so that they can be computed easily for tax purposes.

Keeping Project Records

Often students wish to keep accounts on their supervised farming program. Even though the farming program may be small compared to an entire farm business, the accounting principles we have just discussed apply equally as well.

You can check up on the financial progress you are making in your supervised farming program by comparing your net worth from year to year, just as a farm operator does. Likewise, you should follow the same basic principles in calculating project income that are used in making out a net income statement. To get a true picture of the performance of your farming program during the year, it is necessary to compute income on an inventory basis. Depreciation schedules should be set up on items such as the equipment used in project work in the manner already discussed.

Problems in project accounting

The student keeping project records is confronted with several problems that do not occur in keeping accounts for the entire farm business. These difficulties arise principally because projects are closely related to the other enterprises of the farm. Often Dad's buildings, machinery, and equipment are used for the student's supervised farming program. As a result, the problem of what proportion of these expenses to charge to the project arises. For example, suppose you use one tenth of your father's barn to house a sheep enterprise. How much of the total yearly cost of the building should be charged to your project? One method is to allocate the barn costs between your own and your father's business on the percentage of floor space used by each. If you use your father's tractor on your project, how much should be charged to you for its services? One approach is to base the charge on the prevailing custom rate. Another is to estimate the total cost for the number of hours the tractor will be used on the farm during the year. Then you can allocate the cost to your project on the basis of the percentage of hours you used the tractor.

A problem of the appropriate charge to make for land arises with crop projects. Suppose you had some land in corn. How much rent would you credit to the land? Would you charge the same as if the land were in a legume crop, for example? If your project accounts are to reflect the true income-producing ability of corn, it is important that your rental figure include a charge for the decrease in fertility caused by the corn. On the other hand, rental rates on legume crops should reflect the soil-building qualities of legumes. Usually prevailing crop-share rental rates best reflect these differences among crops. Because of the close interrelationship among crops in the cropping system, a project involving only one crop does not present a realistic picture of the cropping problem. If possible, crop projects should be organized to include all the crops grown in a typical rotation.

Making the accounts useful

In project accounting, the use that will be made of the accounts should be considered in planning how they will be kept. Usually one of their chief purposes is to give you experience in using records to appraise the performance of your supervised farming program. If accounts are to be useful for this purpose, it is important that expenses be treated realistically. For example, feed should be charged at market prices, even though it is given to you by your father. Depreciation on equipment used in the project should be charged as an expense, even though the equipment is borrowed. Only in this way will the income figures that are arrived at be meaningful.

Problems

1. Examine a number of farm account books commonly used in your area. Study the books to find where the items necessary to compute net worth are summarized. Do the same thing for the net income statement. Which account book do you think is best?

2. The information given below was taken from the account book of a cornbelt farmer. Select an account book recommended for your area. From the information given below:

   (a) Enter the asset and liability items for the beginning of the year, and compute the net worth of this farm business.

   (b) Enter receipts and all expense items, including livestock purchases and depreciation, for the year. Individual receipt and expense items are furnished for several months to give you practice in making these entries. However, the totals for the entire year are also given to reduce the time required for doing the exercise.

   (c) Enter the inventory and liability items for the end of the year.

   (d) Compute net farm income for the year.

   (e) Determine net worth at the end of the year, and compute the increase or decrease in net worth during the year.

Inventory of Feed, Livestock, and Land, December 31, 1952

Price per unit is indicated by @

Assets

2,100 bu ear corn @ $1.50 per bu	$ 3,150
50 tons cane silage @ $8.00 per ton	400
1,200 bu oats @ $0.88 per bu	1,056
22 tons alfalfa hay @ $20 per ton	440
15 tons straw @ $15 per ton	225
1,400 lb oil meal @ $4.50 per cwt	63
30 cwt hog concentrate @ $5.50 per cwt	165
4 sows (1,200 lb) @ $20 per cwt	240
13 bred gilts (3,900 lb) @ $22 per cwt	858

Inventory of Feed, Livestock, and Land, December 31, 1952 (Cont.)

20 spring pigs (4,400 lb) @ $23 per cwt	1,012
46 fall pigs (3,400 lb) @ $25 per cwt	850
1 boar (350 lb)	75
12 cows being milked @ $250 per head	3,600
1 dry cow	260
1 bull	400
14 dairy calves under 1 yr @ $70 per head	980
3 yearlings @ $150 per head	450
4 2-year-olds @ $220 per head	880
300 laying hens @ $1.25 per hen	375
Cash on hand	1,500
Cash value of life insurance	2,300
160 acres of land @ $240 per acre	38,400

Liabilities

Mortgage on land	$ 6,000
Unpaid interest on mortgage	100
Note at the bank	1,000
Feed bill (unpaid)	400
Veterinary fees (unpaid)	75

Machinery and Equipment Inventory, December 31, 1952, and Depreciation Schedule

Year Bought	Item	Original Cost	Life, yr	Depreciation, 1953	Value at End of 1952
1941	Manure spreader	$ 220	20	$ 11	$ 99
1942	Hay rack	70	10	—	—
1947	Trailer (4-wheel)	260	10	26	130
1949	Field chopper	1,700	10	170	1,190
1942	Disk	40	20	2	20
1950	Cultivator	200	10	20	160
1941	Corn planter	60	20	3	27
1945	Seeder	50	10	5	15
1947	Corn sheller	180	20	9	135
	Small tools	50	—	—	50
1948	Milking machine	200	10	20	120
1944	4 hoghouses	600	15	40	280
1950	Self-feeder	50	10	5	40
1946	Brooder house	200	10	20	80
1942	Plow	150	10	Traded old plow for new	
1952	Plow	—	10	plow in 1953 plus $90	
1951	Mower	300	10	$ 30	$ 270
1946	Truck	1,800	15	120	1,080
1950	Tractor	2,195	15	153	1,889
	Auto (farm share)*		10		800

* A new car was purchased in 1953 for $1,150 plus the old one.

Building Inventory, December 31, 1952, and Depreciation Schedule

	Depreciation per year	Value at End of 1952
Barn	$30	$690
Barn	15	170
Corn crib	10	220
Corn crib	30	435
Silo	10	340
Hoghouse	5	50
Feeding floor	2	44
Feeding floor	1	32
Poultry house	3	221
Hen house	35	990
Granary and brooder house	4	216
Lumber for barn	5	200
Steel tank	3	2
Wiring	2	56
Gates, etc.	5	60
Deep well force pump	15	455
Posts and wire	4	88
Fencing	30	517
Tile	2	956

Inventory of Feed, Livestock, and Land, December 31, 1953 (Cont.)

Assets

3,800 bu ear corn @ $1.50 per bu	$ 5,700
50 tons silage (cane) @ $8.00 per ton	480
600 bu oats @ $.80 per bu	564
20 tons corn silage @ $8.00 per ton	160
80 tons alfalfa @ $20 per ton	1,600
15 tons straw @ $15 per ton	225
200 lb hog concentrate @ $5.50 per cwt	11
200 lb salt @ $1.50 per cwt	3
12 sows (4,800 lb) @ $19 per cwt	912
12 bred gilts (3,000 lb) @ $23 per cwt	690
31 spring pigs (8,000 lb) @ $23 per cwt	1,840
83 fall pigs (6,200 lb) @ $25 per cwt	1,550
1 boar (300 lb)	77
1 cow being milked	170
2 beef calves under 1 year (1,000 lb) @ $25 per cwt	250
35 feeder cattle (30,000 lb) @ $26 per cwt	7,800
240 laying hens @ $1.00 per hen	240
260 pullets @ $1.25 per pullet	325
Cash on hand	2,000
Cash value of life insurance	2,400
160 acres of land @ $240 per acre	38,400

Inventory of Feed, Livestock, and Land, December 31, 1953 (Cont.)

Liabilities

Mortgage on land	$ 5,000
Unpaid interest on mortgage	80
Note at the bank	2,000

Receipts

January 1953

5	Cream check		$ 65.62
5	Milk check		93.01
3	Eggs	127½ doz	50.10
12	Market hogs (19 head)	4240 lb	932.80
17	Eggs	120 doz	35.62
20	Cream		58.14
20	Milk		73.57
24	Eggs	120 doz	41.52
22	Patronage dividend from cooperative elevator		53.14
31	Eggs	120 doz	42.40
	Director's fee for signing cream checks		4.00

February 1953

5	Cream check		$100.89
5	Milk check		74.52
2	Three calves to Boone Sales Co.	810 lb	174.55
7	Eggs	115½ doz	41.13
15	Gas tax refund		8.12
20	Cream		120.10
21	Eggs	120 doz	48.55
28	Patronage refund		38.59
	Director's fee for signing cream checks		4.00

March 1953

6	Dispersal sale of dairy cattle	33 head	$7,774.50
5	Cream check		100.89
15	Eggs	60 doz	24.42
15	Eggs	54 doz	21.87
20	Cream check		87.67
28	Eggs	97½ doz	34.80
31	Market hogs (6 head)	1860 lb	453.54
	Eggs	120 doz	50.00
	Director's fee for signing cream checks		4.00

Inventory of Feed, Livestock, and Land, December 31, 1953 (Cont.)

Total Receipts for Year
(These totals include receipts during
January, February, and March)

Hog sales	$6,586.34
Beef sales	294.55
Dairy cows (dispersal of dairy herd)	7,074.50
Poultry sales	76.00
Egg sales	2,222.41
Dairy product sales	1,019.41
Crop sales (804 bu of corn)	957.00
Receipts from custom work	220.00
Other miscellaneous receipts	112.73

Expenditures

January 1953

6	Oyster shells	300 lb	$ 3.90
9	Farm Business Association dues		19.20
6	Farm Bureau dues		15.00
4	Grinding		2.75
9	Olson's motor oil (auto)		2.04
14	L. G. Benson (interest)		8.00
13	Calf feed	100 lb	8.80
1	Boone County DHIA		20.00
20	Lights (½ or farm share)		7.84
20	Calf feed	100 lb	8.90
20	Laying mash	200 lb	10.80
26	Overhauling pickup truck		85.00
26	Farmers Seed Co. for seed corn		40.00
18	Grinding to O. Lansing		2.75
29	Interest on note to bank		17.52
15	Car license		28.00
15	Truck license		30.00
24	Oyster shells	100 lb	1.30
29	Laying mash	200 lb	10.50
12	Laying mash	200 lb	10.60
12	Calf feed	100 lb	8.90
28	Antifreeze for car		.90
30	Veterinary service		6.00
31	Grinding feed		2.75

Total Farm Expenses for Year
(Includes January)

Hired labor	$ 237.50
Feed bought	1,887.63
Truck and machine hire	386.72
Tractor fuel, oil, and grease	329.09
Auto expense	417.25 (total)

Inventory of Feed, Livestock, and Land, December 31, 1953 (Cont.)

Machinery repairs	485.20
Building and improvement repairs	176.75
Seed and fertilizer	490.93
Veterinary fees and miscellaneous livestock expenses	325.80
Telephone and electricity	102.52 (total)
Farm organization dues, farm magazines, etc.	91.20
Property taxes	480.00
Fire and wind insurance	233.00
Total interest paid	491.00

Livestock Purchases for Year

Date	Item	No.	Weight	Amount
Mar. 22	Red leg chicks	300		$ 54.22
Mar. 30	Hyline pullets	225		135.00
Apr. 7	Heifer to butcher	1	825	178.00
Aug.	Feeder pigs	34		510.00
Oct. 13	Steer	1	525	175.88
Oct. 13	Feeder steers	34	26,320	7,274.80
Oct. 13	Calves	2	860	292.40
Nov. 5	Board	1	250	77.50

Supplementary Information

Home-Used Products

Dairy	$201
Eggs (175 doz)	48
Poultry	50
Hogs (one butchered)	60
Cattle (one-half)	69
	$428

Crop Record	Acres	Total Production
Corn	67	5,000 bu
Silage (cane)	4	40 tons
Oats	36	1,620 bu
Alfalfa	31	90 tons
Total crop acres	138	
Sweet clover pasture	5	Valued at $60 (total)
Untillable blue grass pasture	5	Valued at $40 (total)
Farmstead	8	
Roads	4	
Straw harvested	8	Valued at $67 (total)
Stalks harvested	4	Valued at $36 (total)

Inventory of Feed, Livestock, and Land, December 31, 1953 (Cont.)

Other Information

Sows	15 spring litters	11 fall litters
Pigs farrowed	120 pigs in spring	110 pigs in fall
Pigs weaned	88 pigs in spring	84 pigs in fall
Average number of laying hens on hand during yr		360

Acres owned	160
Acres in legume	36
Grain used for seed	75 bu oats
Hired labor	1 month
Operator labor	12 months
Family labor	1 month
Auto expense chargeable to farm business	50%

References

Case, H. C. M., and Paul E. Johnston, *Principles of Farm Management,* Chapter 14, J. B. Lippincott Co., Chicago, Philadelphia, New York, 1953.

Doneth, J. C., and B. R. Bookout, "Farm Business Inventory and Net Worth Statement," *Mich. State Coll. Ext. Folder* F-154.

Efferson, J. Norman, *Farm Records and Accounts,* Chapters 4, 5, 6, and 12, John Wiley & Sons, New York, 1949.

Hart, V. B., and M. Slade Kendrick, *Cornell Ext. Bull.* 902.

Hopkins, John A., and Earl O. Heady, *Farm Records,* 3d Ed., Iowa State College Press, Ames, 1949.

Hopkins, John A., and William G. Murray, *Elements of Farm Management,* 4th Ed., Chapter 23, Prentice-Hall, New York, 1953.

Robertson, Lynn S., and Ralph H. Woods, *Farm Business Management,* Chapter 15, J. B. Lippincott Co., Chicago, Philadelphia, New York, 1946.

"1953 Farmer's Income Tax," *Iowa Agr. Ext. Serv. Pamphlet* 209, sponsored by North Central Farm Management Extension Committee, 1953.

21

Using Records to
Analyze the Farm Business

In the previous section we saw how farm accounts could be used to check on the financial standing of the farm business and for income tax purposes. With comparatively little added effort, farm records can be extended to provide a basis for further analyzing the farm business. Such an analysis can point to the strong and weak points of the farming program. It can help the farm manager in making needed adjustments.

Management Problems

1. Using information from financial accounts.
2. Keeping crop production records.
3. Keeping livestock production records.

Using Information from Financial Accounts

What information from financial accounts can be of use in evaluating the performance of the farm business? How should you go about analyzing the business? Our task in this section is to find the answer to these two questions.

Farm Business Associations

Farm Business Associations have been organized in some states to help farmers analyze the performance of their business. These organizations are usually sponsored by the state college, but are supported by the farmer members. Usually, there are 125 to 175 members in each association who keep farm accounts and hire a fieldman cooperatively. The fieldman consults with them on accounting and management problems. At the end of the year, he prepares a summary of all the accounts kept by the members of the association. These summaries are useful because they enable the farmer to compare the performance of his business with that of other farms in the association. This provides the farm manager with guideposts for analyzing the performance of his own business.

In many states, farm business association summaries are available through the state college to farmers who are not members of the associations. Thus nonmembers can use these summaries as a basis for comparing the performance of their business, if they are willing to keep and summarize an accurate account of their own business.

Comparison of net income

Net farm income is the most widely used measure of the over-all performance of the farm business. But how can you tell whether you are getting a satisfactory return from the resources you have put into the business? One way is to compare this year's farm income with what the income has been in previous years. A more stimulating approach is to compare your income with that from similar farm businesses in your locality. Usually the comparisons are more meaningful if they are made among farms of similar type and size. However, it is also interesting to see how farmers who put more resources into the business or followed a different type of farming made out.

In comparing the success of a group of farms on the basis of net income, it is best to add together the income of both the tenant and landlord on rented farms. This makes possible a meaningful comparison of tenant- and owner-operated farms. If only the tenant's income were used in comparing a large group of farms, part of which were owner-operated, the rented farms would tend to show up poorly. On the other hand, owner-operated farms would rank higher among the group than their performances really justified.

Operator's earnings

Attempts have been made to refine comparisons of the over-all performance of farms by using operators' earnings or management return as measures of earnings rather than net income.

To arrive at the operator's earnings, you must first compute net income. From this you subtract a charge for the services of the land, capital, and labor other than the operator's that were used in the business. The steps involved in computing the operator's earnings may be summarized as follows:

1. Compute net farm income for the whole farm business.

2. Determine a rental charge for all land used in the business, regardless of whether the farm is tenant- or owner-operated.

3. Calculate an interest charge for all capital invested in machinery, equipment, livestock, and feed.

4. Make an estimate of the value of family labor used during the year.

5. Subtract the sum of items two, three, and four from net income to get the operator's labor earnings.

The basic data needed to make these computations are already available in farm accounts that have been kept for computing net worth and net income on an inventory basis. Rental, interest, and wage rates used in making land, capital, and family labor charges should be in line with prevailing market rates. Wages for hired labor and interest on borrowed capital should not be subtracted from net income in arriving at the operator's earnings. These items have already been entered as expenses in arriving at net income.

Many farm management workers believe that comparison of farms on the basis of operators' earnings gives a more accurate indication of their performance than net income alone. The charges made for land, capital, and family labor tend to correct for variations in income arising out of differences in the quantities of these resources used in the business. As with net income, comparisons of operators' earnings are most meaningful among farms of the same type and size.

Operators' earnings also can be used by farmers to compare the income they are making on the farm with that of a man working for wages. For example, suppose a farmer who owned his farm debt-free and whose equipment and livestock were paid for had a net income of $8,000 and an operator's earnings of $4,000. The $4,000 difference between net income and operator's earnings represents a return on the money he has invested in land, livestock, and equipment. If he chooses to work at some other occupation, he could still expect to get a comparable return from his capital. Therefore, for his earnings in another occupation to compare favorably with farming on a dollar-and-cents basis, he would have to earn $4,000 in wages.

Management return

Management return, a measure closely related to operator's labor earnings, is used in some states to compare earnings. The two measures are computed in the same way, with one exception: A charge for the operator's labor is subtracted from net farm income along with rent on land and interest on working capital in computing management return. Although this measure goes one step further than operator's labor earnings, it actually serves the same purpose. It is also subject to the same limitations.

When management return is above zero, the farmer supposedly has realized a greater return than if he had hired out his resources (including his own labor) at going market rates. When management return drops below zero, it means that the land, labor, and capital being used in the farm business are not yielding a return comparable with going rental, interest, and wage rates.

Interpreting measures of farm earnings

How should you interpret measures of farm earnings? What does a high operator's labor earnings or management return mean? What importance should you attach to low earnings? In interpreting high earnings, you should make sure that the favorable showing was not due to some accounting irregularity before concluding that the business has performed well. For example, a large income for one year may be the result of selling a dairy herd that had been carried in the inventory at a value well below current market prices, or the favorable showing for a single year may be due to following an exploitive farming program that will not continue to yield high returns year after year. In other cases large earnings may be caused by rising prices and the resulting increase in inventory values.

Nor do low earnings always indicate that the business is poorly organized and managed. They may have resulted from a sharp drop in inventory prices, or they may be due to unavoidable crop failure. If the low earnings can definitely be traced to either of these causes, they should not be taken as evidence that changes are needed in the management of the business. However, low earnings that cannot be explained by temporary misfortunes should be regarded as danger signals. Studying farm records and accounts can help locate some of the causes, but improving the business often is not easy. A detailed analysis of the business requires a broad knowledge of economic principles and tools as they apply to farming. These have been covered in the preceding chapters in the text.

Size of business

One of the first things to examine in attempting to find the reason for an unsatisfactory income is the size of the business. Three measures of size of business, man work units, total capital managed, and the value of gross production, can be computed from farm accounts. We studied how to estimate man work units in Chapter 20. Total capital managed is the value of all land, machinery, livestock, feed, and equipment used in the farm business. Usually an average of the beginning and ending inventories is employed in figuring it.

To compute the total value of gross production, you should make the following calculations:

1. Add together the value of the ending inventory of crops and livestock and all receipts during the year from sale of crops and livestock.

2. Add together the value of the beginning inventory of crops and livestock and purchases of livestock and feed.

3. Subtract the total obtained in step 2 from the total obtained in step 1.

The total value of gross production is sometimes referred to as gross profits. The influence of size of business on income was discussed in Chapter 19.

Gross production per worker

The value of gross production per worker is sometimes used as a measure of labor efficiency. To compute this ratio, the value of gross production is divided by the number of workers on the farm. To determine the number of workers employed on the farm, you must first add up the total man-months of labor used. A man-month of labor is the equivalent of one man working full time for 26 days. After you have determined the total man-months of labor, divide it by 12 to arrive at the equivalent in terms of full-time workers through the year. The labor force on the farm is usually made up of the operator, several family members working part time, plus some hired labor.

Low gross production per worker is often found on farms that are too small. But in some cases output per worker may be low even though the volume of production for the whole farm business is satisfactory. When this situation exists, the manager should try to find the reason. Does the low output result from maintaining enterprises that normally have a high labor requirement, or does it result from inefficient use of labor? If so, is the work program poorly planned? Should more labor-saving equipment and machinery be purchased?

Power and machinery cost per crop acre

This ratio is of value in appraising the efficiency with which the power and machinery are used. The basic data for computing power and machinery investment per crop acre can be found in the account book, since they are needed to determine net income. The first step is to list and total all power and machinery expense items. These should include fuel and oil, repairs, depreciation, and any miscellaneous items connected with operating machinery. If custom work is hired, its costs should be included in the total. However, that part of the custom work bill which represents a payment for hired labor should not be included. The cost of keeping horses should be treated as power costs if the horses are used for farm work.

Total machine costs should be divided by the total number of crop-acres on the farm in order to arrive at power and machinery cost per crop-acre. Neither permanent nor rotation pasture should be included in crop-acres.

What use can be made of the power and machinery cost figure? It is most valuable in making comparisons among farms following a similar type of farming. Farmers should not strive necessarily to keep power and machinery costs at the lowest possible figure. However, if machine costs appear to be out of line, the farm operator should attempt to find out why. It may be that he can justify the higher cost on the basis of saving labor or getting work done in a timely manner. On the other hand, the high cost may be due to overinvestment in machinery, low annual use, or lack of care in maintaining and operating machines. Methods of reducing power and machinery costs were discussed in Chapter 13.

Power and machinery investment per acre

Another measure of machinery efficiency closely related to cost per crop-acre is investment per crop-acre. We have stressed repeatedly the importance of holding down the investment in machinery where capital is limited. Therefore, under these conditions, it is especially important to make a careful analysis of power and machinery investment. The total investment in tractors and machinery can be obtained from the depreciation schedule in the account book. If horses are used for farm work, they should be included. Crop-acres should be computed by the method explained in the previous section.

Keeping Crop Production Records

What crop records should be kept? One simple but useful record is a history of the crops grown. A map on which the fields have been drawn in, together with the acreages in each field should form the basis of the crop record. If the cropping program followed on the farm is fairly uniform from year to year, this task is not difficult. Once the acreages have been measured, they can be used year after year. Irregular fields are much more difficult to measure than square or rectangular fields. This is especially true if the farm has been laid out so that it can be farmed on the contour. Many farmers have found the measurements made by the Agricultural Stabilization and Conservation (formerly the PMA) office helpful. This agency has instruments not usually available to the typical farmer that enable their workers to estimate acreages accurately. If you have an aerial map of the farm, you can make reasonably accurate measurements of irregular fields by the use of a transparent, celluloid scale designed for this purpose.

Keeping a record of the crops grown in each field helps in planning the cropping program in future years. You may think that a record of this type is unnecessary because you can remember back as many years as you need to. But, if the cropping program is irregular, this is often more difficult than you may think. The same map can be used for a number of years. Along with the crop that was grown, a record should also be kept of the lime, fertilizer, and manure that was applied.

In addition to a record of the crops grown and soil management practices, both total production and yield per acre should be estimated for the crops that are harvested. Usually these estimates can be made without involving a great deal of time. If the farmer knows the capacity of his bins, he can estimate the proportion of the total crop produced in each field on the basis of the number of loads coming from each. To do this, he should keep a record of the number of loads harvested from each field. If he does not know the capacity of his storage facilities, he can estimate them sufficiently accurately by using the procedure explained in the preceding chapter. Once the total production from the field has been estimated, yield per acre can be determined by dividing the total production by the number of acres in the field.

Hay yields are somewhat more difficult to estimate than grain yields because estimates based on measurements are less accurate. When hay is baled, several bales should be weighed and the yield estimate made on the basis of the total number of bales harvested. If hay is put up with a loader, farmers can usually make a fairly accurate estimate of the size of the load after they have weighed a number of loads.

When part of the field has been fertilized and part has not, or when two crop varieties are planted in the same field, the information obtained from the crop record will be more useful if yield estimates are made for each part of the field. This facilitates comparing yields from different practices or crop varieties and helps in making next year's plans.

In addition to supplying information of value in planning the cropping system, the crop record also helps in evaluating the performance of the livestock program. This is true because an accurate record of crop production helps in compiling feed records. Its use for this purpose will be explained in the next section on livestock records.

Keeping Livestock Production Records

Checking livestock numbers

How can the farmer be sure that all livestock on hand at the start of the year or raised or purchased during the year are accounted for in his records? One method is to make a livestock check. This helps discover any sales, purchases, livestock deaths that might have been overlooked in keeping farm accounts. It is also useful in working out the average number of certain classes of livestock on hand during the year. This figure is needed to estimate rate of livestock production, a problem to be discussed later.

Suppose you wish to check hog numbers to see that they were all accounted for, how would you proceed? The following relationship provides the basis for the check:

The sum of
1. The number on hand at the start of the year plus
2. The number weaned during the year plus
3. The number purchased during the year
must equal the sum of
1. The number on hand at the end of the year plus
2. The number sold during the year plus

3. The number died plus

4. The number butchered for home use.

If these two sums are not equal, an error has been made somewhere. The next step is to find out where by checking more closely. Farmers may find, for example, that several hogs had been sold that were not entered in the account book, or they may discover that they have made a mistake in making a count for the inventory. In other cases, hogs may have died that were not accounted for.

What information must a farmer have in order to make an accurate check on hog numbers? First, he needs a record of purchases and sales as well as of the numbers on hand at the beginning and the end of the year. Since this information is needed anyway in order to compute net income, no extra work is involved. In addition, he needs a count of the number of pigs weaned and the number that die after weaning.

Estimating rates of livestock production

Many farmers find it helpful in studying their farming operations to compute the number of pounds of butterfat produced per cow, eggs laid per hen, and pigs weaned per litter. In order to determine

Figure 158. Some dairymen belong to Dairy Herd Improvement Associations. Members of these groups keep records of the milk produced and feed consumed by each cow in the herd.

butterfat production per cow or eggs laid per hen, you must know the average number of cows or hens on hand during the year. You could use an average of the opening and closing inventories as an estimate of this figure, but, if the number of hens or cows changed markedly during the year, this method could be badly in error. Keeping a running inventory from month to month will furnish a more accurate estimate of the average number on hand during the year.

An illustration of how the livestock checking system can be used in maintaining a running inventory of the dairy herd is shown in Table 79. You will notice that the method used is the same as for hogs, except that "heifers freshened" replaces "pigs weaned." Once a running inventory has been made for the year, you can find the average number of cows milked during the year by taking an average of the monthly inventories. In the example found in Table 79, the average number of cows milked during the year was 20.9.

Table 79. Running Inventory and Check of Cows in Dairy Herd

	Jan.	Feb.	Mar.	Apr.	May	June	July	Aug.	Sept.	Oct.	Nov.	Dec.
No. on hand, beginning of month	21	20	22	21	23	22	22	22	23	19	18	18
No. purchased	0	0	0	1	0	0	0	0	0	0	0	0
No. of heifers freshened	0	2	0	1	0	1	0	1	0	0	0	0
Total no. to be accounted for	21	22	22	23	23	23	22	23	23	19	18	18
No. sold	1	0	1	0	1	0	0	0	4	1	0	0
No. died	0	0	0	0	0	1	0	0	0	0	0	0
No. on hand end of month	20	22	21	23	22	22	22	23	19	18	18	18
Total no. accounted for	21	22	22	23	23	23	22	23	23	19	18	18

The system of checking illustrated above becomes even more useful with the poultry flock because the number fluctuates more widely during the year and the number on hand at the start of the month is more difficult to estimate. Rather than count the number of birds in the flock at the start of each month, many flock owners keep track of the hens that are sold, die, or are butchered for home use each month. If this information is kept accurately, they can determine the number on hand at the start of each month without making a count.

To compute butterfat production per cow, farmers must know the total production of butterfat during the year, in addition to the average number of cows milked. Dairymen who sell cream can determine the total number of pounds of butter fat sold from their cream slips. To this they should add any butterfat used in the household in the form of milk. If whole milk is sold, the total number of pounds of butterfat can be estimated by multiplying the number of pounds of milk by the average per cent of butterfat contained in it. Once the total pounds of butterfat produced on the farm have been determined, the average output per cow can be estimated by dividing the output by the average number of cows on the farm during the year.

A similar procedure can be used to estimate the number of eggs laid per hen. Some poultry raisers prefer to keep a running account of the rate of lay. They do this by dividing the average number of eggs laid each day during the month by the number of hens in the flock.

How should you interpret these rates of production or livestock yields? Is the highest rate always the most profitable? The answer to these questions is that the profitability of high rates of production depends on the costs incurred in achieving them. At low rates of production, housing and equipment costs and labor required per unit of output produced are likely to be high. If the total cost is the same, cows producing more milk or hens laying more eggs will be more profitable. However, beyond a point, higher rates of production can be achieved only at the expense of higher costs because of the law of diminishing returns. Thus, the farm operator must balance the added costs against the added returns in pushing to higher levels of production. These problems were discussed in the chapters on livestock management.

Feed records

Feed costs typically make up 60 to 80 per cent of the cost of producing livestock products. For this reason, records of feed consumed by the different classes of livestock on the farm are useful in analyzing the livestock program. Most farmers do not keep detailed feed records because of the amount of time that would be involved. However, by careful planning, simplified methods can be developed that reduce the work of record keeping.

Most feed records are set up to estimate the return per $100 feed fed to each class of livestock. In order to do this, it is necessary to determine the gross value of each type of livestock produced. This involves little extra effort since the basic information needed to arrive at the value of livestock production is recorded in accounts kept on the inventory basis. In addition, the quantity of feed fed to each class of livestock must be determined and a value placed on it.

The crop and feed check

Estimating the amount of feed fed to each class of livestock is the most difficult part of keeping a feed record. What is the best way to make these estimates? Few farmers weigh the feed that goes to each class of livestock every day because of the extra work that would be involved. Usually sufficient accuracy can be achieved by weighing the amount of feed once a month or every time the ration is changed.

One device that can help insure greater accuracy in feed records is the crop and feed check. With this system the amount of feed fed is checked against that available as a result of production on the farm, purchases, and inventory supplies. The basic relationship used in the feed check is as follows:

The sum of
1. The total on hand at the beginning of the year plus
2. The total raised during the year plus
3. The amount purchased

minus
1. The amount on hand at the end of the year plus
2. The amount sold during the year plus
3. The amount used for seed plus

equals the amount available for feed.

The next step is to add up the total amount of feed fed to each class of livestock. If all records have been kept accurately, the total amount fed should equal the amount available for feed as determined by the relationship shown above. An illustration of the way in which a feed check can be made is shown in Table 80. The figures are presented in round numbers so that you can follow through the illustration more easily.

You will notice that in the example the amount of feed actually fed exactly equals that estimated as available for feeding purposes. This does not often happen in practice. If the difference between the two figures is not great, finding the source of the inaccuracy is not important, but, if large differences appear, you should attempt to find the reason. There are several possible sources of error. Perhaps you have made a mistake in inventorying feeds, or you may have overlooked some purchases or sales. The difference may be due to over- or underestimating the amount of feed produced. Any of the mistakes mentioned above will result in inaccuracies in the estimate of the amount available for feed. Of course, mistakes can also be made in determining the amount of feed fed to livestock. Thus, when large discrepancies appear in the feed check, estimates of the amount of feed fed should be re-examined and adjustments made where they appear justified.

You will notice that the crop and feed check helps to uncover mistakes in crop sales and feed purchases. It also helps to point

Table 80. Crop and Feed Check

	Corn, bu	Oats, bu	Hay, tons	Protein Supplement, cwt	Silage
1. On hand at beginning of year	4,000	1,000	20	5	0
2. Raised during year	5,000	1,500	31	0	0
3. Purchased	0	0		190	0
4. Total to be accounted for (sum of items 1, 2, and 3)	9,000	2,500	51	195	0
5. On hand at end of year	3,500	1,200	26	10	0
6. Sold during year	0	0	0	0	0
7. Used for seed	0	200	0	0	0
8. Total accounted for other than feed (sum of items 5, 6, and 7)	3,500	1,400	26	10	0
9. Total remaining for feed (Item 4 minus item 8)	5,500	1,100	25	185	0
10. Fed to hogs	3,800	500	1	135	0
11. Fed to cattle	1,500	200	24	20	0
12. Fed to dairy cows	0	0	0	0	0
13. Fed to other dairy cattle	0	0	0	0	0
14. Fed to poultry	200	400	0	30	0
15. Fed to sheep	0	0	0	0	0
16. Total fed (sum of items 10, 11, 12, 13, 14, and 15)	5,500	1,100	25	185	0

up errors in inventorying feeds and in estimating total crop production.

Methods of computing returns per $100 feed fed

Now let us see how the information contained in feed records and in the crop and feed check can be used to compute returns per $100 feed fed. Suppose, for example, you wished to determine returns per $100 feed fed to hogs. The first step is to compute the value of hogs produced as follows:

Value of hogs on hand at end of year	$ 3,000	Value of hogs on hand at end of year	$2,500
Hog sales	9,000	Hog purchases	100
Value of hogs butchered for home use	100		
	$12,100		$ 2,600

$12,100 minus $2,600 equals $9,500, the total value of hogs produced during the year.

The second step is to estimate the total value of feed fed to hogs during the year. You can estimate the quantities of feed fed from the crop and feed check. All purchased feeds should be valued at the price you paid for them. Feeds such as corn, grain, and hay should be valued on the basis of what they would net at the farm if they were sold. Pastures should be charged at rental rates prevailing in the community for pasture of comparable quality. If you use the information from the crop and feed check illustration in Table 80, the value of feed fed to hogs would be as follows:

3,800 bu of corn at $1.50 per bu	$5,700.00
500 bu of oats at $0.70 per bu	350.00
135 cwt of protein supplement at $5.50 per cwt	742.50
1 ton of alfalfa hay at $24 per ton	24.00
7 acres of pasture at $14 per acre	91.00
Total value of feed fed to hogs	$6,907.50

The third and final step is to divide total returns from hogs by feed costs and then multiply the dividend by 100. Therefore, $\frac{\$9,500.00}{\$6,907.50} \times 100 = \$137.53$, the return per $100 feed fed to hogs.

Interpreting returns per $100 feed fed

How can estimates of returns per $100 feed fed to each class of livestock be used to improve the farm business? First, you should bear in mind that feed returns furnish no information concerning the other costs that enter into livestock production. If you realized a return of $100 for every $100 feed fed, you would be meeting feed costs, but you would have no return to cover such costs as labor, veterinary fees, housing, and equipment expenses. Since these other costs are greater with some classes of livestock than with others, the amount of return per $100 feed fed necessary to break even differs among enterprises.

For example, we found in Chapter 8 that costs other than feed are less for hogs than for dairying. Therefore, a feed return of $137 would usually allow a hog producer to make a small profit, but the same return from a dairy enterprise likely would not permit the farm operator to meet all his costs.

Feed-return figures are most useful if you can compare them with returns from the same class of livestock on other farms. Suppose you find that, on the average, a large group of hog producers realized $150 return per $100 feed fed, while you got only $137. The difference is sufficiently great to suggest that something is wrong with your hog program. The trouble may be due to a low selling price resulting from poor timing of production and marketing, or the low returns may be due to high-cost gains caused by a poor ration or by disease and parasite troubles.

Since most farms have several livestock enterprises, feed returns as a whole may be satisfactory in spite of the poor performance of one or two enterprises. High returns on some classes of livestock may make up for unprofitable enterprises. Feed records will aid in uncovering such a situation. Their principal function is to indicate when something is wrong. However, they will not show the cause of the trouble. You can determine this only after a detailed analysis of the enterprise as explained in Chapters 9 through 12.

Problems

1. Secure a copy of the most recent summary of the Farm Business Association in your area. If there are no business associations in your state, obtain a report from a near-by state. What measure is used to compare earnings among farms? What other measures of the performance of the farm business are used?

2. Using the information presented on the farm business at the end of Chapter 20, compute the following:

(a) Operator's earnings.

(b) Value of total gross production.

(c) Value of gross production per worker.

(d) Power and machinery cost per acre.

3. Prepare a map of your home farm, and write in the crops that were grown in each field for as many years in the past as you can get sufficient information. Enter the types and amounts of fertilizer applied to each field during the past cropping season. Make estimates of the yields obtained from each field during the last year.

4. Make out two forms similar to that in Table 79 and keep running inventories on the two most important livestock enterprises on your home farm.

5. Examine the record book used for keeping records on your project or supervised farming program. Does it contain the information necessary for computing returns per $100 feed fed? If so, compute returns per $100 feed fed from any livestock enterprises you have carried on? How do they compare with the returns realized on farms in the Farm Business Association in your area or in a neighboring area? How do you account for any differences?

References

Case, H. C. M., and Paul E. Johnston, *Principles of Farm Management*, Chapter 14, J. B. Lippincott Co., Chicago, Philadelphia, New York, 1953.

Forster, G. W., *Farm Organization and Management*, 3d Ed., Chapter 22, Prentice-Hall, New York, 1953.

Hopkins, John A., and Earl O. Heady, *Farm Records*, 3d Ed., Chapters 3, 4, and 17, Iowa State College Press, Ames, 1949.

Hopkins, John A., and William G. Murray, *Elements of Farm Management*, 4th Ed., Chapter 23, Prentice-Hall, New York, 1953.

Robertson, Lynn S., and Ralph H. Woods, *Farm Business Management*, Chapter 15, J. B. Lippincott Co., Chicago, Philadelphia, New York, 1946.

Index

Abstract of title, 74
Accounts, on partnership farms, 419
  reasons for keeping, 405
  receivable in net worth statement, 411, 412
Accrual method of accounting, 413, 415
Acreage control programs, participation in, 358
  problems created by, 361
  risk arising from, 371
Acres per farm in United States, changes in, 399
Added costs balancing with added returns, 126, 132
Added returns balancing with added costs, 126, 132
Aerial maps, 442
Agreement to purchase, 74
Agricultural Adjustment Act, 359
Alfalfa, average yield from, 117
  cost of production of, 105
Allen, Carl W., 154
Alternative returns, principle of, in allocating labor, 251, 313
  in farm machinery decisions, 290
  in fertilizer decisions, 130
  in planning farm buildings, 339, 345
  statement of, 33
Animal units, 391
April, work schedule for, 318
Artificial drying of corn, 242
Artificial heat, providing, 214
Assets, definition of, 95, 406
  in net worth statement, 412
Auction sales, buying feeder cattle at, 365
  selling purebred cattle at, 188
August, work schedule for, 319

Balancing added costs and added returns, in feeding dairy cows, 241

Balancing added costs and added returns, in fertilizer application, 126
  in improving forage quality, 246, 247
  in marketing hogs, 204
  in pasture improvement, 122, 123
  in poultry housing, 263
Balancing feed requirements with crop production, 298
Banks, commercial, as source of farm mortgage credit, 85
  as source of production credit, 90
Bargaining in buying, 364
Barger, E. L., 289
Beef cows, capital requirements of, 181
  cost and returns from, 226
  economy in housing, 227
  feed requirements for, 171, 172
  hay and pasture required for, 175
  labor required for, 177
  returns per $100 feed fed from, 167
  utilizing forage through, 154
Beef production, in range areas, 217
  management problems, 217
  specialization in, 217
Bloat, losses from, 184
Bonus arrangements for hired help, 331
Bookhout, B. R., 255
Bran, seasonal price pattern of, 366
Breed associations, 188
Brown, L. H., 255
Budgets, adjusting for year-to-year changes, 308
  choosing alternatives for, 294
  cropping system, 297
  estimating yields for, 303
  interpreting, 306, 307
  livestock program, 299, 300
  partial, 309
    advantages of, 310
    summary of, 310

Budgets, purposes of, 292
  refining, 306
  selecting prices for, 299
  use of economic principles in, 294
Buffer strips, 149
Buildings, appraisal of obsolete, 67
  arranging on farmstead, 336, 337
  costs in budgets, 304
  on rented farms, 48
  special rents for, 54
  valuing on basis of cost of production, 73
Bull, cost of keeping, 249
Butterfat prices, seasonal pattern of, 252
Butterfat production per cow, computing, 446
  interpreting, 446
Buying of feed to increase farm output, 401
  of supplies, factors to consider in, 363
  increasing importance of, 363
  obtaining help in, 367
  time spent in, 366
Buying and selling economies on large farms, 397

Calves, efficiency of gain on, 219
Capital, gains and losses, forms for reporting, 427
  methods of calculating, 426
  influence of limited quantities, 9
  items of, 8
  making best use of, 31
  managed, as a measure of farm size, 72
  position, effect on livestock program, 164
  reducing need for on beginning farms, 35
  requirements for conservation, 153
Capitalization rate, effect of lowering, 70
  selection of, 68
Cargill, B. F., 255
Cash method of accounting, 413
Cash leases, 40
  advantages to tenants of, 41
  sliding scale, 42

Catron, Damon, 207
Cattle, change in number on farms, 353
  feeding, adapting programs to the feed supply, 223
  break-even points in, 221, 222
  differences in programs, 218
  indirect returns from, 222
  of low-quality animals, 220
  price margin in, 217, 218
  prices, of slaughter steers, 225
  seasonal trends in, 225
  sources of profits in, 217, 218
  timing of programs, 224
  use of low-grade roughage in, 224
  value of gain over feed cost in, 217, 218
Central farrowing houses, 213
Check list of jobs, 318
Checking livestock numbers, 443
Cheese production, increases in, 235
Chore routine, savings possible in, 321
  simplifying, 320
  travel in, 320
Circular travel, providing for, 326
Collateral, 98
Combining, cost of, 276
Commodity Credit Corporation, 359
Compensation for unexhausted improvements, 48, 53
Competitive relationship, 113
Complementary relationship, 111
Conservation, changes in cropping patterns resulting from, 151
  compensation for, 53
  influence of financial position on, 150
  on rented farms, 47, 48
Contouring, 142, 151
  effect on soil loss, 146
  experience in working with, 157
  returns from, 146
Contract, buying on, 81
Contract of sale, 74
Control of anemia, 214
Corn, applying fertilizer to, 126
  cost of production of, 104
  gross income-producing ability of, 103

Corn, labor required to produce, 105
 silage, estimating tons of, 407
 yield when used as silage, 117
Corn-hog ratio, 351, 352
Cornstalks, marketing through livestock, 160
Credit, long term, 81, 99
 amortizing, 86, 99
 criticisms of, 84
 determining provisions of, 86
 prepayment privileges, 88
 repayment schedule for, 86
 sources of, 82
 production, 88
 budgeting, 92, 93
 productive use of, 94
 sources of, 89
 rating, establishing a good, 98
 factors influencing, 99
 use during price declines, 350
 using for farm buildings, 339
Credits, 418
Crop and feed check, computing, 447
 examples of, 448
 uses of, 448
Crop-share leases, 42
 risk under, 43
Cropping program, management problems in planning, 102
 planning, long run, 114
 short run, 112
Cropping systems, on rented farms,
 55
Crops, estimating gross income from,
 102
 high income, 102
 intertilled, 142
 production records, methods of
 keeping, 442
 use of, 443
 projects, accounting problems with,
 428
 rotations, advantages of, 109
 comparing returns from, 110
 difficulties in following, 120
 experiments with, 115
 influence of fertilizer on, 115
 problems in establishing, 119
 selecting profitable, 110

Crops, rotations, use of budgets in
 selecting, 114
 yield per acre in selecting, 111
Cultivating corn, cost of, 276
Custom work, cost of, 281
 for other farmers, 279
 hiring, 280, 281
 influence of capital position on,
 281

Dairy chores, saving labor in, 255
Dairy cows, artificial breeding of, 249
 capital requirements of, 181
 fall and wintering freshening of, 252
 feed required for replacements, 171
 feeding, adjusting to differences
 among individuals, 239
 effect of heavier feeding on, 240
 effect of price changes on, 243
 most profitable grain-milk ratio,
 244
 hay and pasture required for, 175
 most profitable rate of production
 of, 241
 production pattern of, 252
 returns per $100 feed fed from, 167
 risks involved with, 183
 utilizing forage through, 154
Dairy farms, crop rotations on, 116
 pasture programs on, 120
Dairy Herd Improvement Associations, 249
Dairy housing, cost in relation to size
 of herd, 397
Dealers as source of credit, 89
Debits, 418
December, work schedule for, 319
Decisions, qualifications for making
 and carrying out, 7
 on beginning farms, 36
 seeking advice in making, 36
Deed, warranty, 74
Demand for farm products, 355
Depreciation, buildings, 338
 estimates for appraisal purposes, 67
 machinery, 271
 methods of estimating, 408
 straight line, 409
Depressions, 349

Diminishing returns, in applying fertilizer, 126, 127
in egg production, 261, 263
in feeding dairy cows, 241
principle of, 126, 132
Disease, as cost in hog production, 194
as source of risk, 370
Diversification, of enterprises, 374
of marketing, 199
Down payment, minimum in buying a farm, 64
Drainage, on rented farms, 51
poor, recognizing, 72
Drawing up leasing terms, 45
Drylot, feeding cattle in, 172
feeding hogs in, 168, 208
Dual-purpose cattle, returns per $100 feed fed from, 167

Economy of gains in relation to marketing weight for hogs, 205
Egg-feed ratio, 260, 261
Eggs, prices, seasonal pattern of, 264
production, distribution in the United States, 258
fixed cost of, 260
increase in efficiency of, 256
needed to break even, 260, 261
seasonal pattern of, 264, 265
variable cost of, 260
Eggs laid per hen, estimating, 446
interpreting, 446
Electricity as a source of power, 288
Engene, S. A., 270
Enterprise agreements, 18
Enterprises, problems in combining, 10, 184, 185
Equipment, labor-saving, 331
Erosion, soil, controlling, 115
planning field layouts to reduce, 118
symbols on maps, 142
Estimating feed requirements, 298
Exchange arrangements, advantages of, 280
brood sows, 35
feed, 35
machinery, 279

Expenses, budget of, 302, 304, 311
classifying household and farm, 416
deductible, 425
hog production, 197, 199
repairs as, 417, 418
sharing on rented farms, 48

Family goals, choosing, 11
conflicts in, 14
gearing to income, 15
Farm appraisal, based on cash-rental rates, 71
safeguards in, 72
steps in, 64
Farm buildings, flexibility in, 339
low-cost structures, 342
overinvesting in, 338
permanent, 343
planning, 338, 339
remodeling, 345
temporary, 343
Farm Business Associations, 436
Farm expenses, estimating, 302, 304
Farm owners, methods of becoming, 57
responsibility on rented farms of, 55
Farm ownership, achieving the goal of, 58
advantages of, 58
disadvantages of, 59
pride in, 59
Farm real-estate prices, fluctuations in, 60
Farm work simplification, purposes of, 325
steps in, 322
Farmers Home Administration, 84, 92
Farmstead, costs of, 334
model layouts of, 336
planning the arrangement of, 335
Fayette soils, 132
February, work schedule for, 318
Federal Land Banks, organization of, 83
purposes of, 83
Feed, carts, 321
records, importance of, 446
use of, 447

Feed, requirements, variations in, 169
reserves for drouth years, 378
supply, influence of conservation program on, 151, 152
providing a balanced, 109, 120
selecting an economical, 120
Feeder cattle, capital requirements of, 181
feed required for, 172, 178, 180
hay and pasture required for, 175
information on prices of, 365
labor requirements for, 177
returns per $100 feed fed from, 167
Feeds, influence of prices on, 206
most profitable combination of, 206
Fences, cost of moving, 148
types of, 119
Fertilizers, balancing, 133
estimating response from, 135
high analysis, 125
increase in consumption of, 129
meaning of formulas, 124
most profitable rate of application of, 125, 130
planning a program for, 124
plant nutrients in, 125
sharing cost of, 51
FFA projects, as a step to establishment in farming, 20
using skills acquired in, 164
Field layout, effect of livestock program on, 118
planning the, 117
rearranging for conservation plans, 147
Field renting, 400
Financial progress, measures of, 406, 413
Finding a farm to rent, influence of financial position, 30
preparation for, 29
sources to contact in, 29
Fixed cost, in adjusting to price changes, 354
in machine operation, 270
in milk production, 248
relationship to annual use, 275

Flexibility, in adjusting to price changes, 354
in work schedule, 317
Flock size, adjusting to price changes, 259
Floyd silt loam, 135
Forages, comparison of average yield from, 117
competitive to grain, 113, 114
complementary to grain, 111
high quality, cost of producing, 245
effect on grain requirements, 239
effect on milk production, 245
making profitable use of, 152, 153
methods of increasing supply of, 123
on dairy farms, 120
quality needed for different livestock enterprises, 169
Fractional quarters, 76
Fruit crops, risk in producing, 373
Futures market, 377

Gasoline tax refunds, 416
Goals of farm business, choice of, 12
conflicts in, 14
influence of leisure on, 13
Grade-A milk, meaning of, 234
risk in producing, 371
Grain, total production of, influence of forage on, 111, 112
sacrificing, to produce forage, 115
Grain-milk ratio, in feeding dairy cows, 244
Grain storage, priority of, in building program, 345
Grass silage, 246, 247
Grassed waterways, 149
Grazing, controlled, 122
rotational, 122
Great Plains area, risk in, 374
Gross income, computing, for appraisal purposes, 67
from crops, 103
Gross production, as measure of size of business, 392
per worker, 440
Gross profits, 440
Gullying of soil, 138

Hail damage, estimating, 382
Hand stripping, eliminating, 321
Hay, cost of mow finishing, 247
  estimating amount of, 406
  harvesting equipment for, 154
  improving quality of, 246
Heady, E. O., 154, 207, 289
Hedging, 377
High-priority jobs, 317
Hilly land, planning cropping programs for, 138
Hired labor, adequate housing for, 327
  on large farms, 399
  personal treatment of, 327
  selecting, 328
  supervising, 328
Hogs, capital requirements of, 181
  controlling protein fed to, 212
  early farrowing of, 202
  fall farrowing of, 202
  feed requirements for, 170
  free-choice feeding of, 212
  hay and pasture required for, 175
  labor required for, 177, 178
  limited grain-feeding programs for, 203
  marketing weights on one-litter system, 198
  most profitable marketing weight of, 203
  prices, cyclical movements in, 351
  production, concentration in the cornbelt, 195
    control of disease and parasites, 193
    cost on Indiana farms, 198
    differences in efficiency in, 194
    sanitation measures in, 213
    timing to fit seasonal price trends, 201
  raising on concrete, 213
  raising on pasture, 197
  risks involved in, 183
Household, equipment, competition with farm business, 34
  farm products used in, 306
  keeping a record of products used in, 416

Housing, dairy cost of, 254
  pen type, 254
Housing costs, for beef cow herds, 226
Human uncertainties, 370

Ida-Monona soil area, 152
Illinois Farm Business Associations, 166, 196, 222
Improvements and buildings, return from, 50
Income, as goal for farm business, 11
  estimating through budgets, 306
  variations in, 7
Income-sharing arrangements, accounting procedures to use in, 25
  advantages of, 16
  causes of low income, 25
  conditions necessary for success, 19
  dividing income, 22
  evaluating contributions of land and labor, 23
  minimum wage guarantees, 26
  partners not related, 26
  provisions to include in, 22
  steps in making, 18
Increasing risk, principle of, 97
Individuals, as source of farm mortgage credit, 85
  as source of production credit, 90
Inflation, 349
Information, gathering, 4
  sources of, 5
Inputs, purchased by farmers, 362
Insecurity of tenure, effects of, 48
  reducing, 52
Insurance, as item in machine service, 271
  automobile, 384
  extended coverage, 380
  fire and windstorm, 379
  hail, 382
  keeping policies effective, 381
  liability, 378, 383
Insurance companies as source of farm credit, 82
Interest as cost in machine ownership, 271

Interest of farm operator, effect on livestock program, 164
Interest rate, 80, 83, 84, 86, 98
Income tax, accrual basis of reporting, 421
cash basis of reporting, 420
check list of expenses, 425
deductible expenses, 426
forms, 421, 422, 423, 424
Inventories, feed, supplies, and livestock, 406, 418
land and buildings, 410
opening and closing, 414
taking, 406
Iowa Farm Business Associations, 206

January, work schedule for, 318
Jennings, Ralph D., 241
Joint checking accounts, 420
Judging livestock, 189
July, work schedule for, 319
June, work schedule for, 318

Klein, John W., 241

Labor, influence of limited supply of, 9
requirements, distribution of, 315
effect of building design on, 342
in crop production, 105, 109
on livestock farms, 315
peaks in, 316
reducing with big cow herds, 227
Labor supply, effect on choice of livestock enterprises, 163
Lamb feeding, death loss in, 231
price margin in, 230
sources of return from, 230
timing, 231
Lambs, feeder, early, 230
returns per $100 feed fed from, 167
seasonal prices of, 230
Land, hilly, cropping systems on, 102
in farms operated by tenants, 41
meaning of, 8
poor, tendency to overvalue, 72
values, comparing for United States, 69

Land, values, effect of neighborhood and location on, 62
index numbers of, 61
Land-use maps, symbols used on, 140, 142
uses of, 140, 143
Large farms, cost of output on, 394
sources of increased efficiency on, 394
use of high capacity machines on, 396
Large machines, capital requirements of, 285
saving labor with, 285
Laying hens, culling, 264
mortality of, 260, 264
nutritional requirements of, 259
Laying house, level of crowding, 260
Leases, advantages of written, 46
long term, 52
period of, 47
provisions to include in, 47
Leasing arrangements, cash, 30
crop share, 42
influence of community custom on, 46
patterning father-son agreements after, 27
terms of, 45
to fit, 27
types of, 39
Least-cost combination, influence of price changes on, 209
of corn and soybean oil meal in pork production, 209, 210
relation to rate of gain, 211
Legal descriptions, interpreting, 74
metes and bounds, 76
Liabilities, definition of, 95, 406
Lightning, losses from, 184
Liming, compensation for, 53
Limited capital, attempting farm ownership with, 60
Livestock enterprises, differences in, 163
fitting to resources of the farm, 184
expenses, estimates for budgets, 305
management problems with, 163

Livestock enterprises, production as source of income, 160
concentration in cornbelt, 161
to keep fertility on the farm, 160
program, influence of cropping system on, 115
Livestock-share leases, description of, 43
drawbacks to tenants of, 44
Loans, farm mortgage, held by principal lenders, 82
products needed to repay, 97
purposes of, 81
short term, ability to repay, 98
budgeting, 92, 93
criticisms of, 90
for consumption purposes, 94
for purchase of machinery, 95
purposes of, 98
sources of, 89, 99
Location, influence on land values of, 62
Low-priority work, 317
Low-producing farms, causes of, 387
distribution of, 387
Low-risk enterprises, 374

Machine costs, methods of reducing, 278
on large farms, 399
relationship to annual use, 276
Machine sheds, 342
Machinery repairs, classification of, 274
cost of, 271
Maintaining reserves to reduce risk, 377
Man-months of labor, computing, 440
Man-work units, as measure of size of business, 390
method of computing, 391
Management, appraising performance of, 8
as input in production, 8
errors in, 6
importance of, 6
return, 438
steps involved in, 1

Managers, qualities of superior, 7
specialized, 6
test of good, 9
March, work schedule for, 318
Market milk, cost of producing, 237
prices received for, 235
Market news information, 357
Marketing, programs, diversifying, 376
quotas, 360
weight, most profitable, influence of feed costs on, 205
influence of price trends on, 205
Markets, effect on livestock programs of, 165
Marshall soils, 154
May, work schedule for, 318
McGurk, J. L., 155
McKee, Dean, 207
McLean County, Illinois, 140
Mechanical barn cleaner, 331
Mechanization, increase in, 268
Merchants, as source of credit, 89, 99
Milk, cost of producing, 249
dependability of market for, 237
factors in choosing market for, 236
production per cow, increasing through breeding and selecting, 248
increasing through feeding and care, 250
influence of grain feeding on, 241
influence of high-quality forage on, 245
seasonal pattern of prices of, 251
Mortgages, chattel, 80
first, 81
recording, 80
Mosher, M. L., 169
Murphy, Roger C., 395
Mutual insurance companies, assessment privileges of, 380
operating principles of, 378

National Farm Loan Associations, 83
Negligence, liability for, 383
Net income statement, computing by accrual method, 413
definition of, 406

Net income statement, example of, 419
parts of, 413
summarizing, 418
Net worth statement, definition of, 95, 406
effect of falling prices on, 95
effect of rising prices on, 97
example of, 412
interpreting changes in, 411
use for credit purposes, 411
Norton, L. J., 155
November, work schedule for, 319
Nutrients, balance of, in pork production, 206

Oats, cost of production of, 104
gross income-producing ability of, 103
labor required to produce, 105
yield as forage crop, 117
October, work schedule for, 319
Off-the-farm income, 415
One-litter system, description of, 198
farrowing dates under, 198
Operating costs of machinery, 273
Operator's earnings, differences in, 393
methods of computing, 438
Opportunity cost, in allocating labor, 313
in dairy production, 251
in farm machinery decisions, 130
in fertilizer decisions, 130
in planning farm buildings, 339, 345
Order buyers, 367
Original cost, method of determining, 415
use in depreciation schedule, 408, 409
Outlook reports, accuracy of, 357
to reduce price risk, 373
use of, 355, 356
Owner-operated farms, compared to rented farms, 48
freedom of management on, 59
shortage of capital on, 60
Ownership, pride of, 4
Owning machinery in partnership, 279

Pastures, fertilizing permanent, 123
for August and September, 122
grazing too early, 122
putting into rotation, 122
reducing labor needs on, 197
renting additional, 123
rotated, 122
Picking corn, cost of, one-row picker, 277, 284
two-row picker, 277, 284
Plat books, 76
Portable houses, advantages of, 214
disadvantages of, 214
Poultry, capital requirements of, 181
feed requirements for, 171
labor required for, 177, 178, 180
returns per $100 feed fed, 167
Power and machinery, cost per acre, 441
investment per acre, 441
Power requirements on contoured land, 147
Price, changes, as source of risk, 369
since 1800, 348
cycles, adjusting to, 353
cattle, 352, 353
causes of, 349
hogs, 352
differentials, influence on most profitable marketing weight for hogs, 205
effect of higher, on land values, 70
fluctuations, as factor in decision making, 2
for appraisal purposes, 66
forces determining, 355
index of, 348
paid by farmers, 350
parity, defined, 359
received by farmers, 350
support programs, adjusting to, 358
for perishable products, 362
influence on farming risks, 369
storage privileges under, 360
Production credit associations, 91
Project agreements, 17
Project records, 427
Promissory note, 79, 89, 94

Pullet flocks, cost of, 267
  production from, 264
Purebred livestock, advantages of, 190
  advertising, 190
  characteristics of, 188
  fluctuations in prices of, 190
  selling, 189
  showing, 189

Qualifications for renting a farm, 29
Quonset-type structures, 340, 341

Rate of capital turnover in livestock
    production, 181
Rate of lay, increase in, 256
Rate of planting, effect of dry years
    on, 133
  influence of level of fertility on, 132
Rates of livestock production, esti-
    mating, 444
Receipts, estimating, 306, 307
Recessions, 349
Red clover, seasonal price pattern of
    seed, 366
  yield compared to other crops, 117
Rental terms, determining for ap-
    praisal purposes, 67
Rented farms, influence of divided
    management on, 52
  insecurity of tenure on, 48
  sharing returns on, 51
  special rents for buildings on, 54
Renting land to increase farm size,
    400
Repairs, treatment in farm accounts,
    417
Replacement flock, cost of, 267
  culling, 267
  managing, 266
Resources, farm, analysis in budget-
    ing, 294
  classification of, 8
  differences in quantity of, 9
Returns per $100 feed fed, changes in,
    168
  interpreting, 449
  meaning of, 166
  steps in computing, 449

Risk, adjusting to, 372
  avoiding, 13
  effect of rotations on, 109
  effect on beginning farmers, 372
  in one-crop areas, 374
  influence on livestock program, 164
  reducing, as a goal in farming, 371
Roads, influence on land values, 63
Rorholm, Niels, 270
Roughages, low quality, for beef cow
    herds, 169
  for sheep, 169
Running inventories, 445

Sand, recognizing presence of, 72
Sanitation, in hog production, 339
  in producing milk, 237
Sauer, E. L., 155
Saving gilts from fall litters, 199
Sections, numbering of, 75
Security, providing, 11
Security of tenure, on owner-operated
    farms, 58
  on rented farms, 52
Seeding failures, 117, 119
September, work schedule for, 319
Sharing costs and returns on rented
    farms, 54
Sheep, fluctuations in numbers, 228
  management problems of, 228
  returns per $100 feed fed from farm
    flocks, 166
  specialization in, 228
Shelling corn, cost of, 278
Silo unloader, 331
Size of farm business, effect on in-
    come, 390, 393
  measures of, 386, 388
  methods of increasing, 400
Size of flock, relationship of costs to,
    267
Size of machine, influence on labor
    required, 283, 284
  selecting, 283
Size of tractor, 286
Skill of operator, effect on livestock
    program, 164
Skim milk, as substitute for protein
    supplement, 238

Skim milk, nutrients in, 235
  value as hog and poultry feed, 236
Small tools, providing adequate, 326
Soil, erosion, 140
  measuring slope of, 142
  resources, examining for appraisal purposes, 65
  series, 140
  tests, 134, 135
  topography, effect on livestock program, 163
  type, 140
Soil conservation, increase in grain production from, 152
  most profitable level of, 139
  public interest in, 139
  supporting practices, as substitutes for grasses and legumes in rotation, 146
  using, 145
  timing of cost and returns from, 156
  transition period in adopting, 157
Soil Conservation Service, 150
Soybean oil meal, in pork production, 207
  seasonal price pattern of, 366
Soybeans, cost of production of, 104
  gross income-producing ability of, 103
  labor required to produce, 105
Specialization, risks in, 375
Speculation in land, dangers of, 61
Spraying crops as management problem, 278
Starting to farm, 28
Storage, grain, cost of, 397
  locating, 322
  requirements, effect of rotation on, 110
Strip cropping, 142
Substitution, principle of, complications in applying, 210
  in dairy production, 173
  statement of, 208
Supervised farming programs, appraising performance of, 429
Supply, influence on prices, 356, 357

Taxes, influence on farm values, 73
Technical assistance, using, 150
Tenant purchase loans, 85
Tenants, qualities landowners desire in, 30
Terracing, cost of, 148
  effect of heavy rain on, 148
  experience in working with, 152
Three-litter system, 198
Time and motion studies, 320
Timeliness of operations, effect of high capacity machines on, 286
  importance of, 283
  in hiring machines, 283
  planning to improve, 319
Timing of production, 10
Timothy, yield compared to other forages, 117
Tractor-hours required for field operations, 289
Tractor power, cost of, 288, 289
Travel, in feeding dairy cows, 323
  reducing, in chore routine, 322
Truck crops, risk in producing, 374
Turkey production, risks involved in, 183
Two-litter system, disadvantages of, 199
  distribution of labor, 198
  farrowing dates under, 198
Two-year-old cattle, efficiency of gain on, 219

U.S. Department of Agriculture, 357
Used machinery, buying, 286

Value of gross production, method of computing, 440
Variable cost, in adjusting to price changes, 354
  in machine operation, 270

Wage agreements, as step in taking over family farm, 17
  dangers in prolonging, 17
  terms of, 329
Water supply as influence on field layout, 118

Weather, adjusting to changes in, 308
   as factor in decision making, 2
   risks arising from, 369
Wheat, winter, gross income-produc-
   ing ability of, 103
Windbreaks, 337
Wool, return from, 230
Wooster and Canfield soils, 110
Work areas, arranging, 325
Work schedule, planning, 319
Working off the farm, 403

Workmen's Compensation Insurance,
   383

Yearlings, efficiency of gain on, 219
Yields, due to low productivity, 74
   effect of lowering on land values, 70
   estimates, county, 102
     for appraisal purposes, 66
     for use in budgeting, 114
     township, 102
   history of, 66